MATHEMATICS

FOR CLASS 6

R S Aggarwal, MSc, PhD

Bharati Bhawan

PUBLISHERS & DISTRIBUTORS

Published by

BHARATI BHAWAN (Publishers & Distributors)

4271/3 Ansari Road, Daryaganj, NEW DELHI 110 002, Phone: 23286557
A-61 B/2 Sector 63, NOIDA 201 307, Phone: 4757400
Thakurbari Road, PATNA 800 003, Phone: 2670325
10 Raja Subodh Mallick Square, KOLKATA 700 013, Phone: 22250651
No. 98 Sirsi Circle, Mysore Road, BENGALURU 560 018, Phone: 26740560
Hemsee Heights, Kutchery, Circular Road, RANCHI 834 001, Phone: 2361066

First edition 1993
Seventh edition 2010
Revised print 2012
2016 print

Mathematics for Class 6
Printed at Manipal Technologies Limited, Manipal

Preface

It gives me great pleasure in presenting the new edition of this book. It is in accordance with the latest syllabus.

In the books of this series, the emphasis is on the fundamentals. Mathematical ideas have been explained in the simplest possible way. The text is lucid and to the point. Each chapter has a large number of self-explanatory solved problems to illustrate the concepts and methods. The solved problems are followed by an adequate number of exercises. Care has been taken to grade the problems in such a way that students move from basic to intricate problems with ease.

A large number of objective questions have been included, which will help students quickly test their knowledge and skill. Also included are test papers for CCE.

Over the years I have received a number of suggestions from teachers. I am grateful to all of them. I also thank my sons Deepak and Vikas for assisting me in revising the books of this series.

Author

Contents

1. Number System 1
2. Factors and Multiples 23
3. Whole Numbers 45
4. Integers 61
5. Fractions 80
6. Simplification 105
7. Decimals 110
8. Algebraic Expressions 128
9. Linear Equations in One Variable 138
10. Ratio, Proportion and Unitary Method 148
11. Line Segment, Ray and Line 163
12. Parallel Lines 170
13. Angles and Their Measurement 175
14. Constructions (Using Ruler and a Pair of Compasses) 184
15. Polygons 190
16. Triangles 193
17. Quadrilaterals 199
18. Circles 205
19. Three-Dimensional Shapes 210
20. Two-Dimensional Reflection Symmetry (Linear Symmetry) 215
21. Concept of Perimeter and Area 220
22. Data Handling 234
23. Pictograph 236
24. Bar Graph 240
25. Activities 245
    Answers 275

1 | Number System

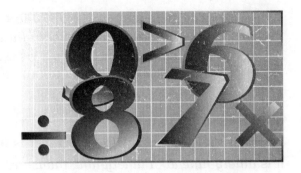

Numbers play an important role in mathematics. We have studied about counting numbers in primary classes. However, we shall review them here and extend our study to have the ideas of larger numbers.

We may express numbers in figures as well as in words.

NOTATION *Writing a number in figures is called notation.*

NUMERATION *Writing a number in words is called numeration.*

HINDU-ARABIC SYSTEM OF WRITING NUMBERS

In the Hindu-Arabic system, we use ten symbols, namely 0, 1, 2, 3, 4, 5, 6, 7, 8 and 9, called *digits* or *figures*, to represent any number.

*A group of digits, denoting a number, is called a **numeral.***

We use place-value system to represent a number.

For a given numeral, we start from the extreme right as: *Ones, Tens, Hundreds, Thousands, Ten thousands, Lakhs, Ten lakhs, etc.*

EXAMPLE 1. *Given below are some numbers arranged in a place-value table. Write each number in words and put it in the expanded form.*

PERIOD →	Lakhs		Thousands		Ones		
	Ten lakhs	Lakhs	Ten thousands	Thousands	Hundreds	Tens	Ones
(i)				9	6	3	8
(ii)			8	2	7	6	5
(iii)		3	5	6	8	0	4
(iv)	5	9	7	3	4	8	2

Solution (i) The given numeral is **'9638'**.

It is '*nine thousand six hundred thirty-eight*'.

In expanded form, we write it as:

$$9638 = (9 \times 1000) + (6 \times 100) + (3 \times 10) + (8 \times 1).$$

(ii) The given numeral is **'82765'**.

It is '*eighty-two thousand seven hundred sixty-five*'.

In expanded form, we write it as:

$$82765 = (8 \times 10000) + (2 \times 1000) + (7 \times 100) + (6 \times 10) + (5 \times 1).$$

(iii) The given numeral is **'356804'**.

It is '*three lakh fifty-six thousand eight hundred and four*'.

In expanded form, we write it as:

$$356804 = (3 \times 100000) + (5 \times 10000) + (6 \times 1000) + (8 \times 100) + (0 \times 10) + (4 \times 1).$$

1

(iv) The given numeral is '**5973482**'.

It is *fifty-nine lakh seventy-three thousand four hundred eighty-two*.

In expanded form, we write it as:

$$5973482 = (5 \times 1000000) + (9 \times 100000) + (7 \times 10000) + (3 \times 1000) + (4 \times 100)$$
$$+ (8 \times 10) + (2 \times 1).$$

NUMBER SYSTEM EXTENDED FURTHER

We know that the largest 7-digit number is **9999999**.

It is *ninety-nine lakh ninety-nine thousand nine hundred ninety-nine*.

On adding 1 to it, we get

$(9999999 + 1) = $ **10000000,** called *one crore.*

Thus, the smallest 8-digit number is one crore.

The largest 8-digit number is **99999999**.

It is *nine crore ninety-nine lakh ninety-nine thousand nine hundred ninety-nine*.

Thus, we extend our place-value chart to have

Ones, Tens, Hundreds, Thousands, Ten thousands, Lakhs, Ten lakhs, Crores and Ten crores, etc.

EXAMPLE 2.   *Given below are the numerals*
(i) 75624908 and (ii) 853172069.
Put them in the place-value chart. Write them in words.
Put each one of them in the expanded form.

Solution   The new place-value chart is given below.

PERIOD →	Crores		Lakhs		Thousands		Ones		
	Ten crores	Crores	Ten lakhs	Lakhs	Ten thousands	Thousands	Hundreds	Tens	Ones
(i)		7	5	6	2	4	9	0	8
(ii)	8	5	3	1	7	2	0	6	9

(i) The given numeral is **75624908.**

It is *seven crore fifty-six lakh twenty-four thousand nine hundred eight*.

Its expanded form is:

$$75624908 = (7 \times 10000000) + (5 \times 1000000) + (6 \times 100000) + (2 \times 10000)$$
$$+ (4 \times 1000) + (9 \times 100) + (0 \times 10) + (8 \times 1).$$

(ii) The given numeral is **853172069.**

It is *eighty-five crore thirty-one lakh seventy-two thousand sixty-nine*.

Its expanded form is:

$$853172069 = (8 \times 100000000) + (5 \times 10000000) + (3 \times 1000000) + (1 \times 100000)$$
$$+ (7 \times 10000) + (2 \times 1000) + (0 \times 100) + (6 \times 10) + (9 \times 1).$$

PERIODS   *Crores, lakhs, thousands and hundreds are known as periods.*

SEPARATING PERIODS IN HINDU-ARABIC SYSTEM

The various periods are:

(Crores), (Lakhs), (Thousands), (Hundreds + Tens + Ones)

We insert comma after each period.

EXAMPLE 1. *Write 75624908, separating periods.*

Solution Separating periods, we have

Crores	Lakhs	Thousands	Ones		
			H	T	O
7	56	24	9	0	8

Using commas, we write it as **7,56,24,908.**

EXAMPLE 2. *Write 853172069, separating periods.*

Solution Separating periods, we have

Crores	Lakhs	Thousands	Ones		
			H	T	O
85	31	72	0	6	9

Using commas, we write it as **85,31,72,069.**

FACE VALUE OF A DIGIT IN A NUMERAL

The face value of a digit remains as it is, whatever place it may be occupying in the place-value chart.

Thus, the face value of 4 is always 4, wherever it may be.

PLACE VALUE OF A DIGIT IN A NUMERAL

The place value of a digit in a numeral depends upon the place it occupies in the place-value chart.

If 5 occurs at ones place, its place value = 5 ones = (5×1) = 5.

If 5 occurs at tens place, its place value = 5 tens = (5×10) = 50.

If 5 occurs at hundreds place, its place value = 5 hundreds = (5×100) = 500, and so on.

Some more examples are given below.

EXAMPLE *Consider the numeral* **'72934806'.**

In this numeral, we have

place value of 6 = 6 ones = (6×1) = 6;

place value of 0 = 0 tens = (0×10) = 0;

place value of 8 = 8 hundreds = (8×100) = 800;

place value of 4 = 4 thousands = (4×1000) = 4000;

place value of 3 = 3 ten thousands = (3×10000) = 30000;

place value of 9 = 9 lakhs = (9×100000) = 900000;

place value of 2 = 2 ten lakhs = (2×1000000) = 2000000;

place value of 7 = 7 crores = (7×10000000) = 70000000.

SOLVED EXAMPLES

EXAMPLE 1. *Separate the periods of the numeral '93574862' by commas and write it in words.*

Solution Separating periods, we have

Crores	Lakhs	Thousands	Ones		
			H	T	O
9	35	74	8	6	2

Using commas, we write it as **9,35,74,862.**

In words, we write it as:

'nine crore thirty-five lakh seventy-four thousand eight hundred sixty-two'.

EXAMPLE 2. *Find the difference of the place values of the two 7s in 75810764.*

Solution The place value of 7 at crores place = 7 crores = $(7 \times 10000000) = 70000000$.

The place value of 7 at hundreds place = 7 hundreds = $(7 \times 100) = 700$.

Required difference = $(70000000 - 700) = 69999300$.

EXAMPLE 3. *How many 5-digit numbers are there in all?*

Solution The largest 5-digit number = 99999.

The smallest 5-digit number = 10000.

Number of all 5-digit numbers = $(99999 - 10000) + 1$

$= (89999 + 1) = 90000$.

Hence, the number of all 5-digit numbers is ninety thousand.

EXAMPLE 4. *How many 8-digit numbers are there in all?*

Solution The largest 8-digit number = 99999999.

The smallest 8-digit number = 10000000.

Number of all 8-digit numbers = $(99999999 - 10000000) + 1$

$= (89999999 + 1) = 90000000$

= nine crores.

Hence, there are in all nine crores of 8-digit numbers.

EXAMPLE 5. *Write the smallest 8-digit number having four different digits.*

Solution Four smallest digits are 0, 1, 2, 3.

Hence, the required number is 10000023.

EXAMPLE 6. *Write all 3-digit numbers using the digits* 1, 3, 5, *taking each digit only once.*

Solution Keeping 1 at the ones place, the numbers formed are 351 and 531.

Keeping 3 at the ones place, the numbers formed are 153 and 513.

Keeping 5 at the ones place, the numbers formed are 135 and 315.

So, the required numbers are

351, 531, 153, 513, 135 and 315.

INTERNATIONAL SYSTEM OF NUMERATION

In the international system of numeration adopted by all the countries throughout the world, the place-value chart is as follows.

PERIOD →	Billions		Millions			Thousands			Ones		
	Ten billions	Billions	Hundred millions	Ten millions	Millions	Hundred thousands	Ten thousands	Thousands	Hundreds	Tens	Ones
				3	4	1	2	5	6	8	0
			TC	C	TL	L	T Th	Th	H	T	O

The number '34125680' in the international system will be read as

'*thirty-four million one hundred and twenty-five thousand six hundred eighty*'.

It is clear from the table that the above number in the Hindu-Arabic system is given by

'*three crore forty-one lakh twenty-five thousand six hundred eighty*'.

EXAMPLE 7. *Rewrite each of the following numbers with proper commas, using international place-value chart:*
   (i) 53684   *(ii)* 1286475   *(iii)* 49637582
   Also, write the number name of each in the international system.

Solution Let us arrange the given numerals in an international place-value chart. Then separating the periods, we write them as shown below.

	Millions			Thousands			Ones			
	HM	TM	M	H Th	T Th	Th	H	T	O	
(i)					5	3	6	8	4	53,684
(ii)			1	2	8	6	4	7	5	1,286,475
(iii)		4	9	6	3	7	5	8	2	49,637,582
		C	TL	L	T Th	Th	H	T	O	

In the international system, we write them in words as:

   (i) Fifty-three thousand six hundred eighty-four

   (ii) One million two hundred eighty-six thousand four hundred seventy-five

   (iii) Forty-nine million six hundred thirty-seven thousand five hundred eighty-two

In the Hindu-Arabic system, these numbers are:

   (i) Fifty-three thousand six hundred eighty-four

   (ii) Twelve lakh eighty-six thousand four hundred seventy-five

   (iii) Four crore ninety-six lakh thirty-seven thousand five hundred eighty-two

EXERCISE 1A

1. Write the numeral for each of the following numbers:
   (i) Nine thousand eighteen
   (ii) Fifty-four thousand seventy-three
   (iii) Three lakh two thousand five hundred six
   (iv) Twenty lakh ten thousand eight
   (v) Six crore five lakh fifty-seven
   (vi) Two crore two lakh two thousand two hundred two
   (vii) Twelve crore twelve lakh twelve thousand twelve
   (viii) Fifteen crore fifty lakh twenty thousand sixty-eight

2. Write each of the following numbers in words:
   (i) 63,005   (ii) 7,07,075   (iii) 34,20,019
   (iv) 3,05,09,012   (v) 5,10,03,604   (vi) 6,18,05,008
   (vii) 19,09,09,900 (viii) 6,15,30,807   (ix) 6,60,60,060

3. Write each of the following numbers in expanded form:
   (i) 15,768   (ii) 3,08,927   (iii) 24,05,609
   (iv) 5,36,18,493   (v) 6,06,06,006   (vi) 9,10,10,510

4. Write the corresponding numeral for each of the following:

(i) $6 \times 10000 + 2 \times 1000 + 5 \times 100 + 8 \times 10 + 4 \times 1$

(ii) $5 \times 100000 + 8 \times 10000 + 1 \times 1000 + 6 \times 100 + 2 \times 10 + 3 \times 1$

(iii) $2 \times 10000000 + 5 \times 100000 + 7 \times 1000 + 9 \times 100 + 5 \times 1$

(iv) $3 \times 1000000 + 4 \times 100000 + 6 \times 1000 + 5 \times 100 + 7 \times 1$

5. Find the difference between the place values of the two nines in 79520986.

6. Find the difference between the place value and the face value of 7 in 27650934.

7. How many 6-digit numbers are there in all?

8. How many 7-digit numbers are there in all?

9. How many thousands make a lakh?

10. How many thousands make a crore?

11. Find the difference between the number 738 and that obtained on reversing its digits.

12. What comes just after 9547999?

13. What comes just before 9900000?

14. What comes just before 10000000?

15. Write all 3-digit numbers using 2, 3, 4, taking each digit only once.

16. Write the smallest number of different digits formed by using the digits 3, 1, 0, 5 and 7.

17. Write the largest number of different digits formed by using the digits 2, 4, 0, 3, 6 and 9.

18. Rewrite each of the following numerals with proper commas, using the international place-value chart. Also, write the number name of each in the international system.

(i) 735821   (ii) 6057894   (iii) 56943821

(iv) 37502093   (v) 89350064   (vi) 90703006

19. Write each of the following in figures in the international place-value chart:

(i) Thirty million one hundred five thousand sixty-three

(ii) Fifty-two million two hundred five thousand six

(iii) Five million five thousand five

COMPARISON OF NUMBERS

In order to compare two numbers, we adopt the following rules.

Rule 1. *The number with less digits is less than the number with more digits.*

Rule 2. *Suppose we have to compare two numbers having the same number of digits, then we proceed as under.*

Step 1. *First compare the digits at the leftmost place in both the numbers.*

Step 2. *If they are equal in value then compare the second digits from the left.*

Step 3. *If the second digits from the left are equal then compare the third digits from the left.*

Step 4. *Continue until you come across unequal digits at the corresponding places. Clearly, the number with greater such digit is the greater of the two.*

The following examples will make the ideas more clear.

SOLVED EXAMPLES

EXAMPLE 1. *Which is greater: 24576813 or 9897686 ?*

Solution Here, we have to compare 24576813 and 9897686.
Clearly, 24576813 consists of 8 digits while 9897686 contains 7 digits.
We know that a number with more digits is greater.
∴ 24576813 > 9897686.

EXAMPLE 2. *Which is greater: 96850374 or 96721895 ?*

Solution Let us arrange the given numbers in a place-value chart, as shown below.

Crores	Ten lakhs	Lakhs	Ten thousands	Thousands	Hundreds	Tens	Ones
9	6	8	5	0	3	7	4
9	6	7	2	1	8	9	5

Clearly, both the numbers have 8 digits.
At the crores place both have the same digit, namely, 9.
At the ten lakhs place both have the same digit, namely, 6.
But, at the lakhs place, the first number has 8 while the second has 7.
Clearly, 8 > 7.
∴ 96850374 > 96721895.

EXAMPLE 3. *Arrange the following numbers in ascending order:*
3763214, 18340217, 984671, 3790423, 18431056

Solution Let us arrange the given numbers in a place-value chart, as shown below.

Crores	Ten lakhs	Lakhs	Ten thousands	Thousands	Hundreds	Tens	Ones
		3	7	6	3	2	1	4
1	8	3	4	0	2	1	7
		9	8	4	6	7	1
		3	7	9	0	4	2	3
1	8	4	3	1	0	5	6

Out of the given numbers one is a 6-digit number, two are 7-digit numbers and two are 8-digit numbers.
6-digit number is 984671.
In 7-digit numbers we have 3763214 < 3790423.
In 8-digit numbers we have 18340217 < 18431056.
Hence, the given numbers in ascending order are:
984671 < 3763214 < 3790423 < 18340217 < 18431056.

EXAMPLE 4. *Arrange the following numbers in descending order:*
63872604, 4965328, 63890503, 5023145, 576943

Solution Let us arrange the given numbers in a place-value chart.

Ten crores	Crores	Ten lakhs	Lakhs	Ten thousands	Thousands	Hundreds	Tens	Ones
	6	3	8	7	2	6	0	4
		4	9	6	5	3	2	8
	6	3	8	9	0	5	0	3
		5	0	2	3	1	4	5
			5	7	6	9	4	3

In 8-digit numbers, clearly 63890503 > 63872604 (9 T Th > 7 T Th).

In 7-digit numbers, clearly 5023145 > 4965328 (5 TL > 4 TL).

The 6-digit number is 576943, which is clearly the smallest.

∴   63890503 > 63872604 > 5023145 > 4965328 > 576943.

Hence, the given numbers in descending order are:
    63890503, 63872604, 5023145, 4965328, 576943.

EXERCISE 1B

Fill in each of the following boxes with the correct symbol > or <:

1. 1003467 ☐ 987965
2. 3572014 ☐ 10235401
3. 3254790 ☐ 3260152
4. 10357690 ☐ 11243567
5. 27596381 ☐ 7965412
6. 47893501 ☐ 47894021

Arrange the following numbers in descending order:

7. 63521047, 7354206, 63514759, 7355014, 102345680
8. 5032786, 23794206, 5032790, 23756819, 987876
9. 190909, 1808088, 16060666, 16007777, 181888, 1808090
10. 199988, 1704382, 200175, 1702497, 201200, 1712040

Arrange the following numbers in ascending order:

11. 9873426, 24615019, 990357, 9874012, 24620010
12. 56943201, 5694437, 56944000, 5695440, 56943300
13. 700087, 8014257, 8015032, 10012458, 8014306
14. 1020304, 893245, 980134, 1021403, 893425, 1020216

WORD PROBLEMS ON NUMBER OPERATIONS

ILLUSTRATIVE EXAMPLES

EXAMPLE 1.   *A businessman earned ₹ 3648970 in the year 2014. Next year, his earning was increased by ₹ 956880. What was his earning in the year 2015?*

Solution   Earning of the man in the year 2014 = ₹ 3648970

Increase in earning during next year = ₹ 956880

Man's earning in the year 2015 = ₹ (3648970 + 956880) = ₹ 4605850.

	1	1	1	1	1		
	TL	L	T Th	Th	H	T	O
	3	6	4	8	9	7	0
+		9	5	6	8	8	0
	4	6	0	5	8	5	0

Hence, the man's earning in the year 2015 is ₹ 4605850.

EXAMPLE 2.   *A survey shows that the population of Andhra Pradesh is 98306965, that of Karnataka is 89627598 and that of Kerala is 46308927. What is the total population of these three states?*

Solution We have:

Population of Andhra Pradesh = 98306965.

Population of Karnataka = 89627598.

Population of Kerala = 46308927.

Total population of the three states = (98306965 + 89627598 + 46308927)

	2	2	1		2	2	1	2	
	TC	C	TL	L	T Th	Th	H	T	O
	9	8	3	0	6	9	6	5	
+		8	9	6	2	7	5	9	8
+		4	6	3	0	8	9	2	7
	2	3	4	2	4	3	4	9	0

The total population of the three states is 234243490.

EXAMPLE 3. *The difference between two numbers is 9476583. If the smaller number is 6873547, find the greater number.*

Solution We have:

Difference between the two numbers = 9476583.

Smaller number = 6873547.

Hence, greater number = (9476583 + 6873547)

	1	1	1	1	1	1	1	
	C	TL	L	T Th	Th	H	T	O
	9	4	7	6	5	8	3	
+	6	8	7	3	5	4	7	
1	6	3	5	0	1	3	0	

Hence, the greater number is 16350130.

EXAMPLE 4. *The population of a city in the year 2014 was 14693675. In the following year, the population became 18002403. Find the increase in the population.*

Solution We have:

Population in the year 2015 = 18002403.

Population in the year 2014 = 14693675.

Increase in population = (18002403 – 14693675)

	C	TL	L	T Th	Th	H	T	O
	1	8	0	0	2	4	0	3
–	1	4	6	9	3	6	7	5
		3	3	0	8	7	2	8

Hence, the increase in population is 3308728.

EXAMPLE 5. *There was a stock of 17380245 quintals of wheat in a godown of the Food Corporation of India. Out of this stock, 2756744 quintals of wheat was sent to Haryana and 4863108 quintals to Punjab. How much is the balance stock now?*

Solution We have:

Total stock of wheat = 17380245 quintals.

Quantity of wheat sent to Haryana
= 2756744 quintals.

Quantity of wheat sent to Punjab
= 4863108 quintals.

Total quantity of wheat taken out of the godown
= (2756744 + 4863108) quintals
= 7619852 quintals.

	1	1				1		
		2	7	5	6	7	4	4
+		4	8	6	3	1	0	8
		7	6	1	9	8	5	2

	1	7	3	8	0	2	4	5
–		7	6	1	9	8	5	2
		9	7	6	0	3	9	3

Balance stock of wheat in the godown = (17380245 − 7619852) quintals

= 9760393 quintals.

EXAMPLE 6. *The cost of a steel almirah is ₹ 22875. What is the cost of 465 such almirahs?*

Solution   Cost of 1 almirah = ₹ 22875.

Cost of 465 almirahs = ₹ (22875 × 465)

= ₹ 10636875.

Hence, the cost of 465 almirahs is ₹ 10636875.

```
        2  2  8  7  5
     ×        4  6  5
     1  1  4  3  7  5
  1  3  7  2  5  0  ×
  9  1  5  0  0  ×  ×
1  0  6  3  6  8  7  5
```

EXAMPLE 7. *6895 screws can be packed in one carton. How many screws can be packed in 1685 such cartons?*

Solution   We have:

Number of screws in 1 carton

= 6895.

Number of screws in 1685 cartons

= (6895 × 1685)

= 11618075.

```
        6  8  9  5
     ×  1  6  8  5
     3  4  4  7  5
  5  5  1  6  0  ×
4  1  3  7  0  ×  ×
6  8  9  5  ×  ×  ×
1  1  6  1  8  0  7  5
```

Hence, the number of screws in 1685 cartons is 11618075.

EXAMPLE 8. *The mass of each gas cylinder is 16 kg 250 g. What is the total mass of 18 such cylinders?*

Solution   Mass of 1 cylinder = 16 kg 250 g.

Mass of 18 cylinders = (16 kg 250 g) × 18

= 292 kg 500 g.

Hence, the total mass of 18 cylinders is 292 kg 500 g.

(+4)	
kg	g
16	250
	× 18
292	500

EXAMPLE 9. *The piece of cloth required for a shirt is 2 m 85 cm. How much cloth will be required for 16 such shirts?*

Solution   We have:

Cloth required for 1 shirt = 2 m 85 cm.

Cloth required for 16 shirts = (2 m 85 cm) × 16

= 45 m 60 cm.

Hence, the cloth required for 16 shirts = 45 m 60 cm.

(+13)	
m	cm
2	85
	× 16
45	60

EXAMPLE 10. *The cost of 16 flats constructed by UP Awas and Vikas Parishad is ₹ 24809520. What is the cost of each flat?*

Solution   We have:

Total cost of 16 flats = ₹ 24809520.

Cost of each flat = (₹ 24809520) ÷ 16

= ₹ 1550595.

Hence, the cost of each flat is ₹ 1550595.

```
16) 24809520 (1550595
    − 16
      88
    − 80
      80
    − 80
       95
     − 80
      152
    − 144
        80
      − 80
         ×
```

EXAMPLE 11. *For making 16 shirts, 44 metres of cloth is needed. How much cloth is required for each shirt?*

Solution   We have:

Cloth required for 16 shirts   = 44 m.

Cloth required for each shirt = (44 m) ÷ 16

= 2 m 75 cm.

Hence, the cloth required for each shirt

= 2 m 75 cm.

```
         2 m
    16 ) 44 m
       − 32
         12 m
        × 100
   16 ) 1200 cm ( 75 cm
      − 112
         80
       − 80
          ×
```

EXAMPLE 12. *A car covers 1002 km in 16 hours. At what speed per hour does the car move?*

Solution   Distance covered in 16 hours = 1002 km.

Distance covered in 1 hour   = (1002 km) ÷ 16

= 62 km 625 m.

Hence, the speed of the car is 62 km 625 m per hour.

```
   16 ) 1002 km ( 62 km
      − 96
         42
       − 32
         10 km
       × 1000
   16 ) 10000 m ( 625 m
      − 96
         40
       − 32
         80
       − 80
          ×
```

EXERCISE 1C

1. The number of persons who visited the holy shrine of Mata Vaishno Devi during last two consecutive years was 13789509 and 12976498 respectively. How many persons visited the shrine during these two years?

2. Last year, three sugar factories in a town produced 24809565 bags, 18738576 bags and 9564568 bags of sugar respectively. How many bags were produced by all the three factories during last year?

3. A number exceeds 37684955 by 3615045. What is that number?

4. There were three candidates in an election. They received 687905 votes, 495086 votes and 93756 votes respectively. The number of invalid votes was 13849. If 25467 persons did not vote, find how many votes were registered.

5. A survey conducted on an Indian state shows that 1623546 people have only primary education; 9768678 people have secondary education; 6837954 people have higher education and 2684536 people are illiterate. If the number of children below the age of school admission is 698781, find the total population of the state.

6. In a particular year a company produced 8765435 bicycles. Next year, the number of bicycles produced was 1378689 more than those produced in the preceding year.
How many bicycles were produced during the second year?
How many bicycles were produced during these two years?

7. The sale receipt of a company during a year was ₹ 20956480. Next year, it increased by ₹ 6709570. What was the total sale receipt of the company during these two years?

8. The total population of a city is 28756304. If the number of males is 16987059, find the number of females in the city.

9. By how much is 13246510 larger than 4658642?

10. By how much is 5643879 smaller than one crore?

11. What number must be subtracted from 11010101 to get 2635967?

12. The sum of two numbers is 10750308. If one of them is 8967519, what is the other number?

13. A man had ₹ 20000000 with him. He spent ₹ 13607085 on buying a school building. How much money is left with him?

14. A society needed ₹ 18536000 to buy a property. It collected ₹ 7253840 as membership fee, took a loan of ₹ 5675450 from a bank and collected ₹ 2937680 as donation. How much is the society still short of?

15. A man had ₹ 10672540 with him. He gave ₹ 4836980 to his wife, ₹ 3964790 to his son and the rest to his daughter. How much money was received by the daughter?

16. The cost of a chair is ₹ 1485. How much will 469 such chairs cost?

17. How much money was collected from 1786 students of a school for a charity show if each student contributed ₹ 625?

18. A factory produces 6985 screws per day. How many screws will it produce in 358 days?

19. Mr Bhaskar saves ₹ 8756 every month. How much money will he save in 13 years?

20. A scooter costs ₹ 36725. How much will 487 such scooters cost?

21. An aeroplane covers 1485 km in 1 hour. How much distance will it cover in 72 hours?

22. The product of two numbers is 13421408. If one of the numbers is 364, find the other.

23. If 36 flats cost ₹ 68251500, what is the cost of each such flat?

24. The mass of a cylinder filled with gas is 30 kg 250 g and the mass of the empty cylinder is 14 kg 480 g. How much is the mass of the gas contained in it?

25. From a cloth 5 m long, a piece of length 2 m 85 cm is cut off. What is the length of the remaining piece?

26. In order to make a shirt, a length of 2 m 75 cm of cloth is needed. How much length of the cloth will be required for 16 such shirts?

27. For making 8 trousers of the same size, 14 m 80 cm of cloth is needed. How much cloth will be required for each such trouser?

28. The mass of a brick is 2 kg 750 g. What is the total mass of 14 such bricks?

29. The total mass of 8 packets, each of the same size, is 10 kg 600 g. What is the mass of each such packet?

30. A rope of length 10 m has been divided into 8 pieces of the same length. What is the length of each piece?

ESTIMATION

Before estimation, we must know how to round off a number to the nearest ten, nearest hundred, nearest thousand, etc.

For the same, we need the rules given below:

Rounding a Number to the Nearest Ten

Step 1:   See the *ones digit* of the given number.

Step 2:   If ones digit is less than 5, *replace ones digit by 0, and keep the other digits as they are.*

Step 3:   If ones digit is 5 or more, *increase tens digit by 1, and replace ones digit by 0.*

Rounding a Number to the Nearest Hundred

Step 1 :   See the *tens digit* of the given number.

Step 2 :   If tens digit is less than 5, *replace each one of tens and ones digits by 0, and keep the other digits as they are.*

Step 3 :   If this digit is 5 or more, *increase hundreds digit by 1 and replace each digit on its right by 0.*

Rounding a Number to the Nearest Thousand

Step 1 :   See the *hundreds digit* of the given number.

Step 2 :   If hundreds digit is less than 5, *replace each one of hundreds, tens and ones digits by 0, and keep the other digits as they are.*

Step 3 :   If hundreds digit is 5 or more, *increase thousands digit by 1 and replace each digit on its right by 0.*

We may extend the ideas for larger numbers.

SOLVED EXAMPLES

EXAMPLE 1.   *Round each of the following numbers to the nearest ten:*
          (a) 53   (b) 287   (c) 8364   (d) 2045

Solution   (a) In 53, the ones digit is 3 < 5.
            ∴ the required rounded number = 50.
        (b) In 287, the ones digit is 7 > 5.
            ∴ the required rounded number = 290.
        (c) In 8364, the ones digit is 4 < 5.
            ∴ the required rounded number = 8360.
        (d) In 2045, the ones digit is 5 = 5.
            ∴ the required rounded number = 2050.

EXAMPLE 2.   *Round each of the following numbers to the nearest hundred:*
          (a) 648   (b) 2356   (c) 13768   (d) 1249

Solution   (a) In 648, the tens digit is 4 < 5.
            ∴ the required rounded number = 600.
        (b) In 2356, the tens digit is 5 = 5.
            ∴ the required rounded number = 2400.
        (c) In 13768, the tens digit is 6 > 5.
            ∴ the required rounded number = 13800.
        (d) In 1249, the tens digit is 4 < 5.
            ∴ the required rounded number = 1200.

EXAMPLE 3.   *Round each of the following numbers to the nearest thousand:*
          (a) 5486   (b) 6823   (c) 14380   (d) 23659

Solution   (a) In 5486, the hundreds digit is 4 < 5.
            ∴ the required rounded number = 5000.
        (b) In 6823, the hundreds digit is 8 > 5.
            ∴ the required rounded number = 7000.
        (c) In 14380, the hundreds digit is 3 < 5.
            ∴ the required rounded number = 14000.
        (d) In 23659, the hundreds digit is 6 > 5.
            ∴ the required rounded number = 24000.

Estimation

To estimate means to make a guess. Estimation, thus, gives us a rough idea of the answer to a question involving operations on numbers.

ESTIMATING THE SUMS

EXAMPLE 1. *Estimate the sum (64 + 79) to the nearest ten.*

Solution   64 estimated to the nearest ten = 60.
            79 estimated to the nearest ten = 80.
            Hence, the required estimation = (60 + 80) = 140.

EXAMPLE 2. *Estimate the sum (267 + 132) to the nearest ten.*

Solution   267 estimated to the nearest ten = 270.
            132 estimated to the nearest ten = 130.
            Hence, the required estimation = (270 + 130) = 400.

EXAMPLE 3. *Estimate the sum (274 + 143) to the nearest hundred.*

Solution   274 estimated to the nearest hundred = 300.
            143 estimated to the nearest hundred = 100.
            Hence, the required estimation = (300 + 100) = 400.

EXAMPLE 4. *Estimate the sum (21397 + 27807 + 42505) to the nearest thousand.*

Solution   21397 estimated to the nearest thousand = 21000.
            27807 estimated to the nearest thousand = 28000.
            42505 estimated to the nearest thousand = 43000.
            Hence, the required estimation = (21000 + 28000 + 43000) = 92000.

EXAMPLE 5. *Estimate the difference (673 − 258) to the nearest hundred.*

Solution   673 estimated to the nearest hundred = 700.
            258 estimated to the nearest hundred = 300.
            Hence, the required estimation = (700 − 300) = 400.

EXERCISE 1D

1. Round each of the following numbers to the nearest ten:
   (a) 36   (b) 173   (c) 3869   (d) 16378

2. Round each of the following numbers to the nearest hundred:
   (a) 814   (b) 1254   (c) 43126   (d) 98165

3. Round each of the following numbers to the nearest thousand:
   (a) 793   (b) 4826   (c) 16719   (d) 28394

4. Round each of the following numbers to the nearest ten thousand:
   (a) 17514   (b) 26340   (c) 34890   (d) 272685

Estimate each sum to the nearest ten:

5. (57 + 34)   6. (43 + 78)   7. (14 + 69)
8. (86 + 19)   9. (95 + 58)   10. (77 + 63)
11. (356 + 275)   12. (463 + 182)   13. (538 + 276)

Estimate each sum to the nearest hundred:

14. (236 + 689)   15. (458 + 324)   16. (170 + 395)

17. $(3280 + 4395)$ **18.** $(5130 + 1410)$ **19.** $(10083 + 29380)$

Estimate each sum to the nearest thousand:

20. $(32836 + 16466)$ **21.** $(46703 + 11375)$

22. There are 54 balls in box A and 79 balls in box B. Estimate the total number of balls in both the boxes taken together.

Estimate each difference to the nearest ten:

23. $(53 - 18)$ **24.** $(97 - 38)$ **25.** $(409 - 148)$

Estimate each difference to the nearest hundred:

26. $(678 - 215)$ **27.** $(957 - 578)$ **28.** $(7258 - 2429)$ **29.** $(5612 - 3095)$

Estimate each difference to the nearest thousand:

30. $(35863 - 27677)$ **31.** $(47005 - 39488)$

===

ESTIMATING THE PRODUCTS

ILLUSTRATIVE EXAMPLES

EXAMPLE 1. *Estimate the product of 42 and 58.*

Solution   42 estimated to the nearest ten = 40.
58 estimated to the nearest ten = 60.
Hence, the required estimation = $(40 \times 60) = 2400$.

EXAMPLE 2. *Estimate the product of 34 and 75.*

Solution   34 estimated to the nearest ten = 30.
75 estimated to the nearest ten = 80.
Hence, the required estimation = $(30 \times 80) = 2400$.

EXAMPLE 3. *Estimate the product of 367×231 by rounding off each number to the nearest hundred.*

Solution   367 estimated to the nearest hundred = 400.
231 estimated to the nearest hundred = 200.
Hence, the estimated product = $400 \times 200 = 80000$.

EXAMPLE 4. *Estimate the product of 183×153 by rounding off the first number upwards and the second number downwards.*

Solution   183 estimated upwards = 200.
153 estimated downwards = 100.
Hence, the estimated product = $200 \times 100 = 20000$.

EXERCISE 1E

Estimate each of the following products by rounding off each number to the nearest ten:

1. 38×63 **2.** 54×47 **3.** 28×63

4. 42×75 **5.** 64×58 **6.** 15×34

Estimate each of the following products by rounding off each number to the nearest hundred:

7. 376×123 **8.** 264×147 **9.** 423×158
10. 509×179 **11.** 392×138 **12.** 271×339

Estimate each of the following products by rounding off the first number upwards and the second number downwards:

13. 183×154 **14.** 267×146 **15.** 359×76
16. 472×158 **17.** 680×164 **18.** 255×350

Estimate each of the following products by rounding off the first number downwards and the second number upwards:

19. 356×278 **20.** 472×76 **21.** 578×369

ESTIMATING THE QUOTIENTS

ILLUSTRATIVE EXAMPLE

EXAMPLE   *Find the estimated quotient for each of the following:*
           (i) $627 \div 23$ *(ii)* $985 \div 48$ *(iii)* $74 \div 34$ *(iv)* $694 \div 58$

Solution   (i) $627 \div 23$ is approximately equal to $600 \div 20 = 30$.
           (ii) $985 \div 48$ is approximately equal to $1000 \div 50 = 20$.
           (iii) $74 \div 34$ is approximately equal to $70 \div 30 = 7 \div 3$, which is approximately equal to 2.
           (iv) $694 \div 58$ is approximately equal to $700 \div 60$,

               which is approximately equal to $70 \div 6$,

               which is approximately equal to 12.

EXERCISE 1F

Find the estimated quotient for each of the following:

1. $87 \div 28$ **2.** $83 \div 17$ **3.** $75 \div 23$
4. $193 \div 24$ **5.** $725 \div 23$ **6.** $275 \div 25$
7. $633 \div 33$ **8.** $729 \div 29$ **9.** $858 \div 39$
10. $868 \div 38$

ROMAN NUMERALS

ROMAN NUMERALS One of the early systems of writing numerals is the system of Roman numerals.

There are seven basic symbols to write any numeral.

These symbols are given below.

Roman numeral	I	V	X	L	C	D	M
Hindu-Arabic numeral	1	5	10	50	100	500	1000

If a bar is placed over a numeral, it is multiplied by 1000.

Thus, $\overline{V}$ = 5000 and $\overline{X}$ = 10000, etc.

Using these symbols, we may form all Roman numerals by adopting the rules given below.

RULE 1   *Repetition of a symbol in a Roman numeral means addition.*

CAUTIONS   (i) Only I, X, C, M can be repeated.

(ii) V, L and D are never repeated.

(iii) No symbol in a Roman numeral can be repeated more than 3 times.

EXAMPLES   (i) II = (1 + 1) = 2   (ii) XX = (10 + 10) = 20

(iii) XXX = (10 + 10 + 10) = 30   (iv) CC = (100 + 100) = 200

RULE 2   *A smaller numeral written to the right of a larger numeral is always added to the larger numeral.*

EXAMPLES   (i) VI = (5 + 1) = 6   (ii) VIII = (5 + 1 + 1 + 1) = 8

(iii) XV = (10 + 5) = 15   (iv) LX = (50 + 10) = 60

RULE 3   *A smaller numeral written to the left of a larger numeral is always subtracted from the larger numeral.*

CAUTIONS   (i) V, L and D are never subtracted.

(ii) I can be subtracted from V and X only.

(iii) X can be subtracted from L and C only.

(iv) C can be subtracted from D and M only.

EXAMPLES   (i) IV = (5 − 1) = 4   (ii) IX = (10 − 1) = 9

(iii) XL = (50 − 10) = 40   (iv) XC = (100 − 10) = 90

(v) CD = (500 − 100) = 400   (vi) CM = (1000 − 100) = 900

RULE 4   *When a smaller numeral is placed between two larger numerals, it is always subtracted from the larger numeral immediately following it.*

EXAMPLES   (i) XIV = 10 + (5 − 1) = 14   (ii) XIX = 10 + (10 − 1) = 19

(iii) CXIV = 100 + 10 + (5 − 1) = 114

<table>
<tr><th colspan="9" style="text-align:center">SUMMARY</th></tr>
</table>

1.

Roman numeral	I	V	X	L	C	D	M
Hindu-Arabic numeral	1	5	10	50	100	500	1000

2. Repetition of a Roman numeral means addition.

   RULES (i) Only I, X, C, M can be repeated.

   (ii) V, L and D are never repeated.

   (iii) No symbol can be repeated more than 3 times.

3. Smaller numeral written to the left of a larger numeral means subtraction.

   RULES (i) V, L and D are never subtracted.

   (ii) I can be subtracted from V and X only.

   (iii) X can be subtracted from L and C only.

   (iv) C can be subtracted from D and M only.

SOLVED EXAMPLES

EXAMPLE 1. *Write Roman numeral for each of the numbers from 1 to 20.*

Solution   We may write these numbers as given below.

1	2	3	4	5	6	7	8	9	10
I	II	III	IV	V	VI	VII	VIII	IX	X

11	12	13	14	15	16	17	18	19	20
XI	XII	XIII	XIV	XV	XVI	XVII	XVIII	XIX	XX

EXAMPLE 2. *Express each of the following numbers as a Roman numeral:*

  (i) 23   *(ii)* 26   *(iii)* 29   *(iv)* 31   *(v)* 37   *(vi)* 39   *(vii)* 40

  (viii) 45   *(ix)* 49   *(x)* 51   *(xi)* 63   *(xii)* 72   *(xiii)* 79   *(xiv)* 84

  (xv) 89   *(xvi)* 90   *(xvii)* 92   *(xviii)* 99   *(xix)* 100

Solution   We may write these numbers as given below:

  (i) 23 = XXIII   (ii) 26 = XXVI   (iii) 29 = XXIX

  (iv) 31 = XXXI   (v) 37 = XXXVII   (vi) 39 = XXXIX

  (vii) 40 = XL   (viii) 45 = XLV   (ix) 49 = XLIX

  (x) 51 = LI   (xi) 63 = LXIII   (xii) 72 = LXXII

  (xiii) 79 = LXXIX   (xiv) 84 = LXXXIV   (xv) 89 = LXXXIX

  (xvi) 90 = XC   (xvii) 92 = XCII   (xviii) 99 = XCIX

  (xix) 100 = C

EXAMPLE 3. *Express each of the following numbers as a Roman numeral:*

  (i) 137   *(ii)* 174   *(iii)* 198   *(iv)* 236

  (v) 341   *(vi)* 389   *(vii)* 400   *(viii)* 479

  (ix) 556   *(x)* 596   *(xi)* 625   *(xii)* 769

Solution   We have:

  (i) $137 = 100 + 30 + 7 = $ CXXXVII   (ii) $174 = 100 + 70 + 4 = $ CLXXIV

  (iii) $198 = 100 + 90 + 8 = $ CXCVIII   (iv) $236 = 200 + 30 + 6 = $ CCXXXVI

  (v) $341 = 300 + 40 + 1 = $ CCCXLI   (vi) $389 = 300 + 80 + 9 = $ CCCLXXXIX

  (vii) $400 = $ CD   (viii) $479 = 400 + 70 + 9 = $ CDLXXIX

  (ix) $556 = 500 + 50 + 6 = $ DLVI   (x) $596 = 500 + 90 + 6 = $ DXCVI

  (xi) $625 = 500 + 100 + 20 + 5 = $ DCXXV   (xii) $769 = 500 + 200 + 60 + 9 = $ DCCLXIX

EXAMPLE 4. *Write each of the following in Hindu-Arabic numeral:*

(i) XXIV (ii) XLVI (iii) LXXXVI (iv) XCIX
(v) CLXVI (vi) CCXXVI (vii) CCCXL (viii) CDXLVI

Solution We have:

(i) XXIV = 20 + (5 − 1) = 24
(ii) XLVI = XL + VI = (50 − 10) + (5 + 1) = 46
(iii) LXXXVI = 50 + 30 + 6 = 86
(iv) XCIX = (100 − 10) + (10 − 1) = 99
(v) CLXVI = 100 + 50 + 10 + (5 + 1) = 166
(vi) CCXXVI = 200 + 20 + (5 + 1) = 226
(vii) CCCXL = 300 + (50 − 10) = 340
(viii) CDXLVI = (500 − 100) + (50 − 10) + (5 + 1) = 446

EXAMPLE 5. *Show that each of the following is meaningless. Give reason in each case.*

(i) XXXX (ii) VX (iii) IC (iv) XVV

Solution
(i) No symbol is repeated more than three times.
∴ XXXX is wrong.

(ii) V, L, D are never subtracted.
∴ VX is wrong.

(iii) I can be subtracted from V and X only.
∴ IC is wrong.

(iv) V, L, D are never repeated.
∴ XVV is wrong.

EXERCISE 1G

1. Express each of the following as a Roman numeral:
(i) 2 (ii) 8 (iii) 14 (iv) 29
(v) 36 (vi) 43 (vii) 54 (viii) 61
(ix) 73 (x) 81 (xi) 91 (xii) 95
(xiii) 99 (xiv) 105 (xv) 114

2. Express each of the following as a Roman numeral:
(i) 164 (ii) 195 (iii) 226 (iv) 341
(v) 475 (vi) 596 (vii) 611 (viii) 759

3. Write each of the following as a Hindu-Arabic numeral:
(i) XXVII (ii) XXXIV (iii) XLV (iv) LIV
(v) LXXIV (vi) XCI (vii) XCVI (viii) CXI
(ix) CLIV (x) CCXXIV (xi) CCCLXV (xii) CDXIV
(xiii) CDLXIV (xiv) DVI (xv) DCCLXVI

4. Show that each of the following is meaningless. Give reason in each case.
(i) VC (ii) IL (iii) VVII (iv) IXX

Hint. *(i) V is never subtracted.*
(ii) I can be subtracted from V and X only.
(iii) V, L, D are never repeated.
(iv) IX cannot occur to the left of X.

EXERCISE 1H

OBJECTIVE QUESTIONS

Mark (✓) against the correct answer in each of the following:

1. The place value of 6 in the numeral 48632950 is
    (a) 6   (b) 632950   (c) 600000   (d) 486

2. The face value of 4 in the numeral 89247605 is
    (a) 4   (b) 40000   (c) 47605   (d) 8924

3. The difference between the place value and the face value of 5 in the numeral 78653421 is
    (a) 53416   (b) 4995   (c) 49995   (d) none of these

4. The smallest counting number is
    (a) 0   (b) 1   (c) 10   (d) none of these

5. How many 4-digit numbers are there?
    (a) 8999   (b) 9000   (c) 8000   (d) none of these

6. How many 7-digit numbers are there?
    (a) 8999999   (b) 9000000   (c) 1000000   (d) none of these

7. How many 8-digit numbers are there?
    (a) 99999999   (b) 89999999   (c) 90000000   (d) none of these

8. What comes just before 1000000?
    (a) 99999   (b) 999999   (c) 9999999   (d) none of these

9. Which of the following is not meaningful?
    (a) VX   (b) XV   (c) XXV   (d) XXXV

10. Which of the following is not meaningful?
    (a) CI   (b) CII   (c) IC   (d) XC

11. Which of the following is not meaningful?
    (a) XIV   (b) XVV   (c) XIII   (d) XXII

CCE TEST PAPER-1

A. 1. Write each of the following numerals in words:
   (i) 16, 06, 23, 708 (ii) 14, 23, 08, 915

2. Write each of the following numerals in words:
   (i) 80, 060, 409   (ii) 234, 150, 319

3. Arrange the following numbers in ascending order:
   3903216, 19430124, 864572, 6940513, 16531079

4. Arrange the following numbers in descending order:
   54796203, 4675238, 63240613, 5125648, 589623

5. How many 7-digit numbers are there in all?

6. Write the largest and smallest numbers using each of the digits 1, 4, 6, 8, 0 only once and find their difference.

7. Write the Hindu-Arabic numeral for each of the following:
   (i) CCXLII   (ii) CDLXV   (iii) LXXVI
   (iv) DCCXLI   (v) XCIV   (vi) CXCIX

8. Write the Roman numeral for each of the following:
   (i) 84   (ii) 99   (iii) 145   (iv) 406   (v) 519

9. Write the successor and predecessor of 999999 and find their difference.

10. Round off each of the following to the nearest thousand:
   (i) 1046   (ii) 973   (iii) 5624   (iv) 4368

B. *Mark (✓) against the correct answer in each of the following:*

11. Which of the following Roman numerals is correct?
   (a) XC   (b) XD   (c) DM   (d) VL

12. 1 Lakh = ... thousands.
   (a) 10   (b) 100   (c) 1000   (d) none of these

13. No Roman numeral can be repeated more than ...... times.
   (a) two   (b) three   (c) four   (d) none of these

14. How many times does the digit 9 occur between 1 and 100?
   (a) 11   (b) 15   (c) 18   (d) 20

15. (7268 – 2427) estimated to the nearest hundred is
   (a) 4900   (b) 4800   (c) 4841   (d) 5000

16. One million = ...
   (a) 1 lakh   (b) 10 lakh   (c) 100 lakh   (d) 1 crore

17. 1512 when rounded off to the nearest hundred is
   (a) 1600   (b) 1500   (c) 1510   (d) none of these

18. Which of the symbols are never repeated?
   (a) V, X and C   (b) V, X and D   (c) V, L and D   (d) L, K and C

19. Write 86324805 separating periods in Hindu-Arabic system.

C. 20. *Fill in the blanks:*
   (i) 1 crore = ... lakh
   (ii) 1 crore = ... million
   (iii) 564 when estimated to the nearest hundred is ....
   (iv) The smallest 4-digit number with four different digits is ....

D. Write 'T' for true and 'F' for false in each of the following:

21. The difference in the face value and the place value of 5 in 85419 is 85414.

22. In Roman numerals V, L and D are never subtracted.

23. The successor of the greatest 5-digit number is 100000.

24. The estimated value of 46,530 to the nearest hundred is 46500.

25. 100 lakhs make a million.

_____

2 | Factors and Multiples

In the previous class we have studied the basic ideas about factors and multiples. In this chapter, we shall review these ideas and extend our study to include some new properties. Here, by numbers we would mean only counting numbers. Recall the following two definitions.

FACTOR   *A factor of a number is an exact divisor of that number.*

MULTIPLE   *A number is said to be a multiple of any of its factors.*

EXAMPLE   We know that $15 = 1 \times 15$ and $15 = 3 \times 5$.
This shows that each of the numbers 1, 3, 5, 15 exactly divides 15.
Therefore, 1, 3, 5, 15 are all *factors* of 15.
In other words, we can say that 15 is a *multiple* of each one of the numbers 1, 3, 5 and 15.

Thus, we conclude that

if a number x divides a number y exactly then x is called a factor of y, and y is called a multiple of x.

Clearly, 1 *is a factor of every number.*

And, *every number is a factor of itself.*

It may be noted that 1 *is the only number which has exactly one factor, namely, itself.*

VARIOUS TYPES OF NUMBERS

(i) EVEN NUMBERS *All multiples of 2 are called even numbers.*

For example: 2, 4, 6, 8, 10, 12, etc., are all even numbers.

(ii) ODD NUMBERS *Numbers which are not multiples of 2 are called odd numbers.*

For example: 1, 3, 5, 7, 9, 11, 13, etc., are all odd numbers.

(iii) PRIME NUMBERS *Each of the numbers which have exactly two factors, namely, 1 and itself, is called a prime number.*

For example: The numbers 2, 3, 5, 7, 11, 13, 17, 19, 23, etc., are all prime numbers.

(iv) COMPOSITE NUMBERS *Numbers having more than two factors are known as composite numbers.*

For example: Each of the numbers 4, 6, 8, 9, 10, 12, 14, etc., is a composite number.

IMPORTANT FACTS
   (i) 1 *is neither prime nor composite.*
   (ii) 2 *is the lowest prime number.*
   (iii) 2 *is the only even prime number.* All other even numbers are composite numbers.

FINDING PRIME AND COMPOSITE NUMBERS FROM 1 to 100

A method for finding the prime and composite numbers from 1 to 100 was found by the Greek mathematician **Eratosthenes.**

Under this method, we proceed according to the steps given below.

Step 1.   Prepare a table of numbers from 1 to 100, taking ten numbers in each row, as shown below.

Step 2.   We know that 1 is neither prime nor composite. So, we separate it out by making a box around it.

Step 3.   Encircle ② as a prime number and cross out every multiple of 2.

Step 4.   Encircle ③ as a prime number and cross out every multiple of 3. We need not mark the numbers which have already been crossed out.

Step 5.   Encircle ⑤ as a prime number and cross out every multiple of 5. We need not mark the numbers which have already been crossed out.

Step 6.   Continue this process till the numbers up to 100 are either encircled or crossed-out.

SIEVE OF ERATOSTHENES

1	2	3	4	5	6	7	8	9	10
11	12	13	14	15	16	17	18	19	20
21	22	23	24	25	26	27	28	29	30
31	32	33	34	35	36	37	38	39	40
41	42	43	44	45	46	47	48	49	50
51	52	53	54	55	56	57	58	59	60
61	62	63	64	65	66	67	68	69	70
71	72	73	74	75	76	77	78	79	80
81	82	83	84	85	86	87	88	89	90
91	92	93	94	95	96	97	98	99	100

Note that: (i) 1 is neither prime nor composite.
(ii) All encircled numbers are prime numbers.
(iii) All crossed out numbers are composite numbers.

Thus, all prime numbers from 1 to 100 are:

2, 3, 5, 7, 11, 13, 17, 19, 23, 29, 31, 37, 41, 43, 47, 53, 59, 61, 67, 71, 73, 79, 83, 89, 97

TWIN PRIMES   *Two consecutive odd prime numbers are known as twin primes.*

Pairs of twin primes between 1 and 100 are:

(i) 3, 5	(ii) 5, 7	(iii) 11, 13	(iv) 17, 19
(v) 29, 31	(vi) 41, 43	(vii) 59, 61	(viii) 71, 73

PRIME TRIPLET   *A set of three consecutive prime numbers, differing by 2, is called a prime triplet.*

The only prime triplet is (3, 5, 7).

CO-PRIMES   *Two numbers are said to be co-primes if they do not have a common factor other than 1.*

EXAMPLES   (i) 2, 3   (ii) 3, 4   (iii) 4, 5   (iv) 4, 9   (v) 8, 15

REMARK 1   Two prime numbers are always co-primes.

REMARK 2   Two co-primes need not be prime numbers.

EXAMPLES: 6, 7 are co-primes, while 6 is not a prime number.

9, 10 are co-primes, while none of 9 and 10 is a prime number.

PERFECT NUMBERS *If the sum of all the factors of a number is two times the number, then the number is called a perfect number.*

EXAMPLES   (i) 6 *is a perfect number*, since the factors of 6 are 1, 2, 3, 6 and $(1 + 2 + 3 + 6) = (2 \times 6)$.

(ii) 28 *is a perfect number*, since the factors of 28 are 1, 2, 4, 7, 14, 28 and $(1 + 2 + 4 + 7 + 14 + 28) = (2 \times 28)$.

EXERCISE 2A

1. Define: (i) factor (ii) multiple. Give five examples of each.

2. Write down all the factors of
   (i) 20   (ii) 36   (iii) 60   (iv) 75

3. Write the first five multiples of each of the following numbers:
   (i) 17   (ii) 23   (iii) 65   (iv) 70

4. Which of the following numbers are even and which are odd?
   (i) 32   (ii) 37   (iii) 50   (iv) 58
   (v) 69   (vi) 144   (vii) 321   (viii) 253

5. What are prime numbers? Give ten examples.

6. Write all the prime numbers between
   (i) 10 and 40   (ii) 80 and 100   (iii) 40 and 80   (iv) 30 and 40

7. (i) Write the smallest prime number.
   (ii) List all even prime numbers.
   (iii) Write the smallest odd prime number.

8. Find which of the following numbers are primes:
   (i) 87   (ii) 89   (iii) 63   (iv) 91

9. Make a list of seven consecutive numbers, none of which is prime.
   Hint. *See the sieve of Eratosthenes.*

10. (i) Is there any counting number having no factor at all?
    (ii) Find all the numbers having exactly one factor.
    (iii) Find numbers between 1 and 100 having exactly three factors.

11. What are composite numbers? Can a composite number be odd? If yes, write the smallest odd composite number.

12. What are twin primes? Write all the pairs of twin primes between 50 and 100.

13. What are co-primes? Give examples of five pairs of co-primes. Are co-primes always primes? If no, illustrate your answer by an example.

14. Express each of the following numbers as the sum of two odd primes:
    (i) 36   (ii) 42   (iii) 84   (iv) 98

15. Express each of the following odd numbers as the sum of three odd prime numbers:
    (i) 31   (ii) 35   (iii) 49   (iv) 63

16. Express each of the following numbers as the sum of twin primes:

(i) 36   (ii) 84   (iii) 120   (iv) 144

17. Which of the following statements are true?

    (i) 1 is the smallest prime number.

    (ii) If a number is prime, it must be odd.

    (iii) The sum of two prime numbers is always a prime number.

    (iv) If two numbers are co-primes, at least one of them must be a prime number.

DIVISIBILITY TESTS FOR 2, 3, 4, 5, 6, 7, 8, 9, 10 AND 11

(i) TEST OF DIVISIBILITY BY 2 *A number is divisible by 2 if its ones digit is 0, 2, 4, 6 or 8.*

EXAMPLE 1.   Each of the numbers 30, 52, 84, 136, 2108 is divisible by 2.

EXAMPLE 2.   None of the numbers 71, 83, 215, 467, 629 is divisible by 2.

(ii) TEST OF DIVISIBILITY BY 3 *A number is divisible by 3 if the sum of its digits is divisible by 3.*

EXAMPLE 1.   Consider the number 64275.
            Sum of its digits = (6 + 4 + 2 + 7 + 5) = 24, which is divisible by 3.
            Therefore, 64275 is divisible by 3.

EXAMPLE 2.   Consider the number 39583.
            Sum of its digits = (3 + 9 + 5 + 8 + 3) = 28, which is not divisible by 3.
            Therefore, 39583 is not divisible by 3.

(iii) TEST OF DIVISIBILITY BY 4 *A number is divisible by 4 if the number formed by its digits in the tens and ones places is divisible by 4.*

EXAMPLE 1.   Consider the number 96852.
            The number formed by the tens and ones digits is 52, which is divisible by 4.
            Therefore, 96852 is divisible by 4.

EXAMPLE 2.   Consider the number 61394.
            The number formed by the tens and ones digits is 94, which is not divisible by 4.
            Therefore, 61394 is not divisible by 4.

(iv) TEST OF DIVISIBILITY BY 5 *A number is divisible by 5 if its ones digit is 0 or 5.*

EXAMPLE 1.   Each of the numbers 65, 195, 230, 310 is divisible by 5.

EXAMPLE 2.   None of the numbers 71, 83, 94, 106, 327, 148, 279 is divisible by 5.

(v) TEST OF DIVISIBILITY BY 6 *A number is divisible by 6 if it is divisible by each one of 2 and 3.*
            Note that 2 and 3 are the prime factors of 6.

EXAMPLE 1.   Each of the numbers 18, 42, 60, 114, 1356 is divisible by 6.

EXAMPLE 2.   None of the numbers 21, 25, 34, 52 is divisible by 6.

(vi) TEST OF DIVISIBILITY BY 7 *A number is divisible by 7 if the difference between twice the ones digit and the number formed by the other digits is either 0 or a multiple of 7.*

EXAMPLE 1.   Consider the number 6804.
            Clearly, (680 − 2 × 4) = 672, which is divisible by 7.
            Therefore, 6804 is divisible by 7.

EXAMPLE 2.   Consider the number 137.
              Clearly, $(2 \times 7) - 13 = 1$, which is not divisible by 7.
              Therefore, 137 is not divisible by 7.

EXAMPLE 3.   Consider the number 1367.
              Clearly, $136 - (2 \times 7) = 136 - 14 = 122$, which is not divisible by 7.
              Therefore, 1367 is not divisible by 7.

(vii) TEST OF DIVISIBILITY BY 8 *A number is divisible by 8 if the number formed by its digits in*
hundreds, tens and ones places is divisible by 8.

EXAMPLE 1.   Consider the number 79152.
              The number formed by hundreds, tens and ones digits is 152, which is clearly
              divisible by 8.
              Therefore, 79152 is divisible by 8.

EXAMPLE 2.   Consider the number 57348.
              The number formed by hundreds, tens and ones digits is 348, which is not divisible
              by 8.
              Therefore, 57348 is not divisible by 8.

(viii) TEST OF DIVISIBILITY BY 9 *A number is divisible by 9 if the sum of its digits is divisible*
by 9.

EXAMPLE 1.   Consider the number 65403.
              Sum of its digits = $(6 + 5 + 4 + 0 + 3) = 18$, which is divisible by 9.
              Therefore, 65403 is divisible by 9.

EXAMPLE 2.   Consider the number 81326.
              Sum of its digits = $(8 + 1 + 3 + 2 + 6) = 20$, which is not divisible by 9.
              Therefore, 81326 is not divisible by 9.

(ix) TEST OF DIVISIBILITY BY 10 *A number is divisible by 10 if its ones digit is 0.*

EXAMPLE 1.   Each of the numbers 30, 160, 690, 720 is divisible by 10.

EXAMPLE 2.   None of the numbers 21, 32, 63, 84, etc., is divisible by 10.

(x) TEST OF DIVISIBILITY BY 11 *A number is divisible by 11 if the difference of the sum of its*
digits in odd places and the sum of its digits in even places (starting from the ones
place) is either 0 or a multiple of 11.

EXAMPLE 1.   Consider the number 90728.
              Sum of its digits in odd places = $(8 + 7 + 9) = 24$.
              Sum of its digits in even places = $(2 + 0) = 2$.
              Difference of the two sums = $(24 - 2) = 22$, which is clearly divisible by 11.
              Therefore, 90728 is divisible by 11.

EXAMPLE 2.   Consider the number 863423.
              Sum of its digits in odd places = $(3 + 4 + 6) = 13$.
              Sum of its digits in even places = $(2 + 3 + 8) = 13$.
              Difference of these sums = $(13 - 13) = 0$.
              Therefore, 863423 is divisible by 11.

EXAMPLE 3.   Consider the number 76844.
              Sum of its digits in odd places = $(4 + 8 + 7) = 19$.
              Sum of its digits in even places = $(4 + 6) = 10$.
              Difference of these sums = $(19 - 10) = 9$, which is not divisible by 11.
              Therefore, 76844 is not divisible by 11.

GENERAL PROPERTIES OF DIVISIBILITY

PROPERTY 1. *If a number is divisible by another number, it must be divisible by each of the factors of that number.*

EXAMPLE   We know that 36 is divisible by 12.
               All factors of 12 are 1, 2, 3, 4, 6, 12.
               Clearly, 36 is divisible by each one of 1, 2, 3, 4, 6, 12.

REMARKS   As a consequence of the above result, we can say that
     (i) every number divisible by 9 is also divisible by 3,
     (ii) every number divisible by 8 is also divisible by 4.

PROPERTY 2. *If a number is divisible by each of two co-prime numbers, it must be divisible by their product.*

EXAMPLE 1.   We know that 972 is divisible by each of the numbers 2 and 3. Also, 2 and 3 are co-primes.
               So, according to Property 2, the number 972 must be divisible by 6, which is true.

EXAMPLE 2.   We know that 4320 is divisible by each one of the numbers 5 and 8. Also, 5 and 8 are co-primes.
               So, 4320 must be divisible by 40.
               By actual division, we find that it is true.

EXAMPLE 3.   Consider the number 372.
               It may be verified that the above number is divisible by both 4 and 6.
               But, by actual division, we find that 372 is not divisible by 24.
               Be careful, 4 and 6 are not co-primes.

REMARK   Since two prime numbers are always co-primes, it follows that if a number is divisible by each one of any two prime numbers then the number is divisible by their product.

PROPERTY 3. *If a number is a factor of each of the two given numbers, then it must be a factor of their sum.*

EXAMPLE 1.   We know that 5 is a factor of 15 as well as that of 20.
               So, 5 must be a factor of (15 + 20), that is, 35.
               And, this is clearly true.

EXAMPLE 2.   We know that 7 is a factor of each of the numbers 49 and 63.
               So, 7 must be a factor of (49 + 63) = 112.
               Clearly, 7 divides 112 exactly.

PROPERTY 4. *If a number is a factor of each of the two given numbers then it must be a factor of their difference.*

EXAMPLE 1.   We know that 3 is a factor of each one of the numbers 36 and 24.
               So, 3 must be a factor of (36 – 24) = 12.
               Clearly, 3 divides 12 exactly.

EXAMPLE 2.   We know that 13 is a factor of each one of the numbers 65 and 117.
               So, 13 must be a factor of (117 – 65) = 52.
               Clearly, 13 divides 52 exactly.

TO FIND PRIME NUMBERS BETWEEN 100 AND 200

We know that $15 \times 15 > 200$.

So, we adopt the following rule:

Rule   *Examine whether the given number is divisible by any prime number less than 15. If yes then it is not prime; otherwise it is prime.*

EXAMPLE   *Which of the following are prime numbers?*
       (i) 117   *(ii)* 139   *(iii)* 193

Solution   (i)   Test the divisibility of 117 by each one of the prime numbers 2, 3, 5, 7, 11, 13, taking one by one. We find that 117 is divisible by 13. So, 117 is not a prime number.

           (ii)   Test the divisibility of 139 by each one of the prime numbers 2, 3, 5, 7, 11, 13. We find that 139 is divisible by none of them. So, 139 is a prime number.

           (iii)   Test the divisibility of 193 by each one of the prime numbers 2, 3, 5, 7, 11, 13. We find that 193 is divisible by none of them.
              So, 193 is a prime number.

TO FIND PRIME NUMBERS BETWEEN 100 AND 400

We know that $20 \times 20 = 400$.

Rule   *Examine whether the given number is divisible by any prime number less than 20. If yes then it is not prime; otherwise it is prime.*

EXAMPLE   *Which of the following is a prime number?*
       (i) 263   *(ii)* 323   *(iii)* 361

Solution   (i)   Test the divisibility of 263 by each one of the prime numbers 2, 3, 5, 7, 11, 13, 17, 19. We find that 263 is not divisible by any of these numbers.
              So, 263 is a prime number.

           (ii)   Test the divisibility of 323 by each one of the numbers 2, 3, 5, 7, 11, 13, 17, 19. We find that 323 is divisible by 17.
              $\therefore$ 323 is not a prime number.

           (iii)   Test the divisibility of 361 by each one of the prime numbers 2, 3, 5, 7, 11, 13, 17, 19. We find that 361 is divisible by 19.
              Hence, 361 is not a prime number.

EXERCISE 2B

1. Test the divisibility of the following numbers by 2:
   (i) 2650   (ii) 69435   (iii) 59628
   (iv) 789403   (v) 357986   (vi) 367314

2. Test the divisibility of the following numbers by 3:
   (i) 733   (ii) 10038   (iii) 20701
   (iv) 524781   (v) 79124   (vi) 872645

3. Test the divisibility of the following numbers by 4:
   (i) 618   (ii) 2314   (iii) 63712
   (iv) 35056   (v) 946126   (vi) 810524

4. Test the divisibility of the following numbers by 5:
   (i) 4965   (ii) 23590   (iii) 35208
   (iv) 723405   (v) 124684   (vi) 438750

5. Test the divisibility of the following numbers by 6:
   (i) 2070   (ii) 46523   (iii) 71232
   (iv) 934706   (v) 251780   (vi) 872536

6. Test the divisibility of the following numbers by 7:
   (i) 826   (ii) 117   (iii) 2345
   (iv) 6021   (v) 14126   (vi) 25368

7. Test the divisibility of the following numbers by 8:
   (i) 9364   (ii) 2138   (iii) 36792
   (iv) 901674   (v) 136976   (vi) 1790184

8. Test the divisibility of the following numbers by 9:
   (i) 2358   (ii) 3333   (iii) 98712
   (iv) 257106   (v) 647514   (vi) 326999

9. Test the divisibility of the following numbers by 10:
   (i) 5790   (ii) 63215   (iii) 55555

10. Test the divisibility of the following numbers by 11:
   (i) 4334   (ii) 83721   (iii) 66311
   (iv) 137269   (v) 901351   (vi) 8790322

11. In each of the following numbers, replace * by the smallest number to make it divisible by 3:
   (i) 27*4   (ii) 53*46   (iii) 8*711
   (iv) 62*35   (v) 234*17   (vi) 6*1054

12. In each of the following numbers, replace * by the smallest number to make it divisible by 9:
   (i) 65*5   (ii) 2*135   (iii) 6702*
   (iv) 91*67   (v) 6678*1   (vi) 835*86

13. In each of the following numbers, replace * by the smallest number to make it divisible by 11:
   (i) 26*5   (ii) 39*43   (iii) 86*72
   (iv) 467*91   (v) 1723*4   (vi) 9*8071

14. Test the divisibility of:
   (i) 10000001 by 11   (ii) 19083625 by 11   (iii) 2134563 by 9
   (iv) 10001001 by 3   (v) 10203574 by 4   (vi) 12030624 by 8

15. Which of the following are prime numbers?
   (i) 103   (ii) 137   (iii) 161   (iv) 179
   (v) 217   (vi) 277   (vii) 331   (viii) 397

16. Give an example of a number
   (i) which is divisible by 2 but not by 4.
   (ii) which is divisible by 4 but not by 8.
   (iii) which is divisible by both 2 and 8 but not by 16.
   (iv) which is divisible by both 3 and 6 but not by 18.

17. Write (T) for true and (F) for false against each of the following statements:
   (i) If a number is divisible by 4, it must be divisible by 8.
   (ii) If a number is divisible by 8, it must be divisible by 4.
   (iii) If a number divides the sum of two numbers exactly, it must exactly divide the numbers separately.
   (iv) If a number is divisible by both 9 and 10, it must be divisible by 90.
      Hint. 9 *and* 10 *are co-primes.*
   (v) A number is divisible by 18 if it is divisible by both 3 and 6.
      Hint. 3 *and* 6 *are not co-primes. Consider* 186.

(vi) If a number is divisible by 3 and 7, it must be divisible by 21.

(vii) The sum of two consecutive odd numbers is always divisible by 4.

(viii) If a number divides two numbers exactly, it must divide their sum exactly.

PRIME FACTORIZATION

PRIME FACTOR *A factor of a given number is called a prime factor if this factor is a prime number.*

EXAMPLE 2 and 3 are prime factors of 12.

PRIME FACTORIZATION *To express a given number as a product of prime factors is called prime factorization or complete factorization of the given number.*

EXAMPLE Let us factorize 36 in three different ways as given below:

$$36 = 2 \times 18 \qquad 36 = 3 \times 12 \qquad 36 = 9 \times 4$$
$$2 \times 9 \qquad\qquad 2 \times 6 \qquad\qquad 3 \times 3 \quad 2 \times 2$$
$$3 \times 3 \qquad\qquad 2 \times 3$$

Thus, $36 = 2 \times 2 \times 3 \times 3$; $36 = 3 \times 2 \times 2 \times 3$; $36 = 3 \times 3 \times 2 \times 2$.

We notice here that in each of the prime factorizations, the factors may be arranged differently but, in fact, they are the same.

Thus, we generalise this result as under.

Every composite number can be factorized into primes in only one way, except for the order of primes.

This property is known as *unique factorization property.*

CONCEPT OF POWER

We write, $2 \times 2 = 2^2$ (read as 2 raised to the power 2),

$2 \times 2 \times 2 = 2^3$ (read as 2 raised to the power 3),

$2 \times 2 \times 2 \times 2 = 2^4$ (read as 2 raised to the power 4),

and so on.

Similarly, $3 \times 3 = 3^2, 3 \times 3 \times 3 = 3^3, 3 \times 3 \times 3 \times 3 = 3^4$, and so on.

In general, $a \times a \times \dots$ taken m times $= a^m$.

SOLVED EXAMPLES

EXAMPLE 1. *Give the prime factorization of 1260.*

Solution We use the division method, as shown below.

2	1260
2	630
3	315
3	105
5	35
7	7
	1

$\therefore$ $1260 = 2 \times 2 \times 3 \times 3 \times 5 \times 7 = 2^2 \times 3^2 \times 5 \times 7$.

EXAMPLE 2.   *Give the prime factorization of* 20570.

Solution   We have:

2	20570
5	10285
11	2057
11	187
17	17
	1

Therefore, $20570 = 2 \times 5 \times 11 \times 11 \times 17 = 2 \times 5 \times 11^2 \times 17$.

EXERCISE 2C

Give the prime factorization of each of the following numbers:

1. 12	2. 18	3. 48	4. 56	5. 90
6. 136	7. 252	8. 420	9. 637	10. 945
11. 1224	12. 1323	13. 8712	14. 9317	15. 1035
16. 1197	17. 4641	18. 4335	19. 2907	20. 13915

HCF AND LCM

HIGHEST COMMON FACTOR (HCF) *The greatest number which is a common factor of two or more given numbers, is called their* **highest common factor** *or* **greatest common divisor** *or* **greatest common measure,** *written as HCF or GCD or GCM.*

EXAMPLE   *Let us find the HCF of* 24 *and* 32.

Solution   All the factors of 24 are: 1, 2, 3, 4, 6, 8, 12, 24

All the factors of 32 are: 1, 2, 4, 8, 16, 32

Common factors of 24 and 32 are: 1, 2, 4, 8
Thus, the highest common factor of 24 and 32 is 8.
Hence, HCF of 24 and 32 = 8.

TO FIND HCF (BY PRIME FACTORIZATION METHOD) *We first find the prime factorization of each of the given numbers. Then, the product of all common prime factors, using the least power of each common prime factor, is the HCF of the given numbers.*

SOLVED EXAMPLES

EXAMPLE 1.   *Find the HCF of* 144 *and* 198 *by the prime factorization method.*

Solution   We have:

2	144
2	72
2	36
2	18
3	9
3	3
	1

2	198
3	99
3	33
11	11
	1

$\therefore$ $144 = 2 \times 2 \times 2 \times 2 \times 3 \times 3 = 2^4 \times 3^2.$

And, $198 = 2 \times 3 \times 3 \times 11 = 2 \times 3^2 \times 11.$

$\therefore$ HCF of 144 and 198 $= 2 \times 3^2 = 18.$

EXAMPLE 2. *Find the HCF of 396 and 1080 by the prime factorization method.*

Solution We have:

2	396
2	198
3	99
3	33
11	11
	1

2	1080
2	540
2	270
5	135
3	27
3	9
3	3
	1

So, $396 = 2^2 \times 3^2 \times 11.$

And, $1080 = 2^3 \times 3^3 \times 5.$

Hence, the HCF of 396 and 1080 is $2^2 \times 3^2 = 36.$

EXAMPLE 3. *Find the HCF of 144, 180 and 192 by the prime factorization method.*

Solution We have:

2	144
2	72
2	36
2	18
3	9
3	3
	1

2	180
2	90
3	45
3	15
5	5
	1

2	192
2	96
2	48
2	24
2	12
2	6
3	3
	1

So, $144 = 2 \times 2 \times 2 \times 2 \times 3 \times 3 = 2^4 \times 3^2;$

$180 = 2 \times 2 \times 3 \times 3 \times 5 = 2^2 \times 3^2 \times 5;$

$192 = 2 \times 2 \times 2 \times 2 \times 2 \times 2 \times 3 = 2^6 \times 3.$

Therefore, the HCF of the given numbers $= 2^2 \times 3 = 12.$

TO FIND HCF (BY DIVISION METHOD) *Suppose two numbers are given. Divide the greater number by the smaller one. Next, divide the divisor by the remainder. Go on repeating the process of dividing the preceding divisor by the remainder last obtained till the remainder zero is obtained. Then the last divisor is the required HCF of the given numbers.*

EXAMPLE 4. *Find the HCF of 161 and 345 by the division method.*

Solution We have:

$$
161 \overline{)\ 345\ }(2
$$
$$
\underline{-\ 322}
$$
$$
23 \overline{)\ 161\ }(7
$$
$$
\underline{-\ 161}
$$
$$
\times
$$

Hence, the HCF of 161 and 345 is 23.

EXAMPLE 5.   *Find the HCF of* 513 *and* 783.

Solution   By the division method, we have:

$$513 \overline{)783} (1$$
$$\underline{-513}$$
$$270 \overline{)513} (1$$
$$\underline{-270}$$
$$243 \overline{)270} (1$$
$$\underline{-243}$$
$$27 \overline{)243} (9$$
$$\underline{-243}$$
$$\times$$

Hence, the HCF of 513 and 783 is 27.

TO FIND THE HCF OF MORE THAN TWO NUMBERS *If more than two numbers are given, choose any two of them and find their HCF. The HCF of this HCF and the third number gives the HCF of these three numbers. The HCF of this HCF and the fourth number gives the HCF of these four numbers, and so on.*

EXAMPLE 6.   *Find the HCF of* 136, 170 *and* 255.

Solution   First we find the HCF of 136 and 170.

$$136 \overline{)170} (1$$
$$\underline{-136}$$
$$34 \overline{)136} (4$$
$$\underline{-136}$$
$$\times$$

Thus, the HCF of 136 and 170 is 34.
Now, we find the HCF of 34 and 255.

$$34 \overline{)255} (7$$
$$\underline{-238}$$
$$17 \overline{)34} (2$$
$$\underline{-34}$$
$$\times$$

So, the HCF of 34 and 255 is 17.
Hence, the HCF of 136, 170 and 255 is 17.

EXAMPLE 7.   *Find the greatest number which divides* 285 *and* 1249, *leaving remainders* 9 *and* 7 *respectively.*

Solution   Clearly, we must find the greatest number which divides (285 − 9) and (1249 − 7) exactly.

So, the required number = HCF of 276 and 1242.

$$276 \overline{)1242} (4$$
$$\underline{-1104}$$
$$138 \overline{)276} (2$$
$$\underline{-276}$$
$$\times$$

Hence, the required number = 138.

EXAMPLE 8. *Reduce* $\dfrac{289}{391}$ *to the lowest terms.*

Solution For reducing the given fraction to the lowest terms, we divide its numerator and the denominator by their HCF.

Now, we find the HCF of 289 and 391 as under:

$$289\,)\,391\,(1$$
$$\underline{-\,289}$$
$$102\,)\,289\,(2$$
$$\underline{-\,204}$$
$$85\,)\,102\,(1$$
$$\underline{-\,85}$$
$$17\,)\,85\,(5$$
$$\underline{-\,85}$$
$$\times$$

Hence, the HCF of 289 and 391 is 17.

Now, dividing the numerator and the denominator of the given fraction by 17, we get:

$$\frac{289}{391} = \frac{289 \div 17}{391 \div 17} = \frac{17}{23}.$$

EXAMPLE 9. *The length, breadth and height of a room are 1050 cm, 750 cm and 425 cm respectively. Find the length of the longest tape which can measure the three dimensions of the room exactly.*

Solution The length of the longest tape which can measure the given lengths
$$= \text{HCF of 1050 cm, 750 cm and 425 cm.}$$

First we find the HCF of 1050 and 750.

$$750\,)\,1050\,(1$$
$$\underline{-\,750}$$
$$300\,)\,750\,(2$$
$$\underline{-\,600}$$
$$150\,)\,300\,(2$$
$$\underline{-\,300}$$
$$\times$$

Hence, HCF of 1050 and 750 = 150.

Now, we find the HCF of 150 and 425.

$$150\,)\,425\,(2$$
$$\underline{-\,300}$$
$$125\,)\,150\,(1$$
$$\underline{-\,125}$$
$$25\,)\,125\,(5$$
$$\underline{-\,125}$$
$$\times$$

Hence, HCF of 150 and 425 is 25.

Thus, the HCF of 1050, 750 and 425 is 25.

Hence, the required length = 25 cm.

EXERCISE 2D

Find the HCF of the numbers in each of the following, using the prime factorization method:

1. 84, 98
2. 170, 238
3. 504, 980
4. 72, 108, 180
5. 84, 120, 138
6. 106, 159, 371
7. 272, 425
8. 144, 252, 630
9. 1197, 5320, 4389

Find the HCF of the numbers in each of the following, using the division method:

10. 58, 70
11. 399, 437
12. 1045, 1520
13. 1965, 2096
14. 2241, 2324
15. 658, 940, 1128
16. 754, 1508, 1972
17. 391, 425, 527
18. 1794, 2346, 4761

Show that the following pairs are co-primes:

19. 59, 97
20. 161, 192
21. 343, 432
22. 512, 945
23. 385, 621
24. 847, 1014

Hint. *Two numbers are co-primes if their HCF is 1.*

25. Find the greatest number which divides 615 and 963, leaving the remainder 6 in each case.
26. Find the greatest number which divides 2011 and 2623, leaving remainders 9 and 5 respectively.
27. Find the greatest number that will divide 445, 572 and 699, leaving remainders 4, 5, 6 respectively.
28. Reduce each of the following fractions to the lowest terms:

    (i) $\dfrac{161}{207}$
    (ii) $\dfrac{517}{799}$
    (iii) $\dfrac{296}{481}$

29. Three pieces of timber, 42-m, 49-m and 63-m long, have to be divided into planks of the same length. What is the greatest possible length of each plank?
30. Three different containers contain 403 L, 434 L and 465 L of milk respectively. Find the capacity of a container which can measure the milk of all the containers in an exact number of times.
31. There are 527 apples, 646 pears and 748 oranges. These are to be arranged in heaps containing the same number of fruits. Find the greatest number of fruits possible in each heap. How many heaps are formed?
32. Determine the longest tape which can be used to measure exactly the lengths 7 m, 3 m 85 cm and 12 m 95 cm.

    Hint. *Convert all the lengths to cm and then take the HCF.*

33. A rectangular courtyard is 18 m 72 cm long and 13 m 20 cm broad. It is to be paved with square tiles of the same size. Find the least possible number of such tiles.
34. Find the HCF of

    (i) two prime numbers
    (ii) two consecutive numbers
    (iii) two co-primes
    (iv) 2 and an even number

═══════

LOWEST COMMON MULTIPLE (LCM) *The lowest common multiple of two or more numbers is the smallest number which is a multiple of each of the numbers.*

EXAMPLE   *Let us find the LCM of 4 and 6.*

Solution   Multiples of 4 are: | 4, 8, 12, 16, 20, 24, 28, 32, 36, ... |

Multiples of 6 are: 6, 12, 18, 24, 30, 36, ...

Common multiples of 4 and 6 are: 12, 24, 36, ...

Lowest common multiple of 4 and 6 is 12.

Hence, LCM of 4 and 6 = 12.

TO FIND LCM (BY PRIME FACTORIZATION METHOD) *In order to find the LCM of two or more given numbers we write the prime factorization of each of the given numbers. Then, the required LCM of these numbers is the product of all different prime factors of the numbers, using the greatest power of each common prime factor.*

SOLVED EXAMPLES

EXAMPLE 1. *Find the LCM of 24, 36 and 40 by the prime factorization method.*

Solution   We have:

2	24
2	12
2	6
3	3
	1

2	36
2	18
3	9
3	3
	1

2	40
2	20
2	10
5	5
	1

$\therefore$ $24 = 2^3 \times 3$

$36 = 2^2 \times 3^2$

$40 = 2^3 \times 5$

Hence, the LCM of 24, 36 and 40 is $2^3 \times 3^2 \times 5 = 360$.

EXAMPLE 2. *Find the LCM of 112, 168, 266 by the prime factorization method.*

Solution   We have:

2	112
2	56
2	28
2	14
7	7
	1

2	168
2	84
2	42
3	21
7	7
	1

2	266
7	133
19	19
	1

$\therefore$ $112 = 2^4 \times 7$

$168 = 2^3 \times 3 \times 7$

$266 = 2 \times 7 \times 19$

Therefore, the LCM of the given numbers $= 2^4 \times 3 \times 7 \times 19 = 6384$.

TO FIND LCM (BY DIVISION METHOD) *In this method, we arrange the given numbers in a line, in any order. We divide by a number which divides exactly at least two of the given numbers and carry forward the numbers which are not divisible. This process is repeated till no two of the given numbers are divisible by a common number. The product of the divisors and the undivided numbers is the required LCM of the given numbers.*

EXAMPLE 3. *Find the LCM of 12, 15, 20, 27 by the division method.*

Solution   We have:

3	12, 15, 20, 27
4	4, 5, 20, 9
5	1, 5, 5, 9
	1, 1, 1, 9

Hence, the LCM of the given numbers $= 3 \times 4 \times 5 \times 9 = 540$.

EXAMPLE 4.   *Find the LCM of* 22, 54, 108, 135 *and* 198.

Solution   We have:

2	22, 54, 108, 135, 198
11	11, 27, 54, 135, 99
9	1, 27, 54, 135, 9
3	1, 3, 6, 15, 1
	1, 1, 2, 5, 1

Hence, the LCM of the given numbers $= 2 \times 11 \times 9 \times 3 \times 2 \times 5 = 5940$.

EXAMPLE 5.   *Find the smallest number which when diminished by* 3 *is divisible by* 21, 28, 36 *and* 45.

Solution   We know that the smallest number divisible by 21, 28, 36 and 45 is their LCM. We calculate this LCM as under:

7	21, 28, 36, 45
3	3, 4, 36, 45
3	1, 4, 12, 15
4	1, 4, 4, 5
	1, 1, 1, 5

Hence, the LCM of 21, 28, 36 and 45 is $7 \times 3 \times 3 \times 4 \times 5 = 1260$.

Hence, the required number $= (1260 + 3) = 1263$.

EXAMPLE 6.   *In a shop, there are three clocks which chime at intervals of* 15, 20 *and* 30 *minutes respectively. They all chime together at* 10 *a.m. At what time will they all chime together again?*

Solution   Required time = LCM of 15, 20, 30 minutes.

5	15, 20, 30
3	3, 4, 6
2	1, 4, 2
	1, 2, 1

∴   LCM of 15, 20, 30 $= (5 \times 3 \times 2 \times 2) = 60$.

So, all the clocks will chime together again after 60 minutes, i.e., after 1 hour, i.e., at 11 a.m.

PROPERTIES OF HCF AND LCM OF GIVEN NUMBERS

 (i) *The HCF of a group of numbers is not greater than any of the given numbers.*

 (ii) *The HCF of two co-primes is* 1.

(iii) *The LCM of a group of numbers is not less than any of the given numbers.*

(iv) *The LCM of two co-primes is equal to their product.*

 (v) *The HCF of a group of numbers is always a factor of their LCM.*

EXAMPLE Consider the numbers 12, 16, 36, 40.

Clearly, the HCF of the given numbers $= 4$.

And, their LCM

$\qquad = 2 \times 2 \times 3 \times 2 \times 2 \times 3 \times 5 = 720.$

2	12, 16, 36, 40
2	6, 8, 18, 20
3	3, 4, 9, 10
2	1, 4, 3, 10
	1, 2, 3, 5

Clearly, 4 is a factor of 720.

(vi) *If a and b are two given numbers such that a is a factor of b then their HCF = a and their LCM = b.*

EXAMPLE We know that 8 is a factor of 32.

Then, clearly HCF of 8 and 32 is 8.

And, LCM of 8 and 32 is 32.

(vii) **AN IMPORTANT PROPERTY** *If two numbers are given then the product of the two numbers = the product of their HCF and LCM.*

EXAMPLE Consider the numbers 48 and 60.

We have, $48 = 2 \times 2 \times 2 \times 2 \times 3 = 2^4 \times 3$.

And, $60 = 2 \times 2 \times 3 \times 5 = 2^2 \times 3 \times 5$.

So, the HCF of 48 and 60 is $2^2 \times 3 = 12$.

And, the LCM of 48 and 60 is $2^4 \times 3 \times 5 = 240$.

Now, the product of the given numbers $= 48 \times 60 = 2880$.

Product of their HCF and LCM $= (12 \times 240) = 2880$.

$\therefore$ *product of two numbers = (their HCF) × (their LCM).*

REMARKS Thus, for any two given numbers, we have:

$$\text{(i) LCM} = \frac{\text{(one number)} \times \text{(the other number)}}{\text{their HCF}}$$

$$\text{(ii) HCF} = \frac{\text{(one number)} \times \text{(the other number)}}{\text{their LCM}}$$

EXAMPLE 7. *Find the HCF and the LCM of 1152 and 1664.*

Solution We first find the HCF of the given numbers.

```
1152 ) 1664 ( 1
       -1152
        512 ) 1152 ( 2
             -1024
              128 ) 512 ( 4
                   -512
                    ×
```

$\therefore$ HCF = 128.

And, $\text{LCM} = \dfrac{\text{product of the numbers}}{\text{their HCF}} = \dfrac{1152 \times 1664}{128} = 14976$.

$\therefore$ HCF = 128 and LCM = 14976.

EXAMPLE 8. *The HCF of two numbers is 16 and their product is 3072. Find their LCM.*

Solution We know that

$$\text{LCM} = \frac{\text{product of the given two numbers}}{\text{their HCF}} = \frac{3072}{16} = 192.$$

EXAMPLE 9. *The HCF of two numbers is 23 and their LCM is 1449. If one of the numbers is 161, find the other.*

Solution   We know that

              (one number) × (the other number) = (HCF × LCM).

              Hence, the required number $= \left(\dfrac{23 \times 1449}{161}\right) = 207.$

EXAMPLE 10.   *Can two numbers have 16 as their HCF and 204 as their LCM? Give reason.*

Solution   We know that the HCF of two or more numbers must divide their LCM exactly.
              But, 16 does not divide 204 exactly.

              So, there can be no two numbers with 16 as their HCF and 204 as their LCM.

EXERCISE 2E

Find the LCM of the numbers given below:

1. 42, 63   **2.** 60, 75   **3.** 12, 18, 20   **4.** 36, 60, 72

5. 36, 40, 126   **6.** 16, 28, 40, 77   **7.** 28, 36, 45, 60   **8.** 144, 180, 384

9. 48, 64, 72, 96, 108

Find the HCF and LCM of

10. 117, 221   **11.** 234, 572   **12.** 693, 1078   **13.** 145, 232

14. 861, 1353   **15.** 2923, 3239

16. For each pair of numbers, verify that their product = (HCF × LCM).
   (i) 87, 145   (ii) 186, 403   (iii) 490, 1155

17. The product of two numbers is 2160 and their HCF is 12. Find their LCM.

18. The product of two numbers is 2560 and their LCM is 320. Find their HCF.

19. The HCF of two numbers is 145 and their LCM is 2175. If one of the numbers is 725, find the other.

20. The HCF and LCM of two numbers are 131 and 8253 respectively. If one of the numbers is 917, find the other.

21. Find the least number divisible by 15, 20, 24, 32 and 36.

22. Find the least number which when divided by 25, 40 and 60 leaves 9 as the remainder in each case.

23. Find the least number of five digits that is exactly divisible by 16, 18, 24 and 30.

24. Find the greatest number of five digits exactly divisible by 9, 12, 15, 18 and 24.

25. Three bells toll at intervals of 9, 12, 15 minutes. If they start tolling together, after what time will they next toll together?

26. Three boys step off together from the same place. If their steps measure 36 cm, 48 cm and 54 cm, at what distance from the starting point will they again step together?

27. The traffic lights at three different road crossings change after every 48 seconds, 72 seconds and 108 seconds. If they start changing simultaneously at 8 a.m., after how much time will they change again simultaneously?

28. Three measuring rods are 45 cm, 50 cm and 75 cm in length. What is the least length (in metres) of a rope that can be measured by the full length of each of these three rods?

29. An electronic device makes a beep after every 15 minutes. Another device makes a beep after every 20 minutes. They beeped together at 6 a.m. At what time will they next beep together?

30. The circumferences of four wheels are 50 cm, 60 cm, 75 cm and 100 cm. They start moving simultaneously. What least distance should they cover so that each wheel makes a complete number of revolutions?

EXERCISE 2F

OBJECTIVE QUESTIONS

Mark (✓) against the correct answer in each of the following:

1. Which of the following numbers is divisible by 3?
   (a) 24357806   (b) 35769812   (c) 83479560   (d) 3336433

2. Which of the following numbers is divisible by 9?
   (a) 8576901   (b) 96345210   (c) 67594310   (d) none of these

3. Which of the following numbers is divisible by 4?
   (a) 78653234   (b) 98765042   (c) 24689602   (d) 87941032

4. Which of the following numbers is divisible by 8?
   (a) 96354142   (b) 37450176   (c) 57064214   (d) none of these

5. Which of the following numbers is divisible by 6?
   (a) 8790432   (b) 98671402   (c) 85492014   (d) none of these

6. Which of the following numbers is divisible by 11?
   (a) 3333333   (b) 1111111   (c) 22222222   (d) none of these

7. Which of the following is a prime number?
   (a) 81   (b) 87   (c) 91   (d) 97

8. Which of the following is a prime number?
   (a) 117   (b) 171   (c) 179   (d) none of these

9. Which of the following is a prime number?
   (a) 323   (b) 361   (c) 263   (d) none of these

10. Which of the following are co-primes?
    (a) 8, 12   (b) 9, 10   (c) 6, 8   (d) 15, 18

11. Which of the following is a composite number?
    (a) 23   (b) 29   (c) 32   (d) none of these

12. The HCF of 144 and 198 is
    (a) 9   (b) 12   (c) 6   (d) 18

13. The HCF of 144, 180 and 192 is
    (a) 12   (b) 16   (c) 18   (d) 8

14. Which of the following are co-primes?
    (a) 39, 91   (b) 161, 192   (c) 385, 462   (d) none of these
    Hint. *HCF of co-primes is* 1.

15. $\dfrac{289}{391}$ when reduced to the lowest terms is
    (a) $\dfrac{11}{23}$ (b) $\dfrac{13}{31}$ (c) $\dfrac{17}{31}$ (d) $\dfrac{17}{23}$

16. The greatest number which divides 134 and 167 leaving 2 as remainder in each case is
    (a) 14   (b) 17   (c) 19   (d) 33

17. The LCM of 24, 36, 40 is
    (a) 4   (b) 90   (c) 360   (d) 720

18. The LCM of 12, 15, 20, 27 is
    (a) 270   (b) 360   (c) 480   (d) 540

19. The smallest number which when diminished by 3 is divisible by 14, 28, 36 and 45, is
    (a) 1257   (b) 1260   (c) 1263   (d) none of these

20. The HCF of two co-primes is
    (a) the smaller number   (b) the larger number
    (c) 1   (d) none of these

21. If a and b are co-primes, then their LCM is
    (a) 1   (b) $\dfrac{a}{b}$ (c) ab (d) none of these

22. The product of two numbers is 2160 and their HCF is 12. The LCM of these numbers is
    (a) 12   (b) 25920   (c) 180   (d) none of these

23. The HCF of two numbers is 145 and their LCM is 2175. If one of the numbers is 725, the other number is
    (a) 290   (b) 435   (c) 5   (d) none of these

24. The least number divisible by each of the numbers 15, 20, 24, 32 and 36 is
    (a) 1660   (b) 2880   (c) 1440   (d) none of these

25. Three bells toll together at intervals of 9, 12, 15 minutes. If they start tolling together, after what time will they next toll together?
    (a) 1 hour   (b) $1\dfrac{1}{2}$ hours   (c) $2\dfrac{1}{2}$ hours   (d) 3 hours

---

Things to Remember

1. *Suppose a number x divides a number y exactly. Then, we say that x is a factor of y. Also, in this case, we say that y is a multiple of x.*
2. *1 is the only number having exactly one factor.*
3. *A number having exactly two factors is called a prime number.*
4. *The only even prime number is 2.*
5. *A number is divisible*
    (i) *by 2, if its ones digit is any of 0, 2, 4, 6, 8;*
    (ii) *by 3, if the sum of its digits is divisible by 3;*
    (iii) *by 9, if the sum of its digits is divisible by 9;*
    (iv) *by 5, if its ones digit is 0 or 5;*
    (v) *by 6, if it is divisible by both 2 and 3;*
    (vi) *by 4, if the number formed by the tens and ones digits is divisible by 4;*
    (vii) *by 8, if the number formed by the hundreds, tens and ones digits is divisible by 8;*
    (viii) *by 11, if the difference of the sum of the digits at odd places and the sum of the digits at even places (beginning from the ones place) is either 0 or a multiple of 11.*
6. *The HCF of two co-primes is 1.*
7. *If x is a factor of y then the HCF of x and y is x, and the LCM of x and y is y.*
8. *The HCF of two or more than two numbers is a factor of their LCM.*
9. *The product of the HCF and LCM of two numbers is equal to the product of the numbers.*

CCE TEST PAPER-2

A. 1. Test the divisibility of 5869473 by 11.

2. Test the divisibility of 67529124 by 8.

3. On dividing 5035 by 31, the remainder is 13. Find the quotient.

4. The HCF of two number is 15 and their product is 1650. Find their LCM.

5. Find the least 5-digit number which is exactly divisible by 20, 25, 30.

6. Find the largest number which divides 630 and 940 leaving remainders 6 and 4 respectively.

7. Find the least number which when divided by 16, 36 and 40 leaves 5 as remainder in each case.

8. Write all prime numbers between 50 and 100.

9. Write seven consecutive composite numbers less than 100 having no prime number between them.

10. Can two numbers have 12 as their HCF and 512 as their LCM? Justify your answer.

B. *Mark (✓) against the correct answer in each of the following:*

11. Which of the following are co-primes?

(a) 91 and 72   (b) 34 and 51   (c) 21 and 36   (d) 15 and 20

12. The LCM of two co-prime numbers is their

(a) sum   (b) difference   (c) product   (d) quotient

13. The number which is neither prime nor composite is

(a) 0   (b) 1   (c) 2   (d) 3

14. What least number should be replaced for * so that the number 67301*2 is exactly divisible by 9?

(a) 5   (b) 6   (c) 7   (d) 8

15. Which of the following numbers is divisible by 6?

(a) 67821   (b) 78134   (c) 87432   (d) none of these

16. Which of the following is a prime number?

(a) 143   (b) 131   (c) 147   (d) 161

17. $\dfrac{289}{391}$ when reduced to lowest term is

(a) $\dfrac{13}{17}$ (b) $\dfrac{17}{19}$ (c) $\dfrac{17}{23}$ (d) $\dfrac{17}{21}$

18. Every counting number has an infinite number of

(a) factors   (b) multiples   (c) prime factors   (d) none of these

C. 19. *Fill in the blanks.*

(i) 1 is neither ...... nor ....

(ii) The smallest prime number is ....

(iii) The smallest composite number is ....

(iv) The HCF of two consecutive odd numbers is ....

(v) Two perfect numbers are ...... and ....

D. 20. *Write 'T' for true and 'F' for false statement.*

    (i) Every prime number is odd.

   (ii) Every even number is composite.

  (iii) The sum of two odd numbers is always odd.

  (iv) The sum of two even numbers is always even.

   (v) The HCF of two given numbers is always a factor of their LCM.

3 | Whole Numbers

NATURAL NUMBERS We are already familiar with the counting numbers 1, 2, 3, 4, 5, 6, etc. *Counting numbers are called natural numbers.*

WHOLE NUMBERS *All natural numbers together with '0' are called whole numbers.*

Thus 0, 1, 2, 3, 4, 5, 6, 7, 8, 10, 11, 12, ... are whole numbers.

Clearly, every natural number is a whole number but 0 is a whole number which is not a natural number.

SUCCESSOR OF A WHOLE NUMBER *If we add 1 to a whole number, we get the next whole number, called its successor.*

Thus, the successor of 0 is 1, the successor of 1 is 2, the successor of 12 is 13, and so on.

Every whole number has its successor.

PREDECESSOR OF A WHOLE NUMBER *One less than a given whole number (other than 0), is called its predecessor.*

Thus, the predecessor of 1 is 0, the predecessor of 2 is 1, the predecessor of 10 is 9, and so on.

The whole number 0 does not have its predecessor.

Every whole number other than 0 has its predecessor.

EXAMPLE *Write the successor and predecessor of*
    (i) 1000   (ii) 1005399   (iii) 999999

Solution
  (i) The successor of 1000 = (1000 + 1) = 1001.
       The predecessor of 1000 = (1000 − 1) = 999.
  (ii) The successor of 1005399 = (1005399 + 1) = 1005400.
       The predecessor of 1005399 = (1005399 − 1) = 1005398.
  (iii) The successor of 999999 = (999999 + 1) = 1000000.
       The predecessor of 999999 = (999999 − 1) = 999998.

EXERCISE 3A

1. Write the next three whole numbers after 30999.
2. Write the three whole numbers occurring just before 10001.
3. How many whole numbers are there between 1032 and 1209?
4. Which is the smallest whole number?
5. Write the successor of:
    (i) 2540801   (ii) 9999   (iii) 50904   (iv) 61639
    (v) 687890   (vi) 5386700   (vii) 6475999   (viii) 9999999

6. Write the predecessor of:
   (i) 97   (ii) 10000   (iii) 36900   (iv) 7684320
   (v) 1566391   (vi) 2456800   (vii) 100000   (viii) 1000000

7. Write down three consecutive whole numbers just preceding 7510001.

8. Write (T) for true and (F) for false against each of the following statements:
   (i) Zero is the smallest natural number.
   (ii) Zero is the smallest whole number.
   (iii) Every whole number is a natural number.
   (iv) Every natural number is a whole number.
   (v) 1 is the smallest whole number.
   (vi) The natural number 1 has no predecessor.
   (vii) The whole number 1 has no predecessor.
   (viii) The whole number 0 has no predecessor.
   (ix) The predecessor of a two-digit number is never a single-digit number.
   (x) The successor of a two-digit number is always a two-digit number.
   (xi) 500 is the predecessor of 499.
   (xii) 7000 is the successor of 6999.

OPERATIONS ON WHOLE NUMBERS

We are already familiar with the four basic operations of addition, subtraction, multiplication and division on whole numbers. Now, we shall study the properties of these operations on whole numbers.

PROPERTIES OF ADDITION

(i) CLOSURE PROPERTY *If a and b are any two whole numbers, then $(a + b)$ is also a whole number.*

Let us take some pairs of whole numbers and add them. Check whether the sum is a whole number.

One whole number	Another whole number	Sum	Is the sum a whole number?
9	11	$9 + 11 = 20$	Yes
14	28	$14 + 28 = 42$	Yes
53	40	$53 + 40 = 93$	Yes

Thus, we conclude that the sum of any two whole numbers is a whole number.

(ii) COMMUTATIVE LAW *If a and b are any two whole numbers, then*
$$(a + b) = (b + a).$$

Take a pair of whole numbers. Add them in two different orders and see whether the sum remains the same. Repeat it with more pairs.

EXAMPLES   (i) $(8 + 11 = 19)$ and $(11 + 8 = 19)$
                      Is $(8 + 11) = (11 + 8)$?   Yes.
                 (ii) $(12 + 23 = 35)$ and $(23 + 12 = 35)$
                      Is $(12 + 23) = (23 + 12)$?   Yes.

Thus, we conclude that in whatever order we add two whole numbers, the sum remains the same.

(iii) ADDITIVE PROPERTY OF ZERO *If a is any whole number, then*
$$a + 0 = 0 + a = a.$$

EXAMPLES   We have:

       (i) $235 + 0 = 235$ and $0 + 235 = 235$.

       (ii) $479 + 0 = 479$ and $0 + 479 = 479$.

(iv) ASSOCIATIVE LAW *For any whole numbers a, b, c we always have*
$$(a + b) + c = a + (b + c).$$

EXAMPLE 1.   Let us take three whole numbers, say 9, 12 and 15. Then,

       $(9 + 12) + 15 = 21 + 15 = 36$.

    And, $9 + (12 + 15) = 9 + 27 = 36$.

    $\therefore$ $(9 + 12) + 15 = 9 + (12 + 15)$.

    We may take some more examples and in each case we shall find that in addition of whole numbers, associative law always holds.

REMARK   *While adding three or more numbers, we group them in such a way that the calculation becomes easier. We arrange them suitably and add.*

EXAMPLE 2.   *Find the sum of 645, 287 and 413.*

Solution   We have:

       $645 + 287 + 413 = 645 + (287 + 413)$

                    $= (645 + 700) = 1345$.

EXAMPLE 3.   *Find the sum by suitable rearrangement:*

    (i) $847 + 306 + 453$ *(ii) $1852 + 653 + 1648 + 547$*

Solution   We have:

       (i) $847 + 306 + 453 = (847 + 453) + 306$

                      $= (1300 + 306) = 1606$.

       (ii) $1852 + 653 + 1648 + 547 = (1852 + 1648) + (653 + 547)$

                                $= (3500 + 1200) = 4700$.

EXAMPLE 4.   *Find the sum:*

    (i) $3678 + 999$ *(ii) $34876 + 9999$*

Solution   We have:

       (i) $3678 + 999 = 3678 + (1000 - 1)$

                  $= (3678 + 1000) - 1 = (4678 - 1) = 4677$.

       (ii) $34876 + 9999 = 34876 + (10000 - 1)$

                   $= (34876 + 10000) - 1 = (44876 - 1) = 44875$.

MAGIC SQUARE *A magic square is an arrangement of different numbers in the form of a square such that the sum of the numbers in every horizontal line, every vertical line and every diagonal line is the same.*

One magic square is shown here.

It may be noted that:

Rowwise sum $= (9 + 2 + 7) = (4 + 6 + 8) = (5 + 10 + 3) = 18$.

Columnwise sum $= (9 + 4 + 5) = (2 + 6 + 10) = (7 + 8 + 3) = 18$.

Diagonalwise sum $= (9 + 6 + 3) = (7 + 6 + 5) = 18$.

9	2	7
4	6	8
5	10	3

EXERCISE 3B

1. Fill in the blanks to make each of the following a true statement:
   (i) $458 + 639 = 639 + \ldots\ldots$ (ii) $864 + 2006 = 2006 + \ldots\ldots$
   (iii) $1946 + \ldots\ldots = 984 + 1946$ (iv) $8063 + 0 = \ldots\ldots$
   (v) $53501 + (574 + 799) = 574 + (53501 + \ldots\ldots)$

2. Add the following numbers and check by reversing the order of the addends:
   (i) $16509 + 114$ (ii) $2359 + 548$ (iii) $19753 + 2867$

3. Find the sum: $(1546 + 498) + 3589$.
   Also, find the sum: $1546 + (498 + 3589)$.
   Are the two sums equal?
   State the property satisfied.

4. Determine each of the sums given below using suitable rearrangement.
   (i) $953 + 707 + 647$ (ii) $1983 + 647 + 217 + 353$
   (iii) $15409 + 278 + 691 + 422$ (iv) $3259 + 10001 + 2641 + 9999$
   (v) $1 + 2 + 3 + 4 + 96 + 97 + 98 + 99$ (vi) $2 + 3 + 4 + 5 + 45 + 46 + 47 + 48$

5. Find the sum by short method:
   (i) $6784 + 9999$ (ii) $10578 + 99999$

6. For any whole numbers a, b, c, is it true that $(a + b) + c = a + (c + b)$? Give reasons.

7. Complete each one of the following magic squares by supplying the missing numbers:

   (i) 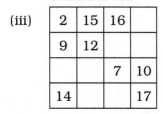   (ii)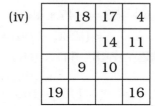

   (iii)

2	15	16	
9	12		
		7	10
14			17

   (iv)

	18	17	4
		14	11
	9	10	
19			16

8. Write (T) for true and (F) for false for each of the following statements:
   (i) The sum of two odd numbers is an odd number.
   (ii) The sum of two even numbers is an even number.
   (iii) The sum of an even number and an odd number is an odd number.

SUBTRACTION IN WHOLE NUMBERS

The operation of subtraction is an inverse process of addition.

   $(14 + 9 = 23) \Rightarrow \{(23 - 9) = 14 \text{ and } (23 - 14) = 9\}$.

PROPERTIES OF SUBTRACTION

(i) *If a and b are two whole numbers such that $a > b$ or $a = b$ then $a - b$ is a whole number; otherwise, subtraction is not possible in whole numbers.*

EXAMPLES   (i) If we subtract two equal whole numbers, we get the whole number 0;

e.g., $(8 - 8) = 0$, $(6 - 6) = 0$, $(25 - 25) = 0$, etc.

(ii) If we subtract a smaller whole number from a larger one, we always get a whole number;

e.g., $(16 - 9) = 7$, $(37 - 8) = 29$, $(23 - 16) = 7$, etc.

(iii) Clearly, we cannot subtract 18 from 13;

i.e., $(13 - 18)$ is not defined in whole numbers.

(ii) *For any two whole numbers a and b, $(a - b) \neq (b - a)$.*

EXAMPLES   (i) $(8 - 5) = 3$ but $(5 - 8)$ is not defined in whole numbers.

(ii) $(26 - 9) = 17$ but $(9 - 26)$ is not defined in whole numbers.

(iii) *For any whole number a, we have: $(a - 0) = a$ but $(0 - a)$ is not defined in whole numbers.*

EXAMPLES   (i) $(9 - 0) = 9$ but $(0 - 9)$ is not defined in whole numbers.

(ii) $(24 - 0) = 24$ but $(0 - 24)$ is not defined in whole numbers.

(iv) *If a, b, c are any three whole numbers, then in general $(\boldsymbol{a} - \boldsymbol{b}) - \boldsymbol{c} \neq \boldsymbol{a} - (\boldsymbol{b} - \boldsymbol{c})$.*

EXAMPLE   Consider the numbers 8, 4 and 2.

$(8 - 4) - 2 = (4 - 2) = 2$.

$8 - (4 - 2) = (8 - 2) = 6$.

$\therefore$ $(8 - 4) - 2 \neq 8 - (4 - 2)$.

(v) *If a, b, c are whole numbers such that $a - b = c$, then $b + c = a$.*

EXAMPLES   (i) $16 - 9 = 7$ $\Rightarrow$ $9 + 7 = 16$.

(ii) $23 - 8 = 15$ $\Rightarrow$ $8 + 15 = 23$.

OBSERVING PATTERNS

Study the following:

(i) $456 - 99 = 456 - 100 + 1 = (457 - 100) = 357$.

(ii) $4962 - 999 = 4962 - 1000 + 1 = (4963 - 1000) = 3963$.

EXERCISE 3C

1. Perform the following subtractions. Check your results by the corresponding additions.

(i) $6237 - 694$ (ii) $21205 - 10899$

(iii) $100000 - 78987$ (iv) $1010101 - 656565$

2. Replace each * by the correct digit in each of the following:

(i)
```
    9 1 7
  - * 5 *
  -------
    5 * 8
```

(ii)
```
    6 1 7 2
  - * * 6 9
  ---------
    2 9 * *
```

(iii)
```
    5 0 0 1 0 0 3
  -   * * 6 9 8 7
  ---------------
      4 8 4 * * * *
```

(iv)
```
    1 0 0 0 0 0 0
  -     * * * * 1
  ---------------
      * 7 0 4 2 *
```

3. Find the difference:

(i) $463 - 9$ (ii) $5632 - 99$ (iii) $8640 - 999$ (iv) $13006 - 9999$

4. Find the difference between the smallest number of 7 digits and the largest number of 4 digits.

5. Ravi opened his account in a bank by depositing ₹ 136000. Next day he withdrew ₹ 73129 from it. How much money was left in his account?

6. Mrs Saxena withdrew ₹ 100000 from her bank account. She purchased a TV set for ₹ 38750, a refrigerator for ₹ 23890 and jewellery worth ₹ 35560. How much money was left with her?

7. The population of a town was 110500. In one year it increased by 3608 due to new births. However, 8973 persons died or left the town during the year. What was the population at the end of the year?

8. Find the whole number n when:

   (i) $n + 4 = 9$ (ii) $n + 35 = 101$ (iii) $n - 18 = 39$ (iv) $n - 20568 = 21403$

MULTIPLICATION OF WHOLE NUMBERS

Let us consider 4 bundles, each consisting of 3 sticks.

Total number of sticks
= 3 + 3 + 3 + 3 = 12.
Also, we may write:
total number of sticks
= 4 times 3, written as 4×3.
∴ $4 \times 3 = 12$.

Again, consider 6 packets of 5 balls each.

Total number of balls
= 5 + 5 + 5 + 5 + 5 + 5 = 30.
Also, we may write:
total number of balls
= 6 times 5, written as 6×5.
Therefore, $6 \times 5 = 30$.

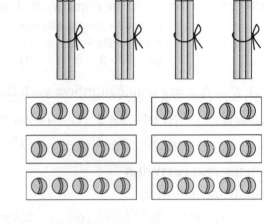

It follows that *multiplication is repeated addition.*

If the numbers are small, we can perform the operation of multiplication mentally as above and find the product.

If the numbers are large, we multiply them using the multiplication tables about which you have learnt earlier.

However, we now list the various properties of multiplication on whole numbers. These properties will help us in finding easily the products of numbers, however large they may be.

PROPERTIES OF MULTIPLICATION OF WHOLE NUMBERS

(i) CLOSURE PROPERTY   *If a and b are whole numbers, then $(a \times b)$ is also a whole number.*

EXAMPLES   Let us take a few pairs of whole numbers and check in each case whether their product is a whole number.

One whole number	Another whole number	Product	Is the product a whole number?
9	8	$9 \times 8 = 72$	Yes
12	7	$12 \times 7 = 84$	Yes
16	10	$16 \times 10 = 160$	Yes

Thus, we see that if we multiply two whole numbers, the product is also a whole number.

(ii) COMMUTATIVE LAW   *If a and b are any two whole numbers then $(a \times b) = (b \times a)$.*

EXAMPLES   (i) $7 \times 5 = 35$ and $5 \times 7 = 35$.

Is $(7 \times 5) = (5 \times 7)$?   Yes.

(ii) $19 \times 12 = 228$ and $12 \times 19 = 228$.

Is $(19 \times 12) = (12 \times 19)$?   Yes.

In general, commutative law of multiplication holds in whole numbers.

(iii) MULTIPLICATIVE PROPERTY OF ZERO   *For   every   whole   number   a,   we   have $(a \times 0) = (0 \times a) = 0$.*

EXAMPLES   (i) $9 \times 0 = 0 \times 9 = 0$ (ii) $37 \times 0 = 0 \times 37 = 0$ (iii) $2386 \times 0 = 0 \times 2386 = 0$

(iv) MULTIPLICATIVE PROPERTY OF 1   *For any whole number a we have: $(a \times 1) = (1 \times a) = a$.*

EXAMPLES   (i) $8 \times 1 = 1 \times 8 = 8$ (ii) $76 \times 1 = 1 \times 76 = 76$ (iii) $2345 \times 1 = 1 \times 2345 = 2345$

(v) ASSOCIATIVE LAW   *If a, b, c are any whole numbers, then $(a \times b) \times c = a \times (b \times c)$.*

EXAMPLE   Take the whole numbers 9, 7 and 10.

$(9 \times 7) \times 10 = 63 \times 10 = 630$.

$9 \times (7 \times 10) = 9 \times 70 = 630$.

$\therefore$ $(9 \times 7) \times 10 = 9 \times (7 \times 10)$.

(vi) DISTRIBUTIVE LAW OF MULTIPLICATION OVER ADDITION   *For any whole numbers a, b, c we have: $a \times (b + c) = (a \times b) + (a \times c)$.*

EXAMPLE   Consider the whole numbers 16, 9 and 8.

$16 \times (9 + 8) = (16 \times 17) = 272$.

$(16 \times 9) + (16 \times 8) = (144 + 128) = 272$.

$\therefore$ $16 \times (9 + 8) = (16 \times 9) + (16 \times 8)$.

(vii) DISTRIBUTIVE LAW OF MULTIPLICATION OVER SUBTRACTION   *For any whole numbers a, b, c we have: $a \times (b - c) = (a \times b) - (a \times c)$.*

EXAMPLE   Consider the whole numbers 11, 6 and 4.

$11 \times (6 - 4) = (11 \times 2) = 22$.

$(11 \times 6) - (11 \times 4) = (66 - 44) = 22$.

$\therefore$ $11 \times (6 - 4) = (11 \times 6) - (11 \times 4)$.

SOLVED EXAMPLES

EXAMPLE 1.   *Multiply 197 by 54.*

Solution   We have:

$$197 \times 54 = 197 \times (50 + 4)$$
$$= 197 \times 50 + 197 \times 4 \ \text{(by distributive law)}$$
$$= 9850 + 788 = 10638.$$

Explanation In order to multiply 197 by 54, we find the products 197×4 and 197×50, and add them.

Thus, we have:

$$
\begin{array}{r}
197 \\
\times\,54 \\
\hline
788 \\
9850 \\
\hline
10638 \\
\end{array}
$$

788   multiplication by 4
9850   multiplication by 50
10638   multiplication by 54

Therefore, we have: $197 \times 54 = 10638$.

EXAMPLE 2. *Multiply 2056 by 87.*

Solution

$$
\begin{array}{r}
2056 \\
\times\,87 \\
\hline
14392 \\
164480 \\
\hline
178872 \\
\end{array}
$$

14392   multiplication by 7
164480   multiplication by 80
178872   multiplication by 87

Therefore, we have: $2056 \times 87 = 178872$.

EXAMPLE 3. *Multiply 1572 by 123.*

Solution

$$
\begin{array}{r}
1572 \\
\times\,123 \\
\hline
4716 \\
31440 \\
157200 \\
\hline
193356 \\
\end{array}
$$

4716   multiplication by 3
31440   multiplication by 20
157200   multiplication by 100
193356   multiplication by 123

Therefore, we have: $1572 \times 123 = 193356$.

EXAMPLE 4. *Find the product: 785×94.*

Solution We have:
$$785 \times 94 = 785 \times (100 - 6)$$
$$= 785 \times 100 - 785 \times 6$$
$$= 78500 - 4710 = 73790.$$

EXAMPLE 5. *Find the value of $968 \times 73 + 968 \times 27$.*

Solution By the distributive law over addition, we have:
$$968 \times 73 + 968 \times 27 = 968 \times (73 + 27)$$
$$= 968 \times 100 = 96800.$$

EXAMPLE 6. *Find the value of $1063 \times 127 - 1063 \times 27$.*

Solution $1063 \times 127 - 1063 \times 27 = 1063 \times (127 - 27)$
$$= 1063 \times 100 = 106300.$$

EXAMPLE 7. *Find the value of $8937 \times 648 + 8937 \times 122 + 8937 \times 230$.*

Solution The given expression $= 8937 \times (648 + 122 + 230)$
$$= 8937 \times 1000 = 8937000.$$

EXAMPLE 8. *Find the product: $4 \times 2995 \times 250$.*

Solution We have:
$$4 \times 2995 \times 250 = (4 \times 250) \times 2995$$

$$= (1000 \times 2995) = 2995000.$$

EXAMPLE 9. *Find the product* $37256 \times 25 \times 40$.

Solution We have:

$$37256 \times 25 \times 40 = 37256 \times (25 \times 40)$$
$$= 37256 \times 1000 = 37256000.$$

EXAMPLE 10. *Find each of the following products:*
(i) 30674×9 *(ii)* 4578×99 *(iii)* 23756×999

Solution We have:

(i) $30674 \times 9 = 30674 \times (10 - 1)$
$$= (30674 \times 10) - (30674 \times 1)$$
$$= (306740 - 30674) = 276066.$$

(ii) $4578 \times 99 = 4578 \times (100 - 1)$
$$= (4578 \times 100) - (4578 \times 1)$$
$$= (457800 - 4578) = 453222.$$

(iii) $23756 \times 999 = 23756 \times (1000 - 1)$
$$= (23756 \times 1000) - (23756 \times 1)$$
$$= (23756000 - 23756) = 23732244.$$

EXERCISE 3D

1. Fill in the blanks to make each of the following a true statement:
   (i) $246 \times 1 = $ ......
   (ii) $1369 \times 0 = $ ....
   (iii) $593 \times 188 = 188 \times $ ....
   (iv) $286 \times 753 = $ ...... $\times 286$
   (v) $38 \times (91 \times 37) = $ ...... $\times (38 \times 37)$
   (vi) $13 \times 100 \times $ ...... $ = 1300000$
   (vii) $59 \times 66 + 59 \times 34 = 59 \times ($ ...... $ + $ ...... $)$
   (viii) $68 \times 95 = 68 \times 100 - 68 \times $ ....

2. State the property used in each of the following statements:
   (i) $19 \times 17 = 17 \times 19$
   (ii) (16×32) is a whole number
   (iii) $(29 \times 36) \times 18 = 29 \times (36 \times 18)$
   (iv) $1480 \times 1 = 1480$
   (v) $1732 \times 0 = 0$
   (vi) $72 \times 98 + 72 \times 2 = 72 \times (98 + 2)$
   (vii) $63 \times 126 - 63 \times 26 = 63 \times (126 - 26)$

3. Find the value of each of the following using various properties:
   (i) $647 \times 13 + 647 \times 7$
   (ii) $8759 \times 94 + 8759 \times 6$
   (iii) $7459 \times 999 + 7459$
   (iv) $9870 \times 561 - 9870 \times 461$
   (v) $569 \times 17 + 569 \times 13 + 569 \times 70$
   (vi) $16825 \times 16825 - 16825 \times 6825$

4. Determine each of the following products by suitable rearrangements:
   (i) $2 \times 1658 \times 50$
   (ii) $4 \times 927 \times 25$
   (iii) $625 \times 20 \times 8 \times 50$
   (iv) $574 \times 625 \times 16$
   (v) $250 \times 60 \times 50 \times 8$
   (vi) $8 \times 125 \times 40 \times 25$

5. Find each of the following products, using distributive laws:
   (i) 740×105
   (ii) 245×1008
   (iii) 947×96
   (iv) 996×367
   (v) 472×1097
   (vi) 580×64
   (vii) 439×997
   (viii) 1553×198

6. Find each of the following products, using distributive laws:
   (i) 3576×9
   (ii) 847×99
   (iii) 2437×999

7. Find the products:

     (i)   458   (ii) 3709   (iii)   4617   (iv) 15208
         $\times\ 67$ $\times\ 89$ $\times\ 234$ $\times\ 542$

8. Find the product of the largest 3-digit number and the largest 5-digit number.

    Hint. $999 \times 99999 = 999 \times (100000 - 1)$. *Now, use distributive law.*

9. A car moves at a uniform speed of 75 km per hour. How much distance will it cover in 98 hours?

10. A dealer purchased 139 VCRs. If the cost of each set is ₹ 24350, find the cost of all the sets together.

11. A housing society constructed 197 houses. If the cost of construction for each house is ₹ 450000, what is the total cost for all the houses?

12. 50 chairs and 30 blackboards were purchased for a school. If each chair costs ₹ 1065 and each blackboard costs ₹ 1645, find the total amount of the bill.

13. There are six sections of Class VI in a school and there are 45 students in each section. If the monthly charges from each student be ₹ 1650, find the total monthly collection from Class VI.

14. The product of two whole numbers is zero. What do you conclude?

15. Fill in the blanks:

      (i)   Sum of two odd numbers is an ...... number.

     (ii)   Product of two odd numbers is an ...... number.

    (iii) $a \neq 0$ and $a \times a = a \ \Rightarrow\ a = ?$

DIVISION IN WHOLE NUMBERS

Division is the inverse operation of multiplication.

Let a and b be two whole numbers. Dividing a by b means finding a whole number c such that
$b \times c = a$ *and we write,* $\boldsymbol{a \div b = c.}$

Thus, $a \div b = c \ \Rightarrow\ \dfrac{a}{b} = c \ \Rightarrow\ a = b \times c.$

EXAMPLES   Dividing 48 by 8 is the same as finding a whole number which when multiplied by 8 gives 48.

             Clearly, such a number is 6, as $8 \times 6 = 48$.

             Similarly, we have:

                  $63 \div 9 = 7, \ \ 84 \div 14 = 6$, etc.

DIVISION ALGORITHM   Suppose 75 is divided by 9, then the quotient is 8 and the remainder is 3.

$$9\ )\ \overline{75}\ (\ 8$$
$$\underline{-\ 72}$$
$$3$$

Clearly, $75 = (9 \times 8) + 3$.

In general, *let a and b be two given whole numbers such that a > b. On dividing a by b, let q be the quotient and r be the remainder.*

Then, we have: $a = bq + r$, *where* $0 \leq r < b$.

This result is known as **division algorithm.**

Thus, ***dividend = (divisor × quotient) + remainder.***

EVEN AND ODD WHOLE NUMBERS *A whole number divisible by 2 is called an even number;*

e.g., 0, 2, 4, 6, 8, etc., are all even numbers.

A whole number which is not divisible by 2 is called an odd number;

e.g., 1, 3, 5, 7, 9, etc., are all odd numbers.

SOLVED EXAMPLES

EXAMPLE 1. *Find the number which when divided by 53 gives 8 as quotient and 5 as remainder.*

Solution   Given: divisor = 53, quotient = 8 and remainder = 5.

By division algorithm, we have:

dividend = (divisor × quotient) + remainder

$= (53 \times 8) + 5$

$= (424 + 5) = 429.$

Hence, the required number is 429.

EXAMPLE 2. *Divide 535 by 31 and check the result by the division algorithm.*

Solution   By actual division, we have:

```
31 ) 535 ( 17
    - 31
     225
    - 217
       8
```

∴   dividend = 535, divisor = 31, quotient = 17 and remainder = 8.

CHECK $(31 \times 17) + 8 = 527 + 8 = 535.$

Hence, the above result is correct.

EXAMPLE 3. *Divide 53068 by 257 and check the result by the division algorithm.*

Solution   By actual division, we have:

```
527 ) 53068 ( 206
    - 514
      1668
    - 1542
       126
```

∴   dividend = 53068, divisor = 257, quotient = 206 and remainder = 126.

CHECK $(257 \times 206) + 126 = 52942 + 126 = 53068.$

Hence, the above result is correct.

PROPERTIES OF DIVISION

(i) *If a and b are nonzero whole numbers, then a ÷ b is not always a whole number.*

EXAMPLE   We know that 7 and 2 are whole numbers.

But, 7 ÷ 2 is not a whole number.

(ii) DIVISION BY 0   *If a is a whole number, then a ÷ 0 is meaningless.*

(iii) *If a is a nonzero whole number, then* $0 \div a = 0$.

EXAMPLES   (i) $0 \div 3 = 0$ (ii) $0 \div 57 = 0$, etc.

EXERCISE 3E

1. Divide and check your answer by the corresponding multiplication in each of the following:
   (i) $1936 \div 16$ (ii) $19881 \div 47$ (iii) $257796 \div 341$
   (iv) $612846 \div 582$ (v) $34419 \div 149$ (vi) $39039 \div 1001$

2. Divide, and find out the quotient and remainder. Check your answer.
   (i) $6971 \div 47$ (ii) $4178 \div 35$ (iii) $36195 \div 153$
   (iv) $93575 \div 400$ (v) $23025 \div 1000$ (vi) $16135 \div 875$

3. Find the value of
   (i) $65007 \div 1$ (ii) $0 \div 879$
   (iii) $981 + 5720 \div 10$ (iv) $1507 - (625 \div 25)$
   (v) $32277 \div (648 - 39)$ (vi) $(1573 \div 1573) - (1573 \div 1573)$

4. Find a whole number n such that $n \div n = n$.

5. The product of two numbers is 504347. If one of the numbers is 317, find the other.

6. On dividing 59761 by a certain number, the quotient is 189 and the remainder is 37. Find the divisor.

7. On dividing 55390 by 299, the remainder is 75. Find the quotient using the division algorithm.

8. What least number must be subtracted from 13601 to get a number exactly divisible by 87?

9. What least number must be added to 1056 to get a number exactly divisible by 23?

10. Find the largest 4-digit number divisible by 16.

11. Divide the largest 5 digit number by 653. Check your answer by the division algorithm.

12. Find the least 6-digit number exactly divisible by 83.

13. 1 dozen bananas cost ₹ 29. How many dozens can be purchased for ₹ 1392?

14. 19625 trees have been equally planted in 157 rows. Find the number of trees in each row.

15. The population of a town is 517530. If one out of every 15 is reported to be literate, find how many literate persons are there in the town.

16. The cost price of 23 colour television sets is ₹ 570055. Determine the cost price of each TV set if each costs the same.

EXERCISE 3F

OBJECTIVE QUESTIONS

Mark (✓) against the correct answer in each of the following:

1. The smallest whole number is
   (a) 1   (b) 0   (c) 2   (d) none of these

2. The least number of 4 digits which is exactly divisible by 9 is
   (a) 1018   (b) 1026   (c) 1009   (d) 1008

3. The largest number of 6 digits which is exactly divisible by 16 is

   (a) 999980   (b) 999982   (c) 999984   (d) 999964

4. What least number should be subtracted from 10004 to get a number exactly divisible by 12?

   (a) 4   (b) 6   (c) 8   (d) 20

5. What least number should be added to 10056 to get a number exactly divisible by 23?

   (a) 5   (b) 18   (c) 13   (d) 10

6. What whole number is nearest to 457 which is divisible by 11?

   (a) 450   (b) 451   (c) 460   (d) 462

7. How many whole numbers are there between 1018 and 1203?

   (a) 185   (b) 186   (c) 184   (d) none of these

8. A number when divided by 46 gives 11 as quotient and 15 as remainder. The number is

   (a) 491   (b) 521   (c) 701   (d) 679

9. In a division sum, we have dividend = 199, quotient = 16 and remainder = 7. The divisor is

   (a) 11   (b) 23   (c) 12   (d) none of these

10. $7589 - ? = 3434$

   (a) 11023   (b) 4245   (c) 4155   (d) none of these

11. $587 \times 99 = ?$

   (a) 57213   (b) 58513   (c) 58113   (d) 56413

12. $4 \times 538 \times 25 = ?$

   (a) 32280   (b) 26900   (c) 53800   (d) 10760

13. $24679 \times 92 + 24679 \times 8 = ?$

   (a) 493580   (b) 1233950   (c) 2467900   (d) none of these

14. $1625 \times 1625 - 1625 \times 625 = ?$

   (a) 1625000   (b) 162500   (c) 325000   (d) 812500

15. $1568 \times 185 - 1568 \times 85 = ?$

   (a) 7840   (b) 15680   (c) 156800   (d) none of these

16. $(888 + 777 + 555) = (111 \times ?)$

   (a) 120   (b) 280   (c) 20   (d) 140

17. The sum of two odd numbers is

   (a) an odd number   (b) an even number (c) a prime number (d) a multiple of 3

18. The product of two odd numbers is

   (a) an odd number   (b) an even number (c) a prime number (d) none of these

19. If a is a whole number such that $a + a = a$, then $a = ?$

   (a) 1   (b) 2   (c) 3   (d) none of these

20. The predecessor of 10000 is

   (a) 10001   (b) 9999   (c) none of these

21. The successor of 1001 is

   (a) 1000   (b) 1002   (c) none of these

22. The smallest even whole number is

   (a) 0   (b) 2   (c) none of these

Things to Remember

1. If a, b, c are whole numbers then
    (i) $a + b$ is a whole number
   (ii) $a \times b$ is a whole number
  (iii) $a - b$ is not necessarily a whole number
   (iv) $a \div b$ is not necessarily a whole number
    (v) $a + b = b + a$
   (vi) $a \times b = b \times a$
  (vii) $(a + b) + c = a + (b + c)$
 (viii) $(a \times b) \times c = a \times (b \times c)$
   (ix) $a \times (b + c) = a \times b + a \times c$
    (x) $a \times (b - c) = a \times b - a \times c$
   (xi) $a + 0 = 0 + a = a$ and $a \times 0 = 0 \times a = 0$
  (xii) $a \times 1 = 1 \times a = a$
2. In general, $(a - b) - c \neq a - (b - c)$.
3. If a is the dividend, b (where $b \neq 0$) is the divisor, q is the quotient and r is the remainder then
   $a = bq + r$.
4. If a is a nonzero whole number, then $a \div 0$ is not defined and $0 \div a = 0$.

CCE TEST PAPER-3

A. 1. How many whole numbers are there between 1064 and 1201?

2. Fill in the blanks.

```
  1000000
-  * * * * 1
   *7042 *
```

3. Use distributive law to find the value of

$$1063 \times 128 - 1063 \times 28.$$

4. Find the product of the largest 5-digit number and the largest 3-digit number using distributive law.

5. Divide 53968 by 267 and check the result by the division algorithm.

6. Find the largest 6-digit number divisible by 16.

7. The cost price of 23 TV sets is ₹ 570055. Find the cost of each such set.

8. What least number must be subtracted from 13801 to get a number exactly divisible by 87?

B. *Mark (✓) against the correct answer in each of the following:*

9. The value of $(89 \times 76 + 89 \times 24)$ is

(a) 890 (b) 8900 (c) 89000 (d) 10420

10. On dividing a number by 53 we get 8 as quotient and 5 as remainder. The number is

(a) 419 (b) 423 (c) 429 (d) none of these

11. The whole number which has no predecessor is

(a) 1 (b) 0 (c) 2 (d) none of these

12. $67 + 33 = 33 + 67$ is an example of

(a) closure property (b) associative property

(c) commutative property (d) distributive property

13. Additive inverse of 36 is

(a) $\dfrac{1}{36}$ (b) 0 (c) –36 (d) none of these

14. Which of the following is not zero?

(a) 0×0 (b) $\dfrac{0}{2}$ (c) $\dfrac{(8-8)}{2}$ (d) $2 + 0$

15. The predecessor of the smallest 3-digit number is

(a) 999 (b) 100 (c) 101 (d) 99

16. The number of whole numbers between the smallest whole number and the greatest 2-digit number is

(a) 88 (b) 98 (c) 99 (d) 101

C. 17. *Fill in the blanks.*

(i) The smallest natural number is ....

(ii) The smallest whole number is ....

(iii) Division by ...... is not defined.

(iv) ...... is a whole number which is not a natural number.

(v) ...... is the multiplicative identity in whole numbers.

D. 18. *Write 'T' for true and 'F' for false in each of the following:*

    (i) 0 is the smallest natural number.

    (ii) Every natural number is a whole number.

    (iii) Every whole number is a natural number.

    (iv) 1 has no predecessor in whole numbers.

E. 19. *Match the following columns on whole numbers:*

Column A	Column B
(a) $137 + 63 = 63 + 137$	(i) Associativity of multiplication
(b) (16×25) is a whole number	(ii) Commutativity of multiplication
(c) $365 \times 18 = 18 \times 365$	(iii) Distributive law of multiplication over addition
(d) $(86 \times 14) \times 25 = 86 \times (14 \times 25)$	(iv) Commutativity of addition
(e) $23 \times (80 + 5) = (23 \times 80) + (23 \times 5)$	(v) Closure property for multiplication

4 Integers

So far we are conversant with only two types of numbers, namely, natural numbers and whole numbers. In this chapter, we shall extend our number system from whole numbers to integers. We shall discuss the representation of integers on the number line, operations on integers and their properties.

INTRODUCTION TO INTEGERS We know that in numbers, when a smaller whole number is subtracted from a larger one, we get a whole number.

But, what about $3 - 5$, $5 - 8$, $11 - 16$, etc.?

Clearly, there are no whole numbers to represent them. So, there is a need to extend our whole number system so as to contain numbers to represent the above differences.

Corresponding to natural numbers $1, 2, 3, 4, 5, 6, ...$, we introduce new numbers denoted by -1, $-2, -3, -4, -5, -6, ...$, called minus one, minus two, minus three, minus four, minus five, minus six, ..., respectively such that $1 + (-1) = 0$, $2 + (-2) = 0$, $3 + (-3) = 0$, and so on.

We say that -1 and 1 are the opposites of each other;

$\quad\quad\quad\quad -2$ and 2 are the opposites of each other;

$\quad\quad\quad\quad -3$ and 3 are the opposites of each other, and so on.

Thus, our new collection together with whole numbers becomes $..., -3, -2, -1, 0, 1, 2, 3, ...$.

These numbers are called **integers.**

The numbers $1, 2, 3, 4, 5, 6, ...$ are called *positive integers*, the numbers $-1, -2, -3, -4, -5, -6, ...$ are called *negative integers* and 0 is an integer which is neither positive nor negative.

In our daily life we come across statements opposite to each other.

We use positive and negative integers for their representation.

EXAMPLE 1. We know that the heights of places are measured as distances from sea level.
We shall represent a height of
    5 km above sea level as +5 km or simply 5 km;
    5 km below sea level as –5 km.

EXAMPLE 2. We know that the freezing point of water is 0°C.
We shall represent a temperature of
    15°C above the freezing point of water as +15°C or simply 15°C;
    15°C below the freezing point of water as –15°C.

EXAMPLE 3. We write:
    a loss of 500 = a gain of –500;
    a withdrawal of rupees 600 = a deposit of rupees –600;
    a decrease of 20 = an increase of –20, etc.

REPRESENTATION OF INTEGERS ON THE NUMBER LINE

We draw a line and fix a point almost in the middle of it. We call it 0. We set off equal distances on the right-hand side as well as on the left-hand side of 0. On the right-hand side, we label the points of division as 1, 2, 3, 4, 5, etc., while on the left-hand side these are labelled as −1, −2, −3, −4, −5, etc., as shown below.

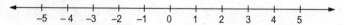

Clearly, 1 and −1 are at equal distances from 0 but in opposite directions.

Similarly, 2 and −2 are at equal distances from 0 but in opposite directions, and so on.

ORDERING OF INTEGERS As a consequence of the above discussion, it follows that we may represent every integer by some point on the number line.

If we represent two integers on the number line, we follow the convention that the number occurring to the right is greater than that on the left. And, the number on the left is smaller than that on the right.

Thus, we have the following examples:

    (i) 3 > 1, since 3 is to the right of 1;

    (ii) 1 > 0, since 1 is to the right of 0;

    (iii) 0 > −1, since 0 is to the right of −1;

    (iv) −1 > −2, since −1 is to the right of −2;

    (v) −2 > −3, since −2 is to the right of −3.

In general, the following results are quite obvious:

  (i) *Zero is less than every positive integer, since 0 is to the left of every positive integer.*

  (ii) *Zero is greater than every negative integer, since 0 is to the right of every negative integer.*

  (iii) *Every positive integer is greater than every negative integer, since every positive integer is to the right of every negative integer.*

  (iv) *The greater the number, the lesser is its opposite.*

    For example: (i) 4 > 3 and −4 < − 3;

               (ii) 7 > 4 and −7 < − 4;

               (iii) 9 > 5 and −9 < − 5.

               Thus, if a and b are two integers such that $a > b$, then $-a < -b$.

               Similarly, if a and b are integers such that $a < b$, then $-a > -b$.

EXAMPLE 1.   *Using the number line, write the integer which is:*
        (i) 3 more than 5   *(ii) 4 more than −1*
        (iii) 5 less than 3   *(iv) 2 less than −3*

Solution (i) We want to know an integer 3 more than 5. So, we start from 5 and proceed 3 steps to the right to obtain 8, as shown below:

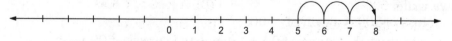

So, 3 more than 5 is 8.

(ii) We want to know an integer 4 more than –1. So, we start from –1 and proceed 4 steps to the right to obtain 3, as shown below:

Hence, 4 more than –1 is 3.

(iii) We want to know an integer 5 less than 3. So, we start from 3 and go to the left by 5 steps to obtain –2, as shown below:

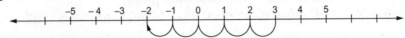

Hence, 5 less than 3 is –2.

(iv) We want to know an integer 2 less than –3. So, we start from –3 and go to the left by 2 steps to obtain –5, as shown below:

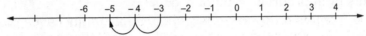

Hence, 2 less than –3 is –5.

EXAMPLE 2. *Fill in the blanks by the appropriate symbol '>' or '<' in each of the following cases:*
  (i) 0 3   *(ii)* –4 0   *(iii)* –9 ...... –15
  (iv) –37 17   *(v)* –10 10   *(vi)* –163 ...... –236

Solution   (i) We know that on the number line, 0 is to the left of 3. So, 0 < 3.
  (ii) Since zero is greater than every negative integer, so –4 < 0.
  (iii) Since 9 < 15, we have –9 > –15.
  (iv) Since every positive integer is greater than every negative integer, we have –37 < 17.
  (v) Every positive integer being greater than every negative integer, we have –10 < 10.
  (vi) Since 163 < 236, we have –163 > –236.

ABSOLUTE VALUE OF AN INTEGER *The absolute value of an integer is the numerical value of the integer regardless of its sign.*

The absolute value of –2, written as |–2|, is 2.
The absolute value of –5, written as |– 5|, is 5.
The absolute value of 5, written as |5|, is 5.
The absolute value of 0, written as |0|, is 0.

Thus, we conclude that the absolute value of an integer is 0 in case of 0, and positive otherwise.

EXERCISE 4A

1. Write the opposite of each of the following:
    (i) An increase of 8
    (ii) A loss of ₹ 7
    (iii) Gaining a weight of 5 kg
    (iv) 10 km above sea level
    (v) 5°C below the freezing point
    (vi) A deposit of ₹ 100
    (vii) Earning ₹ 500
    (viii) Going 6 m to the east
    (ix) 24
    (x) –34

2. Indicate the following using '+' or '–' sign:
    (i) A gain of ₹ 600
    (ii) A loss of ₹ 800
    (iii) 7°C below the freezing point
    (iv) Decrease of 9
    (v) 2 km above sea level
    (vi) 3 km below sea level
    (vii) A deposit of ₹ 200
    (viii) A withdrawal of ₹ 300

3. Mark the following integers on a number line:
   (i) –5   (ii) –2   (iii) 0
   (iv) 7   (v) –13

4. Which number is larger in each of the following pairs?
   (i) 0, –2   (ii) –3, –5   (iii) –5, 2
   (iv) –16, 8   (v) –365, –913   (vi) –888, 8

5. Which number is smaller in each of the following pairs?
   (i) 6, –7   (ii) 0, –1   (iii) –13, –27
   (iv) –26, 17   (v) –317, –603   (vi) –777, 7

6. Write all integers between
   (i) 0 and 6   (ii) –5 and 0   (iii) –3 and 3   (iv) –7 and –5

7. Fill in the blanks by appropriate symbol > or <:
   (i) 0 7   (ii) 0 ...... –3   (iii) –5 ...... –2
   (iv) –15 13   (v) –231 ...... –132   (vi) –6 6

8. Write the following integers in the increasing order:
   (i) 5, –7, –2, 0, 8   (ii) –23, 12, 0, –6, –100, –1
   (iii) –17, 15, –363, –501, 165   (iv) 21, –106, –16, 16, 0, –2, –81

9. Write the following integers in the decreasing order:
   (i) 0, 7, –3, –9, –132, 36   (ii) 51, –53, –8, 0, –2
   (iii) –71, –81, 36, 0, –5   (iv) –365, –515, 102, 413, –7

10. Using the number line, write the integer which is
    (i) 4 more than 6   (ii) 5 more than –6
    (iii) 6 less than 2   (iv) 2 less than –3

11. For each of the following statements, write (T) for true and (F) for false:
    (i) The smallest integer is zero.
    (ii) Zero is not an integer.
    (iii) The opposite of zero is zero.
    (iv) –10 is greater than –6.
    (v) The absolute value of an integer is always greater than the integer.
    (vi) 0 is larger than every negative integer.
    (vii) Every negative integer is less than every natural number.
    (viii) The successor of –187 is –188.
    (ix) The predecessor of –215 is –214.

12. Find the value of
    (i) $|-9|$ (ii) $|-36|$ (iii) $|0|$ (iv) $|15|$
    (v) $-|-3|$ (vi) $7 + |-3|$ (vii) $|7 - 4|$ (viii) $8 - |-7|$

13. (i) Write five negative integers greater than –7.
     (ii) Write five negative integers less than –20.

═══════

OPERATIONS ON INTEGERS

ADDITION OF INTEGERS We have learnt how to add two whole numbers on the number line. We shall extend the same method for addition of integers, using the number line.

Adding –3 to a number means moving 3 steps to the left of the number.

Adding –2 to a number means moving 2 steps to the left of the number, and so on.

SOLVED EXAMPLES

EXAMPLE 1. *Add +7 and –4 on the number line.*

Solution On the number line we start from 0 and move 7 steps to the right to reach a point A. Now, starting from A, we move 4 steps to the left to reach a point B, as shown below.

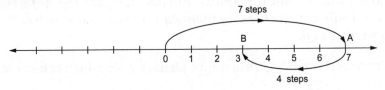

And, B represents the integer 3.

∴ $7 + (-4) = 3$.

EXAMPLE 2. *Add +3 and –8 on the number line.*

Solution On the number line we start from 0 and move 3 steps to the right to reach a point A. Now, starting from A, we move 8 steps to the left to reach a point B, as shown below.

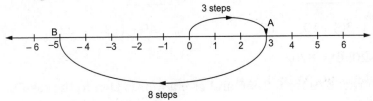

Clearly, B represents the integer –5.

∴ $3 + (-8) = -5$.

EXAMPLE 3. *Add –3 and –6 on the number line.*

Solution On the number line, we start from 0 and move 3 steps to the left to reach a point A. Now, starting from A, we move 6 steps to the left to reach a point B, as shown below.

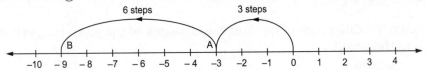

Clearly, B represents –9.

∴ $(-3) + (-6) = -9$.

From the above examples, we obtain the rules for addition of integers, which are given below.

RULES FOR ADDITION OF INTEGERS

RULE 1 *If two positive integers or two negative integers are added, we add their values regardless of their signs and give the sum their common sign.*

EXAMPLE 4. *Add the following integers:*

    (i) +27 and +19   *(ii) –42 and –35*

Solution Using the rule for addition of integers having like signs, we get:

$$
\begin{array}{rl}
\text{(i)} & +27 \\
& +19 \\
\hline
& +46 \\
\hline
\end{array}
\qquad
\begin{array}{rl}
\text{(ii)} & -42 \\
& -35 \\
\hline
& -77 \\
\hline
\end{array}
$$

∴ $27 + 19 = 46$.   ∴ $(-42) + (-35) = -77$.

EXAMPLE 5.   *Add the integers –5928 and –965.*

Solution   Using the rule for addition of integers with like signs, we get:

$$
\begin{array}{r}
-\ 5928 \\
-\ \ \ 965 \\
\hline
-\ 6893 \\
\hline
\end{array}
$$

      $\therefore\ (-5928) + (-965) = -6893.$

RULE 2   *To add a positive and a negative integer, we find the difference between their numerical values regardless of their signs and give the sign of the integer with the greater value to it.*

REMARK   In order to add two integers of unlike signs, we see which is more and by how much.

EXAMPLE 6.   *Add:* *(i)* –36 + 19   *(ii)* 49 + (–27)

Solution   Using the rule for addition of integers with unlike signs, we have:

$$
\text{(i)}\quad
\begin{array}{r}
-\ 36 \\
+\ 19 \\
\hline
-\ 17 \\
\hline
\end{array}
\qquad\qquad
\text{(ii)}\quad
\begin{array}{r}
+\ 49 \\
-\ 27 \\
\hline
+\ 22 \\
\hline
\end{array}
$$

   $\therefore\ (-36) + 19 = -17.$ $\therefore\ 49 + (-27) = 22.$

EXAMPLE 7.   *Add:* (–2056) + 679.

Solution   We subtract 679 from 2056 and give a minus sign to the result.

$$
\begin{array}{r}
-\ 2056 \\
+\ \ 679 \\
\hline
-\ 1377 \\
\hline
\end{array}
$$

    $\therefore\ (-2056) + 679 = -1377.$

EXAMPLE 8.   *Add:* (– 236) + (573).

Solution   We take the difference of the numerical values of the given integers and give a plus sign to the result.

$$
\begin{array}{r}
-\ 236 \\
+\ 573 \\
\hline
+\ 337 \\
\hline
\end{array}
$$

    $\therefore\ (-236) + 573 = 337.$

PROPERTIES OF ADDITION ON INTEGERS

(i) CLOSURE PROPERTY OF ADDITION *The sum of two integers is always an integer.*

EXAMPLES   (i) 3 + 5 = 8, and 8 is an integer.

     (ii) 3 + (–8) = – 5, and –5 is an integer.

     (iii) (–3) + (–9) = – 12, and –12 is an integer.

     (iv) 16 + (–7) = 9, and 9 is an integer.

(ii) COMMUTATIVE LAW OF ADDITION *If a and b are any two integers then* $a + b = b + a.$

EXAMPLES   (i) $(-3) + 8 = 5$, and $8 + (-3) = 5$.

           $\therefore$ $(-3) + 8 = 8 + (-3)$.

           (ii) $(-4) + (-6) = -10$, and $(-6) + (-4) = -10$.

           $\therefore$ $(-4) + (-6) = (-6) + (-4)$.

(iii) ASSOCIATIVE LAW OF ADDITION *If a, b, c are any three integers then* $(a + b) + c = a + (b + c)$.

EXAMPLE   Consider the integers -5, -7 and 3.

           We have: $[(-5) + (-7)] + 3 = (-12) + 3 = -9$.

           And, $(-5) + [(-7) + 3] = (-5) + (-4) = -9$.

           $\therefore$ $[(-5) + (-7)] + 3 = (-5) + [(-7) + 3]$.

(iv) *If a is any integer then $a + 0 = a$ and $0 + a = a$.*

EXAMPLES   (i) $8 + 0 = 8$ (ii) $(-3) + 0 = -3$ (iii) $0 + (-5) = -5$

REMARK   0 is called the *additive identity*.

(v) *The sum of an integer and its opposite is 0.*
Thus, if a is an integer then $a + (-a) = 0$.
a and $-a$ are called opposites or negatives or additive inverses of each other.

EXAMPLE $3 + (-3) = 0$ and $(-3) + 3 = 0$.
           Thus, the additive inverse of 3 is -3.
           And, the additive inverse of -3 is 3.

REMARK   Clearly, the additive inverse of 0 is 0.

SUCCESSOR AND PREDECESSOR OF AN INTEGER

Let a be an integer.

Then, $(a + 1)$ is called the *successor* of a.

And, $(a - 1)$ is called the *predecessor* of a.

EXAMPLES   (i) The successor of 19 is $(19 + 1) = 20$.
           (ii) The successor of -18 is $(-18 + 1) = -17$.
           (iii) The predecessor of 10 is $(10 - 1) = 9$.
           (iv) The predecessor of -20 is $(-20 - 1) = -21$.

EXAMPLE 9.   *Find the sum of -8, 23, -32, -17 and -63.*

Solution $(-8) + 23 + (-32) + (-17) + (-63)$

           $= [(-8) + 23] + (-32) + [(-17) + (-63)]$

           $= [15 + (-32)] + (-80) = (-17) + (-80) = -97$.

EXAMPLE 10.   *Find an integer a such that*
           (i) $2 + a = 0$ *(ii) $a + (-6) = 0$*

Solution   (i) $2 + a = 0 \Rightarrow (-2) + [2 + a] = (-2) + 0$ [adding (-2) on both sides]

           $\Rightarrow [(-2) + 2] + a = -2$ [by associative law of addition and property of 0]

           $\Rightarrow 0 + a = -2$ $[\because (-2) + 2 = 0]$

           $\Rightarrow a = -2$.

         Hence, $a = -2$.

(ii) $a + (-6) = 0$

$\Rightarrow [a + (-6)] + 6 = 0 + 6$ [adding 6 on both sides]

$\Rightarrow a + [(-6) + 6] = 6$ [by associative law of addition and property of 0]

$\Rightarrow a + 0 = 6$ $\qquad [\because (-6) + 6 = 0]$

$\Rightarrow a = 6.$

Hence, $a = 6.$

EXERCISE 4B

1. Use the number line and add the following integers:

   (i) $9 + (-6)$ (ii) $(-3) + 7$ (iii) $8 + (-8)$

   (iv) $(-1) + (-3)$ (v) $(-4) + (-7)$ (vi) $(-2) + (-8)$

   (vii) $3 + (-2) + (-4)$ (viii) $(-1) + (-2) + (-3)$ (ix) $5 + (-2) + (-6)$

2. Fill in the blanks:

   (i) $(-3) + (-9) = \ldots\ldots$ (ii) $(-7) + (-8) = \ldots\ldots$ (iii) $(-9) + 16 = \ldots\ldots$

   (iv) $(-13) + 25 = \ldots\ldots$ (v) $8 + (-17) = \ldots\ldots$ (vi) $2 + (-12) = \ldots\ldots$

3. Add:

   (i) $\begin{array}{r} -\ 365 \\ -\ \ 87 \\ \hline \end{array}$ (ii) $\begin{array}{r} -\ \ 73 \\ -\ 687 \\ \hline \end{array}$

   (iii) $\begin{array}{r} -\ 1065 \\ -\ \ 987 \\ \hline \end{array}$ (iv) $\begin{array}{r} -\ 3596 \\ -\ 1089 \\ \hline \end{array}$

4. Add:

   (i) $\begin{array}{r} -\ 206 \\ +\ \ 98 \\ \hline \end{array}$ (ii) $\begin{array}{r} +\ 178 \\ -\ \ 69 \\ \hline \end{array}$

   (iii) $\begin{array}{r} -\ 103 \\ +\ 312 \\ \hline \end{array}$ (iv) $\begin{array}{r} -\ 493 \\ +\ 289 \\ \hline \end{array}$

5. Find the sum of

   (i) 137 and –354   (ii) 1001 and –13

   (iii) –3057 and 199   (iv) –36 and 1027

   (v) –389 and –1032   (vi) –36 and 100

   (vii) 3002 and –888   (viii) –18, +25 and –37

   (ix) –312, 39 and 192   (x) –51, –203, 36 and –28

6. Find the additive inverse of

   (i) –57   (ii) 183   (iii) 0

   (iv) –1001   (v) 2054

7. Write the successor of each one of the following:

   (i) 201   (ii) 70   (iii) –5

   (iv) –99   (v) –500

8. Write the predecessor of each one of the following:

   (i) 120   (ii) 79   (iii) –8

   (iv) –141   (v) –300

9. Simplify:
    (i) $(-7) + (-9) + 12 + (-16)$ (ii) $37 + (-23) + (-65) + 9 + (-12)$
    (iii) $(-145) + 79 + (-265) + (-41) + 2$ (iv) $1056 + (-798) + (-38) + 44 + (-1)$

10. A car travelled 60 km to the north of Patna and then 90 km to the south from there. How far from Patna was the car finally?

11. A man bought some pencils for ₹ 30 and some pens for ₹ 90. The next day, he again bought some pencils for ₹ 25. Then, he sold all the pencils for ₹ 20 and the pens for ₹ 70. What was his net gain or loss?

12. For each of the following statements write (T) for true and (F) for false:
    (i) The sum of two negative integers is always a negative integer.
    (ii) The sum of a negative integer and a positive integer is always a negative integer.
    (iii) The sum of an integer and its negative is zero.
    (iv) The sum of three different integers can never be zero.
    (v) $|-5| < |-3|$
    (vi) $|8 - 5| = |8| + |-5|$

13. Find an integer a such that
    (i) $a + 6 = 0$ (ii) $5 + a = 0$ (iii) $a + (-4) = 0$ (iv) $-8 + a = 0$

SUBTRACTION OF INTEGERS

We have learnt how to subtract two whole numbers.

We defined subtraction as an inverse process of addition. For example, to subtract 4 from 9 is the same as to find a number which when added to 4 gives 9.

Clearly, the answer is 5.

Thus, $9 - 4 = 5$.

We extend the same idea to subtraction of integers. Suppose we want to subtract (-4) from 6. Clearly, we want a number which when added to (-4) gives 6.

Now, on the number line, find out how many steps should be taken from -4 to reach 6.

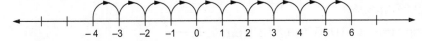

We see that the number of steps taken is 10.

∴ $6 - (-4) = 10$.

Also, we know that $6 + 4 = 10$.

Thus, $6 - (-4) = 6 + 4 = 10$.

RULE   *To subtract one integer from another, we take the additive inverse of the integer to be subtracted and add it to the other integer.*
          Thus, if a and b are two integers then $a - b = a + (-b)$.

SOLVED EXAMPLES

EXAMPLE 1.   *Subtract:*
       (i) 7 from 2   *(ii) −8 from 5*   *(iii) 4 from −9*   *(iv) −7 from −5*

Solution   (i) $2 - 7 = 2 + (\text{negative of } 7) = 2 + (-7) = -5$.
          (ii) $5 - (-8) = 5 + (\text{negative of } -8) = 5 + 8 = 13$.
          (iii) $-9 - 4 = -9 + (\text{negative of } 4) = (-9) + (-4) = -13$.
          (iv) $-5 - (-7) = (-5) + (\text{negative of } -7) = (-5) + 7 = 2$.

EXAMPLE 2.   *Subtract:*
   (i) −2459 *from* 5128   *(ii)* −1040 *from* −687
   (iii) 347 *from* −58   *(iv)* −728 *from* 0

Solution   We have:
   (i) $5128 - (-2459) = 5128 + 2459 = 7587$ [negative of −2459 is 2459]
   (ii) $-687 - (-1040) = -687 + 1040 = 353$ [negative of −1040 is 1040]
   (iii) $-58 - (347) = (-58) + (-347) = -405$ [negative of 347 is −347]
   (iv) $0 - (-728) = 0 + 728 = 728$ [negative of −728 is 728]

EXAMPLE 3.   *The sum of two integers is −27. If one of them is 260, find the other.*

Solution   Let the other number be x. Then,
   $260 + x = (-27)$
   $\Rightarrow \quad x = (-27) - 260 = (-27) + (-260) = -287.$
   Hence, the other number is −287.

PROPERTIES OF SUBTRACTION ON INTEGERS

(i) CLOSURE PROPERTY   *If a and b are integers then (a − b) is also an integer.*

(ii) *If a is any integer then (a − 0) = a.*

(iii) *If a, b, c are integers and a > b then (a − c) > (b − c).*

EXERCISE 4C

1. Subtract:
   (i) 18 from −34   (ii) −15 from 25   (iii) −28 from −43
   (iv) 68 from −37   (v) 219 from 0   (vi) −92 from 0
   (vii) −135 from −250   (viii) −2768 from −287 (ix) 6240 from −271
   (x) −3012 from 6250
2. Subtract the sum of −1050 and 813 from −23.
3. Subtract the sum of −250 and 138 from the sum of 136 and −272.
4. From the sum of 33 and −47, subtract −84.
5. Add −36 to the difference of −8 and −68.
6. Simplify:
   (i) $[37 - (-8)] + [11 - (-30)]$ (ii) $[-13 - (-17)] + [-22 - (-40)]$
7. Find $34 - (-72)$ and $(-72) - 34$. Are they equal?
8. The sum of two integers is −13. If one of the numbers is 170, find the other.
9. The sum of two integers is 65. If one of the integers is −47, find the other.
10. Which of the following statements are true and which are false?
    (i) The sum of two integers is always an integer.
    (ii) The difference of two integers is always an integer.
    (iii) $-14 > -8 - (-7)$
    (iv) $-5 - 2 > -8$
    (v) $(-7) - 3 = (-3) - (-7)$

11. The point A is on a mountain which is 5700 metres above sea level and the point B is in a mine which is 39600 metres below sea level. Find the vertical distance between A and B.

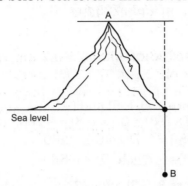

Sea level

12. On a day in Srinagar, the temperature at 6 p.m. was 1°C but at midnight that day, it dropped to –4°C. By how many degrees Celsius did the temperature fall?

MULTIPLICATION OF INTEGERS

RULE 1   *To find the product of two integers with unlike signs, we find the product of their values regardless of their signs and give a minus sign to the product.*

EXAMPLES   (i) $4 \times (-7) = -28$ (ii) $7 \times (-4) = -28$
(iii) $(-9) \times 4 = -36$ (iv) $(-3) \times 7 = -21$

RULE 2   *To find the product of two integers with the same sign, we find the product of their values regardless of their signs and give a plus sign to the product.*

EXAMPLES   (i) $4 \times 13 = 52$ (ii) $(-4) \times (-13) = 52$
(iii) $(-7) \times (-9) = 63$ (iv) $(-18) \times (-10) = 180$

EXAMPLE 1.   *Find each of the following products:*
   (i) $36 \times (-17)$ *(ii) $(-81) \times 15$*
   (iii) $(-23) \times (-18)$ *(iv) $(-60) \times (-21)$*

Solution   (i) $36 \times (-17) = -(36 \times 17) = -612$.
(ii) $(-81) \times 15 = -(81 \times 15) = -1215$.
(iii) $(-23) \times (-18) = 23 \times 18 = 414$.
(iv) $(-60) \times (-21) = 60 \times 21 = 1260$.

PROPERTIES OF MULTIPLICATION ON INTEGERS

(i) CLOSURE PROPERTY OF MULTIPLICATION *The product of two integers is always an integer.*

EXAMPLES   (i) $3 \times 5 = 15$, and 15 is an integer.
(ii) $(-7) \times 3 = -21$, and –21 is an integer.
(iii) $8 \times (-4) = -32$, and –32 is an integer.
(iv) $(-7) \times (-8) = 56$, and 56 is an integer.

(ii) COMMUTATIVE LAW FOR MULTIPLICATION *For any two integers a and b, we have*
   $a \times b = b \times a.$

EXAMPLES (i) $3 \times (-7) = -21$, and $(-7) \times 3 = -21$.
$\therefore \quad 3 \times (-7) = (-7) \times 3$.
(ii) $(-5) \times (-8) = 40$, and $(-8) \times (-5) = 40$.
$\therefore \quad (-5) \times (-8) = (-8) \times (-5)$.

(iii) ASSOCIATIVE LAW FOR MULTIPLICATION *If a, b, c are any three integers then*
$(a \times b) \times c = a \times (b \times c)$.

EXAMPLE 1.   Consider three integers (-7), (-5) and (-8).
We have: $[(-7) \times (-5)] \times (-8) = 35 \times (-8) = -280$.
And, $(-7) \times [(-5) \times (-8)] = (-7) \times 40 = -280$.
$\therefore \quad [(-7) \times (-5)] \times (-8) = (-7) \times [(-5) \times (-8)]$.

EXAMPLE 2.   Consider three integers 3, (-5) and (-7).
We have: $[3 \times (-5)] \times (-7) = (-15) \times (-7) = 105$.
And, $3 \times [(-5) \times (-7)] = 3 \times 35 = 105$.
$\therefore \quad [3 \times (-5)] \times (-7) = 3 \times [(-5) \times (-7)]$.

(iv) DISTRIBUTIVE LAW *If a, b, c be any three integers then* $a \times (b + c) = a \times b + a \times c$.

EXAMPLE 1.   Consider the integers 4, (-5) and (-6).
We have: $4 \times [(-5) + (-6)] = 4 \times (-11) = -44$.
And, $4 \times (-5) + 4 \times (-6) = (-20) + (-24) = -44$.
$\therefore \quad 4 \times [(-5) + (-6)] = 4 \times (-5) + 4 \times (-6)$.

EXAMPLE 2.   Consider the integers (-3), (-4) and (-8).
We have: $(-3) \times [(-4) + (-8)] = (-3) \times (-12) = 36$.
And, $(-3) \times (-4) + (-3) \times (-8) = 12 + 24 = 36$.
$\therefore \quad (-3) \times [(-4) + (-8)] = (-3) \times (-4) + (-3) \times (-8)$.

(v) *For any integer a, we have* $a \times 1 = a$. *The integer 1 is called the multiplicative identity for integers.*

EXAMPLES   (i) $(-3) \times 1 = -3$ (ii) $7 \times 1 = 7$

(vi) *For any integer a, we have* $a \times 0 = 0$.

EXAMPLES   (i) $4 \times 0 = 0$ (ii) $(-4) \times 0 = 0$

EXAMPLE 1.   *Simplify:*
(i) $8 \times (-13) + 8 \times 9$ (ii) $(-12) \times 7 + (-12) \times (-4)$
(iii) $9 \times (-16) + (-12) \times (-16)$ (iv) $10 \times (-31) + 10 \times (-9)$

Solution   Using the distributive law, we have:
(i) $8 \times (-13) + 8 \times 9 = 8 \times [(-13) + 9] = 8 \times (-4) = -32$.
(ii) $(-12) \times 7 + (-12) \times (-4) = (-12) \times [7 + (-4)] = (-12) \times 3 = -36$.
(iii) $9 \times (-16) + (-12) \times (-16) = [9 + (-12)] \times (-16) = (-3) \times (-16) = 48$.
(iv) $10 \times (-31) + 10 \times (-9) = 10 \times [(-31) + (-9)] = 10 \times (-40) = -400$.

EXERCISE 4D

1. Multiply:
   (i) 15 by 9   (ii) 18 by -7 (iii) 29 by -11 (iv) -18 by 13
   (v) -56 by 16   (vi) 32 by -21 (vii) -57 by 0   (viii) 0 by -31
   (ix) -12 by -9 (x) -746 by -8 (xi) 118 by -7 (xii) -238 by -143

2. Find the products:
   (i) $(-2) \times 3 \times (-4)$ (ii) $2 \times (-5) \times (-6)$ (iii) $(-8) \times 3 \times 5$
   (iv) $8 \times 7 \times (-10)$ (v) $(-3) \times (-7) \times (-6)$ (vi) $(-8) \times (-3) \times (-9)$

3. Use convenient groupings and find the values of
   (i) $18 \times (-27) \times 30$ (ii) $(-8) \times (-63) \times 9$
   (iii) $(-17) \times (-23) \times 41$ (iv) $(-51) \times (-47) \times (-19)$

4. Verify the following:
   (i) $18 \times [9 + (-7)] = 18 \times 9 + 18 \times (-7)$
   (ii) $(-13) \times [(-6) + (-19)] = (-13) \times (-6) + (-13) \times (-19)$

5. Complete the following multiplication table:

×	-3	-2	-1	0	1	2	3
-3							
-2							
-1							
0							
1							
2							
3							

6. Which of the following statements are true and which are false?
   (i) The product of a positive integer and a negative integer is negative.
   (ii) The product of two negative integers is a negative integer.
   (iii) The product of three negative integers is a negative integer.
   (iv) Every integer when multiplied with –1 gives its multiplicative inverse.

7. Simplify:
   (i) $(-9) \times 6 + (-9) \times 4$ (ii) $8 \times (-12) + 7 \times (-12)$
   (iii) $30 \times (-22) + 30 \times (14)$ (iv) $(-15) \times (-14) + (-15) \times (-6)$
   (v) $43 \times (-33) + 43 \times (-17)$ (vi) $(-36) \times (72) + (-36) \times 28$
   (vii) $(-27) \times (-16) + (-27) \times (-14)$

DIVISION ON INTEGERS

We know that division of whole numbers is an inverse process of multiplication. We extend the same idea to integers.

EXAMPLE 1. To divide 36 by (–9) means: what integer should be multiplied with (–9) to get 36? Obviously, the answer is –4.
   $\therefore \quad 36 \div (-9) = -4$.

EXAMPLE 2. To divide (–40) by 8 means: what integer should be multiplied with 8 to get (–40)? Obviously, the answer is –5.
   $\therefore \quad (-40) \div 8 = -5$.

EXAMPLE 3. To divide (–35) by (–5) means: what integer should be multiplied with –5 to get (–35)? Obviously, the answer is 7.
   $\therefore \quad (-35) \div (-5) = 7$.

Thus, we have the following rules for division of integers.

RULE 1   *For dividing one integer by another, the two having unlike signs, we divide their values regardless of their signs and give a minus sign to the quotient.*

EXAMPLES   (i) $(-36) \div 9 = -4$ (ii) $72 \div (-8) = -9$

(iii) $(-132) \div 12 = -11$ (iv) $144 \div (-18) = -8$

RULE 2   *For dividing one integer by another, the two having like signs, we divide their values regardless of their signs and give a plus sign to the quotient.*

EXAMPLES   (i) $42 \div 7 = 6$ (ii) $(-42) \div (-6) = 7$

(iii) $(-98) \div (-7) = 14$ (iv) $(-84) \div (-21) = 4$

EXAMPLE 1.   *Divide:*

(i) (-115) by 23 (ii) 168 by (-7)

(iii) (-272) by (-16) (iv) (-324) by (-27)

Solution   (i) $(-115) \div 23 = \dfrac{-115}{23} = -5.$

(ii) $168 \div (-7) = \dfrac{168}{-7} = -24.$

(iii) $(-272) \div (-16) = \dfrac{-272}{-16} = 17.$

(iv) $(-324) \div (-27) = \dfrac{-324}{-27} = 12.$

EXAMPLE 2.   *Fill in the blanks:*

(i) $-273 \div \ldots\ldots = 1$ (ii) $\ldots\ldots \div 137 = -2$

(iii) $\ldots\ldots \div 238 = 0$ (iv) $\ldots\ldots \div (-13) = -5$

Solution   (i) Clearly, we have $-273 \div (-273) = 1$.
So, the required number $= -273$.

(ii) Required number $= 137 \times (-2) = -274$.

(iii) Required number $= 238 \times 0 = 0$.

(iv) Required number $= (-13) \times (-5) = 65$.

REMARKS   (i) When 0 is divided by any integer, the quotient is 0.

(ii) We cannot divide any integer by 0.

PROPERTIES OF DIVISION ON INTEGERS

(i) *If a and b are integers then $(a \div b)$ is not necessarily an integer.*

EXAMPLES   (i) 15 and 4 are both integers, but $(15 \div 4)$ is not an integer.

(ii) (-8) and 3 are both integers, but $[(-8) \div 3]$ is not an integer.

(ii) *If a is an integer and $a \neq 0$ then $(a \div a) = 1$.*

EXAMPLES   (i) $9 \div 9 = 1$ (ii) $(-7) \div (-7) = 1$

(iii) *If a is an integer then $(a \div 1) = a$.*

EXAMPLES   (i) $6 \div 1 = 6$ (ii) $(-3) \div 1 = (-3)$

(iv) *If a is a nonzero integer then $(0 \div a) = 0$, but $(a \div 0)$ is not meaningful.*

EXAMPLES   (i) $0 \div 5 = 0$ (ii) $0 \div (-3) = 0$

(iii) $(5 \div 0)$ is not meaningful.

(v) *If a, b, c are integers then* $(a \div b) \div c \neq a \div (b \div c)$, *unless c = 1.*

EXAMPLE   Let $a = 8$, $b = 4$ and $c = 2$. Then,
$$(a \div b) \div c = (8 \div 4) \div 2 = (2 \div 2) = 1.$$
$$a \div (b \div c) = 8 \div (4 \div 2) = (8 \div 2) = 4.$$
$$\therefore \quad (a \div b) \div c \neq a \div (b \div c).$$
If $c = 1$ then $(a \div b) \div c = (8 \div 4) \div 1 = 2.$
And $a \div (b \div c) = 8 \div (4 \div 1) = 8 \div 4 = 2.$
$\therefore$ in this case $(a \div b) \div c = a \div (b \div c).$

(vi) *If a, b, c are integers and a > b then*
    (i) $(a \div c) > (b \div c)$, *if c is positive*
    (ii) $(a \div c) < (b \div c)$, *if c is negative*

EXAMPLES   (i) $27 > 18$, and 9 is positive
$$\Rightarrow \quad \frac{27}{9} > \frac{18}{9}.$$
     (ii) $27 > 18$, and (-9) is negative
$$\Rightarrow \quad \frac{27}{-9} < \frac{18}{-9}.$$

EXERCISE 4E

1. Divide:
    (i) 85 by -17 (ii) -72 by 18   (iii) -80 by 16
    (iv) -121 by 11   (v) 108 by -12 (vi) -161 by 23
    (vii) -76 by -19 (viii) -147 by -21 (ix) -639 by -71
    (x) -15625 by -125 (xi) 2067 by -1 (xii) 1765 by -1765
    (xiii) 0 by -278 (xiv) 3000 by -100

2. Fill in the blanks:
    (i) $80 \div (\ldots\ldots) = -5$ (ii) $(-84) \div (\ldots\ldots) = -7$ (iii) $(\ldots\ldots) \div (-5) = 25$
    (iv) $(\ldots\ldots) \div 372 = 0$ (v) $(\ldots\ldots) \div 1 = -186$ (vi) $(\ldots\ldots) \div 17 = -2$
    (vii) $(\ldots\ldots) \div 165 = -1$ (viii) $(\ldots\ldots) \div (-1) = 73$ (ix) $1 \div (\ldots\ldots) = -1$

3. Write (T) for true and (F) for false for each of the following statements:
    (i) $0 \div (-6) = 0$ (ii) $(-8) \div 0 = 0$ (iii) $15 \div (-1) = -15$
    (iv) $(-16) \div (-4) = -4$ (v) $(-7) \div (-1) = 7$ (vi) $(-18) \div 9 = -2$
    (vii) $20 \div (-5) = -4$ (viii) $(-10) \div 1 = -10$ (ix) $(-1) \div (-1) = -1$

EXERCISE 4F

OBJECTIVE QUESTIONS

Mark (✓) against the correct answer in each of the following:

1. Which of the following is a true statement?
    (a) $-4 > -3$ (b) $-4 < -3$ (c) -4 and -3 are non-comparable

2. 2 less than -3 is
    (a) -1 (b) 1   (c) -5 (d) 5

3. 4 more than –5 is

  (a) 9   (b) –9   (c) –1   (d) 1

4. 2 less than –7 is

  (a) –9   (b) –5   (c) 5   (d) none of these

5. $7 + |-3| = ?$

  (a) 4   (b) 10   (c) –10   (d) none of these

6. $(-42) + (-35) = ?$

  (a) –7   (b) 7   (c) –77   (d) none of these

7. $(-37) + 6 = ?$

  (a) –43   (b) –31   (c) 31   (d) none of these

8. $49 + (-27) = ?$

  (a) –73   (b) 73   (c) 22   (d) none of these

9. The successor of –18 is

  (a) –19   (b) 17   (c) –17   (d) 19

10. The predecessor of –16 is

  (a) –15   (b) –17   (c) 15   (d) 17

11. The additive inverse of –5 is

  (a) 5   (b) 0   (c) –4   (d) –6

12. $-12 - (-5) = ?$

  (a) –17   (b) –7   (c) 7   (d) none of these

13. $5 - (-8) = ?$

  (a) 3   (b) 13   (c) –3   (d) none of these

14. The sum of two integers is –25. If one of them is 30 then the other is

  (a) 55   (b) 5   (c) –55   (d) none of these

15. The sum of two integers is 20. If one of them is –5 then the other is

  (a) 25   (b) –25   (c) 15   (d) none of these

16. The sum of two integers is –13. If one of them is 8 then the other is

  (a) –5   (b) –21   (c) 21   (d) none of these

17. On subtracting –8 from 0, we get

  (a) –8   (b) 8   (c) none of these

18. $8 + (-8) = ?$

  (a) 16   (b) –16   (c) 0   (d) none of these

19. $(-6) + 4 - (-3) = ?$

  (a) –5   (b) –1   (c) 1   (d) none of these

20. $6 - (-4) = ?$

  (a) 2   (b) –10   (c) 10   (d) none of these

21. $(-7) + (-9) + 12 + (-16) = ?$

  (a) –20   (b) 20   (c) –12   (d) none of these

22. On subtracting 8 from –4, we get

  (a) 4   (b) 12   (c) –12   (d) none of these

23. On subtracting –9 from –6, we get

  (a) –15   (b) –3   (c) 3   (d) none of these

24. On subtracting –5 from 10, we get

  (a) 5   (b) –15   (c) 15   (d) none of these

25. $(-6) \times 9 = ?$

    (a) 54   (b) –54   (c) none of these

26. $(-9) \times 6 + (-9) \times 4 = ?$

    (a) –90   (b) 90   (c) –18   (d) 18

27. $36 \div (-9) = ?$

    (a) 4   (b) –4   (c) none of these

Things to Remember

1. The numbers ..., $-4, -3, -2, -1, 0, 1, 2, 3, 4, ...,$ are integers.
2. 0 is an integer which is neither positive nor negative.
3. 0 is less than every positive integer and greater than every negative integer.
4. If x and y are integers such that $x > y$ then $-x < -y$.
   For example: $17 > 13$ and $-17 < -13$.
5. The absolute value of an integer is its numerical value regardless of its sign.
   Thus, $|-7| = 7$ and $|7| = 7$. Also, $|0| = 0$.
6. To add two integers with like signs, we add their numerical values and give the sign of the addends to the sum.
   Thus, $(-8) + (-7) = -15$ and $8 + 7 = 15$.
7. To add two integers with unlike signs, we take the difference of their numerical values and give the sign of the integer having the greater absolute value to the difference.
   Thus, $(-17) + 9 = -8$ and $17 + (-8) = 9$.
8. For two integers a and b, we define $a - b = a + (-b)$.
9. To subtract an integer b from an integer a, we change the sign of b and add it to a.
10. All properties of operations on whole numbers are satisfied by these operations on integers.
11. If a and b are two integers then $(a - b)$ is also an integer.
12. $-a$ and a are negatives, or additive inverses, of each other.
13. To find the product of two integers with like signs (i.e., both positive or both negative), we multiply their numerical values and give a plus sign to the product.
14. To find the product of two integers with unlike signs (i.e., one positive and one negative), we multiply their numerical values and give a minus sign to the product.
15. The quotient of two negative or two positive integers is always positive.
16. The quotient of one positive and one negative integer is always negative.

CCE TEST PAPER-4

A. 1. What are integers? Write all integers from –5 to 5.

2. In each of the pairs given below, find the larger integer.

   (i) 0, –3   (ii) –4, –6   (iii) –99, 9   (iv) –385, –615

3. Write the following integers in increasing order:

   –18, 16, 0, –5, 8, –36, –1, 1

4. Find the value of:

   (i) $9 - |-6|$ (ii) $6 + |-4|$ (iii) $-8 - |-3|$

5. Write four integers less than –6 and four integers greater than –6.

6. Evaluate:

   (i) $8 + (-16)$ (ii) $(-5) + (-6)$ (iii) $(-6) \times (-8)$ (iv) $(-36) \div 6$

   (v) $30 - (-50)$ (vi) $(-40) \div (-10)$ (vii) $8 \times (-5)$ (viii) $(-30) - 15$

7. The sum of two integers is –12. If one of them is 34, find the other.

8. Simplify:

   (i) $(-24) \times (68) + (-24) \times 32$ (ii) $(-9) \times 18 - (-9) \times 8$

   (iii) $(-147) \div (-21)$ (iv) $16 \div (-1)$

B. *Mark (✓) against the correct answer in each of the following:*

9. The successor of –89 is

   (a) –90   (b) –88   (c) 90   (d) 88

10. The predecessor of –99 is

   (a) –98   (b) –100   (c) 98   (d) 100

11. Additive inverse of –23 is

   (a) $\dfrac{-1}{23}$ (b) $\dfrac{1}{23}$ (c) 23   (d) –23

12. If $(-13 + 6) \square -25 - (-9)$, then the correct symbol in the place holder is

   (a) <   (b) >   (c) =   (d) none of these

13. $? + (-8) = 12$

   (a) –4   (b) –20   (c) 20   (d) 4

14. The integer which is 5 more that (–7) is

   (a) –12   (b) 12   (c) –2   (d) 2

15. What should be added to 16 to get (–31)?

   (a) 15   (b) –15   (c) 47   (d) –47

16. When 34 is subtracted from –36, we get

   (a) 2   (b) –2   (c) 70   (d) –70

C. 17. *Fill in the blanks.*

   (i) $-23 - (?) = 15$.

   (ii) The largest negative integer is ....

   (iii) The smallest positive integer is ....

   (iv) $(-8) + (-6) - (-3) = $ ....

   (v) The predecessor of –200 is ....

D. 18. *Write 'T' for true and 'F' for false in each of the following:*

    (i) 0 is neither positive nor negative.

    (ii) $-(-36) - 1 = -37$.

    (iii) On the number line -10 lies to the right of -6.

    (iv) 0 is an integer.

    (v) $-|-15| = -15$.

    (vi) $|-40| + 40 = 0$.

5 | Fractions

FRACTIONS AND FRACTIONAL NUMBERS

Look at the given figure.

In this figure, a strip has been divided into 7 equal parts.

Out of these 7 equal parts, 4 parts have been shaded.

Clearly, the shaded portion represents **four-sevenths.**

In numeral, we denote it by $\dfrac{4}{7}$ (read as *'four by seven'*).

Here $\dfrac{4}{7}$ is a **fraction** and **four-sevenths** is a **fractional number.**

FRACTIONS ON NUMBER LINE

Suppose we want to denote the fraction $\dfrac{4}{7}$ on the number line.

Take a line segment $\overline{OA}$ of unit length.

Divide OA into 7 equal parts and take 4 parts out of it to reach the point P.

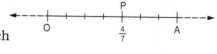

Then, *the point P represents the number* $\dfrac{4}{7}$.

Some more examples are given below.

Fraction	Fractional number			Number line
$\dfrac{1}{2}$	one-half	$\dfrac{1}{2}$		
$\dfrac{1}{4}$	one-quarter	$\dfrac{1}{4}$		
$\dfrac{2}{3}$	two-thirds	$\dfrac{2}{3}$		
$\dfrac{3}{5}$	three-fifths	$\dfrac{3}{5}$		
$\dfrac{5}{8}$	five-eighths	$\dfrac{5}{8}$		

Thus, the fractions shown above are $\dfrac{1}{2}$, $\dfrac{1}{4}$, $\dfrac{2}{3}$, $\dfrac{3}{5}$ and $\dfrac{5}{8}$.

The corresponding fractional numbers are *one-half, one-quarter, two-thirds, three-fifths and five-eighths* respectively.

FRACTION AS A PART OF A COLLECTION

Consider the following figures:

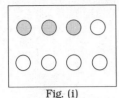
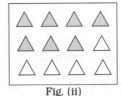
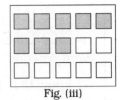

Fig. (i)   Fig. (ii)   Fig. (iii)

Fig. (i) contains a collection of 8 circles, of which 3 circles are shaded.

Shaded circles represent $\dfrac{3}{8}$ *of the collection.*

Fig. (ii) contains a collection of 12 triangles, of which 7 triangles are shaded.

Shaded triangles represent $\dfrac{7}{12}$ *of the collection.*

Fig. (iii) contains a collection of 15 squares of which 8 squares are shaded.

Shaded squares represent $\dfrac{8}{15}$ *of the collection.*

In general, we define a fraction as given below.

FRACTIONS *The numbers of the form* $\dfrac{a}{b}$*, where a and b are natural numbers, are called*

   fractions.

Here, a is called the numerator and b the denominator of the fraction $\dfrac{a}{b}$.

EXAMPLES   (i) $\dfrac{5}{9}$ is a fraction with numerator = 5 and denominator = 9.

             (ii) $\dfrac{8}{17}$ is a fraction with numerator = 8 and denominator = 17.

FRACTIONAL PART OF A COLLECTION

EXAMPLE 1.   *Find* $\dfrac{3}{4}$ *of 12.*

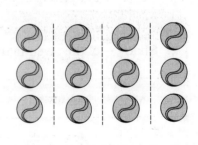

Solution   Consider a collection of 12 balls.
             Divide this collection into 4 equal parts and take
             3 parts out of it.
             Clearly, 3 parts out of 4 parts contain 9 balls.
             $\therefore \ \dfrac{3}{4}$ of 12 balls = 9 balls.

Short Method

$$\frac{3}{4} \text{ of } 12 = \left(\frac{3}{4_1} \times \frac{\cancel{12}^3}{1} \right) = \frac{9}{1} = 9.$$

EXAMPLE 2.   *Find* $\dfrac{5}{8}$ *of 32.*

Solution $\dfrac{5}{8}$ of 32 $= \left(\dfrac{5}{8_1} \times \dfrac{\cancel{32}^4}{1} \right) = \dfrac{20}{1} = 20.$

EXAMPLE 3.   *What fraction of a day is 8 hours?*

Solution   We know that 1 day = 24 hours.

$$\therefore \quad \text{the required fraction} = \frac{8}{24}.$$

EXAMPLE 4.   *What fraction of an hour is 40 minutes?*

Solution   We know that 1 hour = 60 minutes.

$$\therefore \quad \text{the required fraction} = \frac{40}{60}.$$

EXAMPLE 5.   *In the given figure, if we say that the shaded region is $\frac{1}{2}$ of the whole, then what is the error in it?*

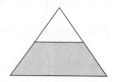

Solution   In the given figure, the shaded region is not equal to the unshaded region.

$$\therefore \quad \text{shaded region is not equal to } \frac{1}{2} \text{ of the whole.}$$

EXERCISE 5A

1. Write the fraction representing the shaded portion:

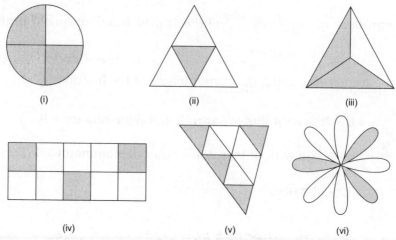

2. Shade $\frac{4}{9}$ of the given figure.

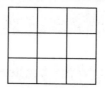

3. In the given figure, if we say that the shaded region is $\frac{1}{4}$, then identify the error in it.

4. Write a fraction for each of the following:
   (i)   three-fourths
   (ii) four-sevenths
   (iii) two-fifths
   (iv) three-tenths
   (v)   one-eighth
   (vi) five-sixths
   (vii) eight-ninths
   (viii) seven-twelfths

5. Write down the numerator and the denominator of each of the fractions given below:

(i) $\dfrac{4}{9}$　　　(ii) $\dfrac{6}{11}$　　　(iii) $\dfrac{8}{15}$　　　(iv) $\dfrac{12}{17}$　　　(v) $\dfrac{5}{1}$

6. Write down the fraction in which

(i) numerator = 3, denominator = 8　　(ii) numerator = 5, denominator = 12

(iii) numerator = 7, denominator = 16　(iv) numerator = 8, denominator = 15

7. Write down the fractional number for each of the following:

(i) $\dfrac{2}{3}$　　(ii) $\dfrac{4}{9}$　　(iii) $\dfrac{2}{5}$　　(iv) $\dfrac{7}{10}$　　(v) $\dfrac{1}{3}$

(vi) $\dfrac{3}{4}$　(vii) $\dfrac{3}{8}$　(viii) $\dfrac{9}{14}$　(ix) $\dfrac{5}{11}$　(x) $\dfrac{6}{15}$

8. What fraction of an hour is 24 minutes?

9. How many natural numbers are there from 2 to 10? What fraction of them are prime numbers?

10. Determine:

(i) $\dfrac{2}{3}$ of 15 pens　　(ii) $\dfrac{2}{3}$ of 27 balls　　(iii) $\dfrac{2}{3}$ of 36 balloons

11. Determine:

(i) $\dfrac{3}{4}$ of 16 cups　　(ii) $\dfrac{3}{4}$ of 28 rackets　　(iii) $\dfrac{3}{4}$ of 32 books

12. Neelam has 25 pencils. She gives $\dfrac{4}{5}$ of them to Meena. How many pencils does Meena get? How many pencils are left with Neelam?

13. Represent each of the following fractions on the number line:

(i) $\dfrac{3}{8}$　　(ii) $\dfrac{5}{9}$　　(iii) $\dfrac{4}{7}$　　(iv) $\dfrac{2}{5}$　　(v) $\dfrac{1}{4}$

PROPER, IMPROPER AND MIXED FRACTIONS

PROPER FRACTIONS *A fraction whose numerator is less than its denominator is called a proper fraction.*

EXAMPLES $\dfrac{2}{3}, \dfrac{5}{8}, \dfrac{7}{11}, \dfrac{0}{4}, \dfrac{8}{15}$, etc., are all proper fractions.

NOTE *Each proper fraction is less than 1.*

IMPROPER FRACTIONS *A fraction whose numerator is greater than or equal to its denominator is called an improper fraction.*

Thus $\dfrac{5}{4}, \dfrac{7}{3}, \dfrac{8}{5}, \dfrac{10}{10}, \dfrac{11}{6}, \dfrac{25}{9}$, *etc., are all improper fractions.*

MIXED FRACTIONS *A combination of a whole number and a proper fraction is called a mixed fraction.*

EXAMPLES $2\dfrac{1}{3}, 3\dfrac{2}{5}, 4\dfrac{5}{7}, 5\dfrac{9}{11}$, etc., are all mixed fractions.

TO CONVERT A MIXED FRACTION INTO AN IMPROPER FRACTION

A mixed fraction = A whole number + A fraction.

EXAMPLES (i) $2\dfrac{3}{5} = 2 + \dfrac{3}{5} = \dfrac{(2 \times 5) + 3}{5} = \dfrac{13}{5}$ (ii) $3\dfrac{4}{7} = 3 + \dfrac{4}{7} = \dfrac{(3 \times 7) + 4}{7} = \dfrac{25}{7}$

Rule *Multiply the whole number with the denominator of the fraction and to this product add the numerator of the fraction. This gives the numerator of the required improper fraction. Its denominator is the same as the denominator of the fractional part.*

TO CONVERT AN IMPROPER FRACTION INTO A MIXED FRACTION

EXAMPLE *Convert $\dfrac{29}{8}$ into a mixed fraction.*

Solution On dividing 29 by 8, we get quotient = 3 and remainder = 5.

$$\therefore \ \frac{29}{8} = 3 + \frac{5}{8} = 3\frac{5}{8}.$$

$$8\,\overline{)\,29\,}\,(\,3$$
$$\underline{-24}$$
$$\quad 5$$

Similarly, $\dfrac{38}{9} = 4 + \dfrac{2}{9} = 4\dfrac{2}{9}.$

TO REPRESENT MIXED FRACTIONS ON NUMBER LINE

EXAMPLE *Represent $2\dfrac{2}{5}$ on the number line.*

Solution Let $OA = AB = BC = 1$ unit.

Then, clearly, $OB = 2$ units and $OC = 3$ units.

Divide BC into 5 equal parts and take 2 parts out of them to reach the point P.

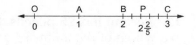

Clearly, P represents the number $2\dfrac{2}{5}.$

SOLVED EXAMPLES

EXAMPLE 1. *Write six improper fractions with denominator 7.*

Solution Clearly, $\dfrac{8}{7}, \dfrac{9}{7}, \dfrac{10}{7}, \dfrac{11}{7}, \dfrac{12}{7}, \dfrac{13}{7}$ are all improper fractions, each with denominator 7.

EXAMPLE 2. *Write six improper fractions with numerator 11.*

Solution Clearly, $\dfrac{11}{2}, \dfrac{11}{3}, \dfrac{11}{4}, \dfrac{11}{5}, \dfrac{11}{6}, \dfrac{11}{7}$ are all improper fractions with numerator 11.

EXAMPLE 3. *Convert each of the following into an improper fraction:*

(i) $3\dfrac{4}{5}$ (ii) $6\dfrac{5}{8}$ (iii) $5\dfrac{7}{9}$ (iv) $11\dfrac{1}{6}$

Solution We have:

(i) $3\dfrac{4}{5} = \dfrac{(3 \times 5) + 4}{5} = \dfrac{19}{5}.$

(ii) $6\dfrac{5}{8} = \dfrac{(6 \times 8) + 5}{8} = \dfrac{53}{8}.$

(iii) $5\dfrac{7}{9} = \dfrac{(5 \times 9) + 7}{9} = \dfrac{52}{9}.$

(iv) $11\dfrac{1}{6} = \dfrac{(11 \times 6) + 1}{6} = \dfrac{67}{6}.$

EXAMPLE 4.   *Convert each of the following into a mixed fraction:*

(i) $\dfrac{23}{5}$ (ii) $\dfrac{37}{6}$ (iii) $\dfrac{45}{8}$ (iv) $\dfrac{50}{7}$

Solution   (i) On dividing 23 by 5, we get

quotient = 4 and remainder = 3.

$$\therefore \quad \frac{23}{5} = 4 + \frac{3}{5} = 4\frac{3}{5}.$$

(ii) On dividing 37 by 6, we get

quotient = 6 and remainder = 1.

$$\therefore \quad \frac{37}{6} = 6 + \frac{1}{6} = 6\frac{1}{6}.$$

(iii) On dividing 45 by 8, we get

quotient = 5 and remainder = 5.

$$\therefore \quad \frac{45}{8} = 5 + \frac{5}{8} = 5\frac{5}{8}.$$

(iv) On dividing 50 by 7, we get

quotient = 7 and remainder = 1.

$$\therefore \quad \frac{50}{7} = 7 + \frac{1}{7} = 7\frac{1}{7}.$$

```
5 ) 23 ( 4
  - 20
  ----
     3

6 ) 37 ( 6
  - 36
  ----
     1

8 ) 45 ( 5
  - 40
  ----
     5

7 ) 50 ( 7
  - 49
  ----
     1
```

EXERCISE 5B

1. Which of the following are proper fractions?

$$\frac{1}{2}, \frac{3}{5}, \frac{10}{7}, \frac{7}{4}, 2, \frac{15}{8}, \frac{16}{16}, \frac{10}{11}, \frac{23}{10}$$

2. Which of the following are improper fractions?

$$\frac{3}{2}, \frac{5}{6}, \frac{9}{4}, \frac{8}{8}, 3, \frac{27}{16}, \frac{23}{31}, \frac{19}{18}, \frac{10}{13}, \frac{26}{26}$$

3. Write six improper fractions with denominator 5.

4. Write six improper fractions with numerator 13.

5. Convert each of the following into an improper fraction:

(i) $5\dfrac{5}{7}$ (ii) $9\dfrac{3}{8}$ (iii) $6\dfrac{3}{10}$ (iv) $3\dfrac{5}{11}$

(v) $10\dfrac{9}{14}$ (vi) $12\dfrac{7}{15}$ (vii) $8\dfrac{8}{13}$ (viii) $51\dfrac{2}{3}$

6. Convert each of the following into a mixed fraction:

(i) $\dfrac{17}{5}$ (ii) $\dfrac{62}{7}$ (iii) $\dfrac{101}{8}$ (iv) $\dfrac{95}{13}$

(v) $\dfrac{81}{11}$ (vi) $\dfrac{87}{16}$ (vii) $\dfrac{103}{12}$ (viii) $\dfrac{117}{20}$

7. Fill up the blanks with '>', '<' or '=':

(i) $\dfrac{1}{2}$ ☐ 1   (ii) $\dfrac{3}{4}$ ☐ 1   (iii) 1 ☐ $\dfrac{6}{7}$ (iv) $\dfrac{6}{6}$ ☐ 1

(v) $\dfrac{3016}{3016}$ ☐ 1   (vi) $\dfrac{11}{5}$ ☐ 1

8. Draw number lines and locate the following points:

(i) $\dfrac{1}{4}, \dfrac{1}{2}, \dfrac{3}{4}, \dfrac{4}{4}$

(ii) $\dfrac{1}{8}, \dfrac{2}{8}, \dfrac{3}{8}, \dfrac{5}{8}, \dfrac{7}{8}$

(iii) $\dfrac{2}{5}, \dfrac{3}{5}, \dfrac{4}{5}, \dfrac{8}{5}$

EQUIVALENT FRACTIONS

Look at the figures given below.

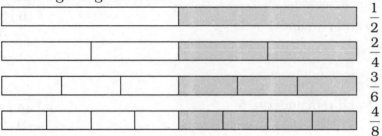

Clearly, the shaded portions of these figures are equal.

$\therefore \quad \dfrac{1}{2} = \dfrac{2}{4} = \dfrac{3}{6} = \dfrac{4}{8}.$

These fractions are called equivalent fractions.

Note that, $\dfrac{1}{2} = \dfrac{1 \times 2}{2 \times 2} = \dfrac{1 \times 3}{2 \times 3} = \dfrac{1 \times 4}{2 \times 4}.$

It shows that *multiplying the numerator and the denominator of a fraction by the same nonzero number does not change the value of the fraction.*

Similarly, *dividing the numerator and the denominator of a fraction by the same nonzero number does not change the value of the fraction.*

All such fractions are known as equivalent fractions.

EQUIVALENT FRACTIONS *Two or more fractions representing the same part of a whole are called equivalent fractions.*

RULE *To get a fraction equivalent to a given fraction, we multiply or divide the numerator and the denominator of the given fraction by the same nonzero number.*

SOLVED EXAMPLES

EXAMPLE 1. *Write four fractions equivalent to each of the following.*

(i) $\dfrac{3}{4}$ (ii) $\dfrac{5}{7}$ (iii) $\dfrac{8}{11}$

Solution

(i) $\dfrac{3}{4} = \dfrac{3 \times 2}{4 \times 2} = \dfrac{3 \times 3}{4 \times 3} = \dfrac{3 \times 4}{4 \times 4} = \dfrac{3 \times 5}{4 \times 5}.$

$\therefore \quad \dfrac{3}{4} = \dfrac{6}{8} = \dfrac{9}{12} = \dfrac{12}{16} = \dfrac{15}{20}.$

Hence, the four fractions equivalent to $\dfrac{3}{4}$ are $\dfrac{6}{8}, \dfrac{9}{12}, \dfrac{12}{16}$ and $\dfrac{15}{20}.$

(ii) $\dfrac{5}{7} = \dfrac{5 \times 2}{7 \times 2} = \dfrac{5 \times 3}{7 \times 3} = \dfrac{5 \times 4}{7 \times 4} = \dfrac{5 \times 5}{7 \times 5}.$

$\therefore \quad \dfrac{5}{7} = \dfrac{10}{14} = \dfrac{15}{21} = \dfrac{20}{28} = \dfrac{25}{35}.$

Hence, the four fractions equivalent to $\dfrac{5}{7}$ are $\dfrac{10}{14}, \dfrac{15}{21}, \dfrac{20}{28}$ and $\dfrac{25}{35}.$

(iii) $\dfrac{8}{11} = \dfrac{8 \times 2}{11 \times 2} = \dfrac{8 \times 3}{11 \times 3} = \dfrac{8 \times 4}{11 \times 4} = \dfrac{8 \times 5}{11 \times 5}$.

$\therefore \quad \dfrac{8}{11} = \dfrac{16}{22} = \dfrac{24}{33} = \dfrac{32}{44} = \dfrac{40}{55}$.

Hence, the four fractions equivalent to $\dfrac{8}{11}$ are $\dfrac{16}{22}, \dfrac{24}{33}, \dfrac{32}{44}$ and $\dfrac{40}{55}$.

EXAMPLE 2.   *Write a fraction equivalent to $\dfrac{3}{4}$ with numerator* 15.

Solution   Let $\dfrac{3}{4} = \dfrac{15}{\square}$.

Clearly, $15 = (3 \times 5)$.

So, we multiply the denominator also by 5.

$\therefore \quad \dfrac{3}{4} = \dfrac{3 \times 5}{4 \times 5} = \dfrac{15}{20}$.

Hence, the required fraction is $\dfrac{15}{20}$.

EXAMPLE 3.   *Write a fraction equivalent to $\dfrac{5}{8}$ with denominator* 56.

Solution   Let $\dfrac{5}{8} = \dfrac{\square}{56}$.

Clearly, $56 = (8 \times 7)$.

So, we multiply the numerator also by 7.

$\therefore \quad \dfrac{5}{8} = \dfrac{5 \times 7}{8 \times 7} = \dfrac{35}{56}$.

Hence, the required fraction is $\dfrac{35}{56}$.

EXAMPLE 4.   *Write a fraction equivalent to $\dfrac{36}{63}$ with numerator* 4.

Solution   Let $\dfrac{36}{63} = \dfrac{4}{\square}$.

Clearly, $4 = 36 \div 9$.

So, we divide the denominator also by 9.

$\therefore \quad \dfrac{36}{63} = \dfrac{36 \div 9}{63 \div 9} = \dfrac{4}{7}$

Hence, the required fraction is $\dfrac{4}{7}$.

EXAMPE 5.   *Write a fraction equivalent to $\dfrac{20}{36}$ with denominator* 9.

Solution   Let $\dfrac{20}{36} = \dfrac{\square}{9}$.

Clearly, $9 = 36 \div 4$.

So, we divide the numerator also by 4.

$\therefore \quad \dfrac{20}{36} = \dfrac{20 \div 4}{36 \div 4} = \dfrac{5}{9}$.

Hence, the required fraction is $\dfrac{5}{9}$.

AN INTERESTING FACT

TO TEST WHETHER TWO GIVEN FRACTIONS ARE EQUIVALENT OR NOT

TEST   *Let $\dfrac{a}{b}$ and $\dfrac{c}{d}$ be two given fractions.*

Cross multiply as shown, $\dfrac{a}{b} \diagdown\!\!\!\!\!\diagup \dfrac{c}{d}$

If $ad = bc$, we say that $\dfrac{a}{b}$ and $\dfrac{c}{d}$ are equivalent, otherwise not.

EXAMPLE 6.   *Show that $\dfrac{5}{8}$ and $\dfrac{20}{32}$ are equivalent fractions.*

Solution   The given fractions are $\dfrac{5}{8}$ and $\dfrac{20}{32}$.

By cross multiplication, we have: $\dfrac{5}{8} \diagdown\!\!\!\!\!\diagup \dfrac{20}{32}$

Now, $5 \times 32 = 160$ and $8 \times 20 = 160$.

$\therefore$ $(5 \times 32) = (8 \times 20)$.

Hence, $\dfrac{5}{8}$ and $\dfrac{20}{32}$ are equivalent fractions.

EXAMPLE 7.   *Show that $\dfrac{7}{12}$ and $\dfrac{36}{60}$ are not equivalent fractions.*

Solution   The given fractions are $\dfrac{7}{12}$ and $\dfrac{36}{60}$.

By cross multiplication, we have: $\dfrac{7}{12} \diagdown\!\!\!\!\!\diagup \dfrac{36}{60}$

Now, $7 \times 60 = 420$ and $12 \times 36 = 432$.

$\therefore$ $7 \times 60 \neq 12 \times 36$.

Hence, $\dfrac{7}{12}$ and $\dfrac{36}{60}$ are not equivalent fractions.

SIMPLEST FORM OF A FRACTION   *A fraction is said to be in the simplest form if the HCF of its numerator and denominator is 1.*

REDUCING A GIVEN FRACTION TO ITS SIMPLEST FORM

METHOD   Let the given fraction be $\dfrac{a}{b}$ and let the HCF of a and b be h.

Then, $\dfrac{a}{b} = \dfrac{(a \div h)}{(b \div h)}$ is in the simplest form.

EXAMPLE 8.   *Show that $\dfrac{7}{10}$ is in the simplest form.*

Solution   Here, numerator = 7 and denominator = 10.

Factors of 7 are 1, 7.

Factors of 10 are 1, 2, 5, 10.

Common factor of 7 and 10 is 1 only.

$\therefore$ HCF of 7 and 10 is 1.

Hence, $\dfrac{7}{10}$ is in the simplest form.

EXAMPLE 9. *Reduce $\dfrac{21}{35}$ to the simplest form.*

Solution   Here, numerator = 21 and denominator = 35.

Factors of 21 are 1, 3, 7, 21.

Factors of 35 are 1, 5, 7, 35.

Common factors of 21 and 35 are 1, 7.

HCF of 21 and 35 is 7.

$\therefore \quad \dfrac{21}{35} = \dfrac{21 \div 7}{35 \div 7} = \dfrac{3}{5}$.

Hence, the simplest form of $\dfrac{21}{35}$ is $\dfrac{3}{5}$.

EXERCISE 5C

1. Write five fractions equivalent to each of the following:

   (i) $\dfrac{2}{3}$ (ii) $\dfrac{4}{5}$ (iii) $\dfrac{5}{8}$ (iv) $\dfrac{7}{10}$

   (v) $\dfrac{3}{7}$ (vi) $\dfrac{6}{11}$ (vii) $\dfrac{7}{9}$ (viii) $\dfrac{5}{12}$

2. Which of the following are the pairs of equivalent fractions?

   (i) $\dfrac{5}{6}$ and $\dfrac{20}{24}$ (ii) $\dfrac{3}{8}$ and $\dfrac{15}{40}$ (iii) $\dfrac{4}{7}$ and $\dfrac{16}{21}$

   (iv) $\dfrac{2}{9}$ and $\dfrac{14}{63}$ (v) $\dfrac{1}{3}$ and $\dfrac{9}{24}$ (vi) $\dfrac{2}{3}$ and $\dfrac{33}{22}$

3. Find the equivalent fraction of $\dfrac{3}{5}$ having

   (i) denominator 30   (ii) numerator 24

4. Find the equivalent fraction of $\dfrac{5}{9}$ having

   (i) denominator 54   (ii) numerator 35

5. Find the equivalent fraction of $\dfrac{6}{11}$ having

   (i) denominator 77   (ii) numerator 60

6. Find the equivalent fraction of $\dfrac{24}{30}$ having numerator 4.

7. Find the equivalent fraction of $\dfrac{36}{48}$ with

   (i) numerator 9   (ii) denominator 4

8. Find the equivalent fraction of $\dfrac{56}{70}$ with

   (i) numerator 4   (ii) denominator 10

9. Reduce each of the following fractions into its simplest form:

   (i) $\dfrac{9}{15}$ (ii) $\dfrac{48}{60}$ (iii) $\dfrac{84}{98}$ (iv) $\dfrac{150}{60}$ (v) $\dfrac{72}{90}$

10. Show that each of the following fractions is in the simplest form:

   (i) $\dfrac{8}{11}$ (ii) $\dfrac{9}{14}$ (iii) $\dfrac{25}{36}$ (iv) $\dfrac{8}{15}$ (v) $\dfrac{21}{10}$

11. Replace $\square$ by the correct number in each of the following:

(i) $\dfrac{2}{7} = \dfrac{8}{\square}$

(ii) $\dfrac{3}{5} = \dfrac{\square}{35}$

(iii) $\dfrac{5}{8} = \dfrac{20}{\square}$

(iv) $\dfrac{45}{60} = \dfrac{9}{\square}$

(v) $\dfrac{40}{56} = \dfrac{\square}{7}$

(vi) $\dfrac{42}{54} = \dfrac{7}{\square}$

═══

LIKE AND UNLIKE FRACTIONS

LIKE FRACTIONS *Fractions having the same denominator are called **like fractions**.*

Thus, $\dfrac{2}{9}, \dfrac{4}{9}, \dfrac{5}{9}, \dfrac{8}{9}$ are all like fractions.

UNLIKE FRACTIONS *Fractions having different denominators are called **unlike fractions**.*

Thus, $\dfrac{1}{2}, \dfrac{3}{4}, \dfrac{5}{6}, \dfrac{7}{9}$ are all unlike fractions.

CONVERTING UNLIKE FRACTIONS INTO LIKE FRACTIONS

RULE *Suppose some unlike fractions are given. Convert each one of them into an equivalent fraction having a denominator equal to the LCM of all the denominators of the given fractions.*

EXAMPLE 1. *Convert the fractions $\dfrac{1}{2}, \dfrac{2}{3}, \dfrac{5}{6}$ and $\dfrac{4}{9}$ into like fractions.*

Solution The given fractions are $\dfrac{1}{2}, \dfrac{2}{3}, \dfrac{5}{6}$ and $\dfrac{4}{9}$.

LCM of 2, 3, 6, 9 = $(2 \times 3 \times 3)$ = 18.

So, we convert each of the given fractions into an equivalent fraction with 18 as the denominator.

2	2, 3, 6, 9
3	1, 3, 3, 9
	1, 1, 1, 3

Thus, we have:

$$\dfrac{1}{2} = \dfrac{1 \times 9}{2 \times 9} = \dfrac{9}{18}; \quad \dfrac{2}{3} = \dfrac{2 \times 6}{3 \times 6} = \dfrac{12}{18};$$

$$\dfrac{5}{6} = \dfrac{5 \times 3}{6 \times 3} = \dfrac{15}{18} \text{ and } \dfrac{4}{9} = \dfrac{4 \times 2}{9 \times 2} = \dfrac{8}{18}.$$

Hence, the required like fractions are $\dfrac{9}{18}, \dfrac{12}{18}, \dfrac{15}{18}$ and $\dfrac{8}{18}$.

COMPARISON OF FRACTIONS

COMPARISON OF LIKE FRACTIONS

RULE 1 *Among two fractions with the same denominator, the one with the greater numerator is the greater of the two.*

EXAMPLES   (i) $\dfrac{8}{9} > \dfrac{5}{9}$ (ii) $\dfrac{7}{11} > \dfrac{6}{11}$ (iii) $\dfrac{9}{10} > \dfrac{7}{10}$

COMPARISON OF FRACTIONS WITH THE SAME NUMERATOR

RULE 2 *Among two fractions with the same numerator, the one with the smaller denominator is the greater of the two.*

EXAMPLES   (i) $\dfrac{5}{6} > \dfrac{5}{8}$ (ii) $\dfrac{3}{5} > \dfrac{3}{7}$ (iii) $\dfrac{9}{10} > \dfrac{9}{11}$

GENERAL METHODS OF COMPARING TWO FRACTIONS

I. METHOD OF CROSS MULTIPLICATION

Let $\dfrac{a}{b}$ and $\dfrac{c}{d}$ be the two given fractions.

Cross multiply, as shown: $\dfrac{a}{b} \diagdown\!\!\!\!\diagdown \dfrac{c}{d}$

Find cross products ad and bc.

(i) *If $ad > bc$ then* $\dfrac{a}{b} > \dfrac{c}{d}.$

(ii) *If $ad < bc$ then* $\dfrac{a}{b} < \dfrac{c}{d}.$

(iii) *If $ad = bc$ then* $\dfrac{a}{b} = \dfrac{c}{d}.$

EXAMPLE 2.   *Compare the fractions $\dfrac{3}{8}$ and $\dfrac{5}{12}.$*

Solution   By cross multiplying, we get:

$3 \times 12 = 36$ and $8 \times 5 = 40.$ $\dfrac{3}{8} \diagdown\!\!\!\!\diagdown \dfrac{5}{12}$

Clearly, $36 < 40.$

Hence, $\dfrac{3}{8} < \dfrac{5}{12}.$

EXAMPLE 3.   *Compare the fractions $\dfrac{5}{9}$ and $\dfrac{6}{11}.$*

Solution   By cross multiplying, we get:

$5 \times 11 = 55$ and $9 \times 6 = 54.$ $\dfrac{5}{9} \diagdown\!\!\!\!\diagdown \dfrac{6}{11}$

Clearly, $55 > 54.$

Hence, $\dfrac{5}{9} > \dfrac{6}{11}.$

II. METHOD OF CONVERTING THE GIVEN FRACTIONS INTO LIKE FRACTIONS

RULE *Change each one of the given fractions into an equivalent fraction with the denominator equal to the LCM of the denominators of the given fractions. Now, the new fractions are like fractions, which may be compared by Rule 1.*

EXAMPLE 4.   *Compare the fractions $\dfrac{5}{6}$ and $\dfrac{8}{9}.$*

Solution   LCM of 6 and 9 $= (3 \times 2 \times 3) = 18.$

Now, we convert each one of $\dfrac{5}{6}$ and $\dfrac{8}{9}$ into an equivalent

$$\begin{array}{c|c} 3 & 6, 9 \\ \hline & 2, 3 \end{array}$$

fraction having 18 as denominator.

$$\therefore \ \frac{5}{6} = \frac{5 \times 3}{6 \times 3} = \frac{15}{18} \text{ and } \frac{8}{9} = \frac{8 \times 2}{9 \times 2} = \frac{16}{18}.$$

Clearly, $\frac{15}{18} < \frac{16}{18}.$

Hence, $\frac{5}{6} < \frac{8}{9}.$

EXAMPLE 5. *Compare the fractions* $\frac{7}{12}$ *and* $\frac{9}{16}.$

Solution LCM of 12 and 16 = $(4 \times 3 \times 4) = 48.$

So, we convert each one of $\frac{7}{12}$ and $\frac{9}{16}$ into an equivalent

4	12, 16
	3, 4

fraction having 48 as denominator.

Now, $\frac{7}{12} = \frac{7 \times 4}{12 \times 4} = \frac{28}{48}$ and $\frac{9}{16} = \frac{9 \times 3}{16 \times 3} = \frac{27}{48}.$

Clearly, $\frac{28}{48} > \frac{27}{48}.$

Hence, $\frac{7}{12} > \frac{9}{16}.$

EXAMPLE 6. *Arrange the fractions* $\frac{2}{3}, \ \frac{1}{6}, \ \frac{5}{9}$ *and* $\frac{7}{12}$ *in ascending order.*

Solution The given fractions are $\frac{2}{3}, \ \frac{1}{6}, \ \frac{5}{9}$ and $\frac{7}{12}.$

LCM of 3, 6, 9, 12 = $(3 \times 2 \times 3 \times 2) = 36.$

So, we convert each one of the given fractions
into an equivalent fraction with denominator 36.

3	3, 6, 9, 12
2	1, 2, 3, 4
	1, 1, 3, 2

Now, $\frac{2}{3} = \frac{2 \times 12}{3 \times 12} = \frac{24}{36}; \ \frac{1}{6} = \frac{1 \times 6}{6 \times 6} = \frac{6}{36};$

$\frac{5}{9} = \frac{5 \times 4}{9 \times 4} = \frac{20}{36}$ and $\frac{7}{12} = \frac{7 \times 3}{12 \times 3} = \frac{21}{36}.$

Clearly, $\frac{6}{36} < \frac{20}{36} < \frac{21}{36} < \frac{24}{36}.$

$\therefore \quad \frac{1}{6} < \frac{5}{9} < \frac{7}{12} < \frac{2}{3}.$

Hence, the given fractions in ascending order are $\frac{1}{6}, \ \frac{5}{9}, \ \frac{7}{12}, \ \frac{2}{3}.$

EXAMPLE 7. *Arrange the fractions* $\frac{4}{5}, \ \frac{7}{10}, \ \frac{8}{15}$ *and* $\frac{17}{30}$ *in descending order.*

Solution The given fractions are $\frac{4}{5}, \ \frac{7}{10}, \ \frac{8}{15}$ and $\frac{17}{30}.$

LCM of 5, 10, 15, 30 = $(5 \times 2 \times 3) = 30.$

So, we convert each of the given fractions into an equivalent
fraction with denominator 30.

5	5, 10, 15, 30
2	1, 2, 3, 6
3	1, 1, 3, 3
	1, 1, 1, 1

Thus, we have

$\frac{4}{5} = \frac{4 \times 6}{5 \times 6} = \frac{24}{30}; \ \frac{7}{10} = \frac{7 \times 3}{10 \times 3} = \frac{21}{30};$

$\frac{8}{15} = \frac{8 \times 2}{15 \times 2} = \frac{16}{30}; \ \frac{17}{30} = \frac{17 \times 1}{30 \times 1} = \frac{17}{30}.$

Clearly, $\dfrac{24}{30} > \dfrac{21}{30} > \dfrac{17}{30} > \dfrac{16}{30}$.

$\therefore \quad \dfrac{4}{5} > \dfrac{7}{10} < \dfrac{17}{30} < \dfrac{8}{15}$.

Hence, the given fractions in descending order are $\dfrac{4}{5}, \dfrac{7}{10}, \dfrac{17}{30}, \dfrac{8}{5}$.

EXERCISE 5D

1. Define like and unlike fractions and give five examples of each.

2. Convert $\dfrac{3}{5}$, $\dfrac{7}{10}$, $\dfrac{8}{15}$ and $\dfrac{11}{30}$ into like fractions.

3. Convert $\dfrac{1}{4}$, $\dfrac{5}{8}$, $\dfrac{7}{12}$ and $\dfrac{13}{24}$ into like fractions.

4. Fill in the place holders with the correct symbol > or <:

  (i) $\dfrac{8}{9} \square \dfrac{5}{9}$
  (ii) $\dfrac{9}{10} \square \dfrac{7}{10}$
  (iii) $\dfrac{3}{7} \square \dfrac{6}{7}$

  (iv) $\dfrac{11}{15} \square \dfrac{8}{15}$
  (v) $\dfrac{6}{11} \square \dfrac{5}{11}$
  (vi) $\dfrac{11}{20} \square \dfrac{17}{20}$

5. Fill in the place holders with the correct symbol > or <:

  (i) $\dfrac{3}{4} \square \dfrac{3}{5}$
  (ii) $\dfrac{7}{8} \square \dfrac{7}{10}$
  (iii) $\dfrac{4}{11} \square \dfrac{4}{9}$

  (iv) $\dfrac{8}{11} \square \dfrac{8}{13}$
  (v) $\dfrac{5}{12} \square \dfrac{5}{8}$
  (vi) $\dfrac{11}{14} \square \dfrac{11}{15}$

Compare the fractions given below:

6. $\dfrac{4}{5}, \dfrac{5}{7}$

7. $\dfrac{3}{8}, \dfrac{5}{6}$

8. $\dfrac{7}{11}, \dfrac{6}{7}$

9. $\dfrac{5}{6}, \dfrac{9}{11}$

10. $\dfrac{2}{3}, \dfrac{4}{9}$

11. $\dfrac{6}{13}, \dfrac{3}{4}$

12. $\dfrac{3}{4}, \dfrac{5}{6}$

13. $\dfrac{5}{8}, \dfrac{7}{12}$

14. $\dfrac{4}{9}, \dfrac{5}{6}$

15. $\dfrac{4}{5}, \dfrac{7}{10}$

16. $\dfrac{7}{8}, \dfrac{9}{10}$

17. $\dfrac{11}{12}, \dfrac{13}{15}$

Arrange the following fractions in ascending order:

18. $\dfrac{1}{2}, \dfrac{3}{4}, \dfrac{5}{6}$ and $\dfrac{7}{8}$

19. $\dfrac{2}{3}, \dfrac{5}{6}, \dfrac{7}{9}$ and $\dfrac{11}{18}$

20. $\dfrac{2}{5}, \dfrac{7}{10}, \dfrac{11}{15}$ and $\dfrac{17}{30}$

21. $\dfrac{3}{4}, \dfrac{7}{8}, \dfrac{11}{16}$ and $\dfrac{23}{32}$

Arrange the following fractions in descending order:

22. $\dfrac{3}{4}, \dfrac{5}{8}, \dfrac{11}{12}$ and $\dfrac{17}{24}$

23. $\dfrac{7}{9}, \dfrac{5}{12}, \dfrac{11}{18}$ and $\dfrac{17}{36}$

24. $\dfrac{2}{3}, \dfrac{3}{5}, \dfrac{7}{10}$ and $\dfrac{8}{15}$

25. $\dfrac{5}{7}, \dfrac{9}{14}, \dfrac{17}{21}$ and $\dfrac{31}{42}$

26. $\dfrac{1}{12}, \dfrac{1}{23}, \dfrac{1}{7}, \dfrac{1}{9}, \dfrac{1}{17}, \dfrac{1}{50}$

27. $\dfrac{3}{7}, \dfrac{3}{11}, \dfrac{3}{5}, \dfrac{3}{13}, \dfrac{3}{4}, \dfrac{3}{17}$

28. Lalita read 30 pages of a book containing 100 pages while Sarita read $\frac{2}{5}$ of the book. Who read more?

29. Rafiq exercised for $\frac{2}{3}$ hour, while Rohit exercised for $\frac{3}{4}$ hour. Who exercised for a longer time?

30. In a school 20 students out of 25 passed in VI A, while 24 out of 30 passed in VI B. Which section gave better result?

═══

ADDITION OF FRACTIONS

ADDITION OF LIKE FRACTIONS

RULE *Sum of like fractions* $= \dfrac{(Sum\ of\ their\ numerators)}{(Common\ denominator)}$.

EXAMPLE 1. *Find the sum:*

     (i) $\dfrac{4}{9} + \dfrac{2}{9}$ *(ii)* $\dfrac{3}{8} + \dfrac{1}{8} + \dfrac{5}{8}$

Solution   We have:

     (i) $\dfrac{4}{9} + \dfrac{2}{9} = \dfrac{(4+2)}{9} = \dfrac{\cancel{6}^{2}}{\cancel{9}_{3}} = \dfrac{2}{3}$.

     (ii) $\dfrac{3}{8} + \dfrac{1}{8} + \dfrac{5}{8} = \dfrac{(3+1+5)}{8} = \dfrac{9}{8} = 1\dfrac{1}{8}$.

ADDITION OF UNLIKE FRACTIONS

RULE *Change the given fractions into equivalent like fractions and then add.*

EXAMPLE 2. *Find the sum:* $\dfrac{8}{9} + \dfrac{5}{12}$.

Solution   LCM of 9 and 12 $= (3 \times 3 \times 4) = 36$.

     Now, $\dfrac{8}{9} = \dfrac{8 \times 4}{9 \times 4} = \dfrac{32}{36}$ and $\dfrac{5}{12} = \dfrac{5 \times 3}{12 \times 3} = \dfrac{15}{36}$.

     $\therefore \quad \dfrac{8}{9} + \dfrac{5}{12} = \dfrac{32}{36} + \dfrac{15}{36} = \dfrac{(32+15)}{36} = \dfrac{47}{36} = 1\dfrac{11}{36}$.

3 | 9, 12
  | 3, 4

36) 47 (1
   − 36
    ‾‾‾‾
     11

Short Method

     LCM of 9 and 12 $= (3 \times 3 \times 4) = 36$.

     $\therefore \quad \dfrac{8}{9} + \dfrac{5}{12} = \dfrac{32+15}{36}$ $\{[36 \div 9 = 4,\ 4 \times 8 = 32]$ and

                                      $[36 \div 12 = 3,\ 3 \times 5 = 15]\}$

              $= \dfrac{47}{36} = 1\dfrac{11}{36}$.

3 | 9, 12
  | 3, 4

EXAMPLE 3. *Find the sum:* $\dfrac{5}{6} + \dfrac{3}{8}$.

Solution   LCM of 6 and 8 $= (2 \times 3 \times 4) = 24$.

     $\therefore \quad \dfrac{5}{6} + \dfrac{3}{8} = \dfrac{20+9}{24}$ $\{[24 \div 6 = 4,\ 4 \times 5 = 20]$ and

                                      $[24 \div 8 = 3,\ 3 \times 3 = 9]\}$

              $= \dfrac{29}{24} = 1\dfrac{5}{24}$.

2 | 6, 8
  | 3, 4

EXAMPLE 4. *Find the sum:* $\dfrac{7}{12} + \dfrac{11}{16} + \dfrac{9}{24}$.

Solution LCM of 12, 16, 24 = $(4 \times 3 \times 2 \times 2) = 48$.

$$\therefore \quad \dfrac{7}{12} + \dfrac{11}{16} + \dfrac{9}{24} = \dfrac{28 + 33 + 18}{48}$$

$$= \dfrac{79}{48}$$

$$= 1\dfrac{31}{48} .$$

$$\begin{cases} 48 \div 12 = 4, \ 4 \times 7 = 28 \\ 48 \div 16 = 3, \ 3 \times 11 = 33 \\ 48 \div 24 = 2, \ 2 \times 9 = 18 \end{cases}$$

4	12, 16, 24
3	3, 4, 6
2	1, 4, 2
	1, 2, 1

EXAMPLE 5. *Find the sum:* $\dfrac{5}{6} + \dfrac{7}{8} + \dfrac{11}{12}$.

Solution We have:

LCM of 6, 8, 12 = $(2 \times 3 \times 2 \times 2) = 24$.

$$\therefore \quad \dfrac{5}{6} + \dfrac{7}{8} + \dfrac{11}{12} = \dfrac{20 + 21 + 22}{24}$$

$$= \dfrac{\cancel{63}^{21}}{\cancel{24}_{8}} = \dfrac{21}{8} = 2\dfrac{5}{8} .$$

$$\begin{cases} 24 \div 6 = 4, \ 4 \times 5 = 20 \\ 24 \div 8 = 3, \ 3 \times 7 = 21 \\ 24 \div 12 = 2, \ 2 \times 11 = 22 \end{cases}$$

2	6, 8, 12
3	3, 4, 6
2	1, 4, 2
	1, 2, 1

EXAMPLE 6. *Find the sum:* $2\dfrac{4}{5} + 1\dfrac{3}{10} + 3\dfrac{1}{15}$.

Solution We have:

$$2\dfrac{4}{5} + 1\dfrac{3}{10} + 3\dfrac{1}{15}$$

5	5, 10, 15
	1, 2, 3

$$= \dfrac{14}{5} + \dfrac{13}{10} + \dfrac{46}{15}$$

LCM of 5, 10, 15 = $(5 \times 2 \times 3) = 30$.

$$= \dfrac{84 + 39 + 92}{30}$$

$$= \dfrac{\cancel{215}^{43}}{\cancel{30}_{6}} = \dfrac{43}{6} = 7\dfrac{1}{6} .$$

$$\begin{cases} [30 \div 5 = 6, \ 6 \times 14 = 84], \\ [30 \div 10 = 3, \ 3 \times 13 = 39] \\ \text{and } [30 \div 15 = 2, \ 2 \times 46 = 92] \end{cases}$$

EXAMPLE 7. *Tanvi bought a notebook for* ₹ $8\dfrac{3}{4}$ *and a pen for* ₹ $10\dfrac{2}{5}$ · *How much money should she pay to the shopkeeper?*

Solution Cost of a notebook = ₹ $8\dfrac{3}{4}$ = ₹ $\dfrac{35}{4}$.

Cost of a pen = ₹ $10\dfrac{2}{5}$ = ₹ $\dfrac{52}{5}$.

Total cost of both the articles = ₹ $\left(\dfrac{35}{4} + \dfrac{52}{5} \right)$ = ₹ $\left(\dfrac{175 + 208}{20} \right)$

$$= ₹ \dfrac{383}{20} = ₹ 19\dfrac{3}{20} .$$

Hence, Tanvi should pay ₹ $19\dfrac{3}{20}$ to the shopkeeper.

EXAMPLE 8. *Three boxes weigh* $18\dfrac{3}{4}$ *kg,* $7\dfrac{1}{2}$ *kg and* $10\dfrac{1}{5}$ *kg respectively. A porter carries all the three boxes. What is the total weight carried by the porter?*

Solution Total weight carried by the porter

$$= \left(18\frac{3}{4} \text{ kg} + 7\frac{1}{2} \text{ kg} + 10\frac{1}{5} \text{ kg}\right)$$

$$= \left(\frac{75}{4} + \frac{15}{2} + \frac{51}{5}\right) \text{kg} = \left(\frac{375 + 150 + 204}{20}\right) \text{kg}$$

$$= \frac{729}{20} \text{ kg} = 36\frac{9}{20} \text{ kg.}$$

Hence, the total weight carried by the porter is $36\frac{9}{20}$ kg.

EXERCISE 5E

Find the sum:

1. $\frac{5}{8} + \frac{1}{8}$

2. $\frac{4}{9} + \frac{8}{9}$

3. $1\frac{3}{5} + 2\frac{4}{5}$

4. $\frac{2}{9} + \frac{5}{6}$

5. $\frac{7}{12} + \frac{9}{16}$

6. $\frac{4}{15} + \frac{17}{20}$

7. $2\frac{3}{4} + 5\frac{5}{6}$

8. $3\frac{1}{8} + 1\frac{5}{12}$

9. $2\frac{7}{10} + 3\frac{8}{15}$

10. $3\frac{2}{3} + 1\frac{5}{6} + 2$

11. $3 + 1\frac{4}{15} + 1\frac{3}{20}$

12. $3\frac{1}{3} + 4\frac{1}{4} + 6\frac{1}{6}$

13. $\frac{2}{3} + 3\frac{1}{6} + 4\frac{2}{9} + 2\frac{5}{18}$

14. $2\frac{1}{3} + 1\frac{1}{4} + 2\frac{5}{6} + 3\frac{7}{12}$

15. $2 + \frac{3}{4} + 1\frac{5}{8} + 3\frac{7}{16}$

16. Rohit bought a pencil for ₹ $3\frac{2}{5}$ and an eraser for ₹ $2\frac{7}{10}$. What is the total cost of both the articles?

17. Sohini bought $4\frac{1}{2}$ m of cloth for her kurta and $2\frac{2}{3}$ m of cloth for her pyjamas. How much cloth did she purchase in all?

18. While coming back home from his school, Kishan covered $4\frac{3}{4}$ km by rickshaw and $1\frac{1}{2}$ km on foot. What is the distance of his house from the school?

19. The weight of an empty gas cylinder is $16\frac{4}{5}$ kg and it contains $14\frac{2}{3}$ kg of gas. What is the weight of the cylinder filled with gas?

SUBTRACTION OF FRACTIONS

SUBTRACTION OF LIKE FRACTIONS

RULE *Difference of like fractions* $= \dfrac{(Difference\ of\ their\ numerators)}{(Common\ denominator)}.$

EXAMPLE 1. *Find the difference:*

(i) $\frac{5}{9} - \frac{2}{9}$ (ii) $\frac{11}{12} - \frac{7}{12}$

Solution   We have:

(i) $\dfrac{5}{9} - \dfrac{2}{9} = \dfrac{5-2}{9} = \dfrac{\cancel{3}^{1}}{\cancel{9}_{3}} = \dfrac{1}{3}$.

(ii) $\dfrac{11}{12} - \dfrac{7}{12} = \dfrac{11-7}{12} = \dfrac{\cancel{4}^{1}}{\cancel{12}_{3}} = \dfrac{1}{3}$.

SUBTRACTION OF UNLIKE FRACTIONS

RULE *Change the given fractions into equivalent like fractions and then subtract.*

EXAMPLE 2.   *Find the difference:* $\dfrac{7}{8} - \dfrac{5}{12}$.

Solution   LCM of 8 and 12 = $(4 \times 2 \times 3) = 24$.

Now, $\dfrac{7}{8} = \dfrac{7 \times 3}{8 \times 3} = \dfrac{21}{24}$ and $\dfrac{5}{12} = \dfrac{5 \times 2}{12 \times 2} = \dfrac{10}{24}$.

$$\therefore \quad \dfrac{7}{8} - \dfrac{5}{12} = \dfrac{21}{24} - \dfrac{10}{24} = \dfrac{21-10}{24} = \dfrac{11}{24}.$$

$$\begin{array}{c|c} 4 & 8,\ 12 \\ \hline & 2,\ 3 \end{array}$$

Short Method

LCM of 8 and 12 = $(4 \times 2 \times 3) = 24$.

$$\therefore \quad \dfrac{7}{8} - \dfrac{5}{12} = \dfrac{21-10}{24} \quad \{[24 \div 8 = 3,\ 3 \times 7 = 21] \text{ and } [24 \div 12 = 2,\ 2 \times 5 = 10]\}$$

$$\begin{array}{c|c} 4 & 8,\ 12 \\ \hline & 2,\ 3 \end{array}$$

$$= \dfrac{11}{24}.$$

EXAMPLE 3.   *Subtract* $3\dfrac{5}{9}$ *from* $5\dfrac{1}{6}$.

$$\begin{array}{c|c} 3 & 6,\ 9 \\ \hline & 2,\ 3 \end{array}$$

Solution $5\dfrac{1}{6} - 3\dfrac{5}{9} = \dfrac{31}{6} - \dfrac{32}{9}$

LCM of 6, 9 = $(3 \times 2 \times 3) = 18$.

$$= \dfrac{93 - 64}{18} \quad \{[18 \div 6 = 3,\ 3 \times 31 = 93] \text{ and } [18 \div 9 = 2,\ 2 \times 32 = 64]\}$$

$$= \dfrac{29}{18} = 1\dfrac{11}{18}.$$

EXAMPLE 4.   *Subtract* $\dfrac{7}{10}$ *from* $4\dfrac{1}{5}$.

$$\begin{array}{c|c} 5 & 5,\ 10 \\ \hline & 1,\ 2 \end{array}$$

Solution $4\dfrac{1}{5} - \dfrac{7}{10} = \dfrac{21}{5} - \dfrac{7}{10}$

LCM of 5, 10 = $(5 \times 2) = 10$.

$$= \dfrac{42 - 7}{10} \quad \{[10 \div 5 = 2,\ 2 \times 21 = 42] \text{ and } [10 \div 10 = 1,\ 1 \times 7 = 7]\}$$

$$= \dfrac{\cancel{35}^{7}}{\cancel{10}_{2}} = \dfrac{7}{2} = 3\dfrac{1}{2}.$$

EXAMPLE 5.   *Subtract* $1\dfrac{5}{6}$ *from* 8.

Solution   We have:

$$8 - 1\dfrac{5}{6} = 8 - \dfrac{11}{6}$$

$$= \frac{8}{1} - \frac{11}{6} \qquad \text{[LCM of 1, 6 = 6]}$$

$$= \frac{48-11}{6} \qquad \{[6 \div 1 = 6, 6 \times 8 = 48] \text{ and } [6 \div 6 = 1, 1 \times 11 = 11]\}$$

$$= \frac{37}{6} = 6\frac{1}{6}.$$

EXAMPLE 6. *Simplify:* $5\frac{1}{6} - 3\frac{1}{4} + 3\frac{1}{3} + 4.$

Solution   We have:

$$5\frac{1}{6} - 3\frac{1}{4} + 3\frac{1}{3} + 4$$

$$
\begin{array}{r|l}
3 & 6,\ 4,\ 3,\ 1 \\
\hline
2 & 2,\ 4,\ 1,\ 1 \\
\hline
 & 1,\ 2,\ 1,\ 1
\end{array}
$$

$$= \frac{31}{6} - \frac{13}{4} + \frac{10}{3} + \frac{4}{1}$$

LCM of 6, 4, 3, 1 = $(3 \times 2 \times 2) = 12.$

$$= \frac{62 - 39 + 40 + 48}{12} \qquad \left\{ \begin{array}{l} [12 \div 6 = 2, 2 \times 31 = 62], [12 \div 4 = 3, 3 \times 13 = 39], \\ [12 \div 3 = 4, 4 \times 10 = 40], [12 \div 1 = 12, 12 \times 4 = 48] \end{array} \right\}$$

$$= \frac{150 - 39}{12} = \frac{\cancel{111}^{37}}{\cancel{12}_4} = \frac{37}{4} = 9\frac{1}{4}.$$

EXAMPLE 7. *Of $\frac{5}{7}$ and $\frac{9}{14}$, which is greater and by how much?*

Solution   Let us compare $\frac{5}{7}$ and $\frac{9}{14}$.

$5 \times 14 = 70$ and $7 \times 9 = 63$ $\frac{5}{7} \diagdown\!\!\!\!\diagup \frac{9}{14}$

Clearly, $70 > 63;$ $\therefore \frac{5}{7} > \frac{9}{14}.$

$$
\begin{array}{r|l}
7 & 7,\ 14 \\
\hline
 & 1,\ 2
\end{array}
$$

Required difference $= \frac{5}{7} - \frac{9}{14}$

LCM of 7, 14 = $(7 \times 2) = 14.$

$$= \frac{10 - 9}{14} \qquad \{[14 \div 7 = 2, 2 \times 5 = 10] \text{ and } [14 \div 14 = 1, 1 \times 9 = 9]\}$$

$$= \frac{1}{14}.$$

Hence, $\frac{5}{7}$ is greater than $\frac{9}{14}$ by $\frac{1}{14}.$

EXAMPLE 8. *The cost of a pen is ₹ $6\frac{2}{3}$ and that of a pencil is ₹ $4\frac{1}{6}$. Which costs more and by how much?*

Solution   Cost of a pen $= ₹\, 6\frac{2}{3} = ₹\, \frac{20}{3} = ₹\, \frac{(20 \times 2)}{(3 \times 2)} = ₹\, \frac{40}{6}.$

Cost of a pencil $= ₹\, 4\frac{1}{6} = ₹\, \frac{25}{6}.$

Clearly, $\frac{40}{6} > \frac{25}{6}$ and so ₹ $6\frac{2}{3} > ₹\, 4\frac{1}{6}.$

So, the cost of a pen is more than the cost of a pencil.

Difference between their costs $= ₹\left(\frac{20}{3} - \frac{25}{6} \right) = ₹\left(\frac{40 - 25}{6} \right)$

$$= ₹\, \frac{15}{6} = ₹\, 2\frac{3}{6} = ₹\, 2\frac{1}{2}.$$

Hence, the cost of a pen is more than the cost of a pencil by ₹ $2\frac{1}{2}.$

EXERCISE 5F

Find the difference:

1. $\dfrac{5}{8} - \dfrac{1}{8}$

2. $\dfrac{7}{12} - \dfrac{5}{12}$

3. $4\dfrac{3}{7} - 2\dfrac{4}{7}$

4. $\dfrac{5}{6} - \dfrac{4}{9}$

5. $\dfrac{1}{2} - \dfrac{3}{8}$

6. $\dfrac{5}{8} - \dfrac{7}{12}$

7. $2\dfrac{7}{9} - 1\dfrac{8}{15}$

8. $3\dfrac{5}{8} - 2\dfrac{5}{12}$

9. $2\dfrac{3}{10} - 1\dfrac{7}{15}$

10. $6\dfrac{2}{3} - 3\dfrac{3}{4}$

11. $7 - 5\dfrac{2}{3}$

12. $10 - 6\dfrac{3}{8}$

Simplify:

13. $\dfrac{5}{6} - \dfrac{4}{9} + \dfrac{2}{3}$

14. $\dfrac{5}{8} + \dfrac{3}{4} - \dfrac{7}{12}$

15. $2 + \dfrac{11}{15} - \dfrac{5}{9}$

16. $5\dfrac{3}{4} - 4\dfrac{5}{12} + 3\dfrac{1}{6}$

17. $2 + 5\dfrac{7}{10} - 3\dfrac{14}{15}$

18. $8 - 3\dfrac{1}{2} - 2\dfrac{1}{4}$

19. $8\dfrac{5}{6} - 3\dfrac{3}{8} + 2\dfrac{7}{12}$

20. $6\dfrac{1}{6} - 5\dfrac{1}{5} + 3\dfrac{1}{3}$

21. $3 + 1\dfrac{1}{5} + \dfrac{2}{3} - \dfrac{7}{15}$

22. What should be added to $9\dfrac{2}{3}$ to get 19?

23. What should be added to $6\dfrac{7}{15}$ to get $8\dfrac{1}{5}$?

24. Subtract the sum of $3\dfrac{5}{9}$ and $3\dfrac{1}{3}$ from the sum of $5\dfrac{5}{6}$ and $4\dfrac{1}{9}$.

25. Of $\dfrac{3}{4}$ and $\dfrac{5}{7}$, which is greater and by how much?

26. Mrs Soni bought $7\dfrac{1}{2}$ litres of milk. Out of this milk, $5\dfrac{3}{4}$ litres was consumed. How much milk is left with her?

27. A film show lasted for $3\dfrac{1}{3}$ hours. Out of this time, $1\dfrac{3}{4}$ hours was spent on advertisements. What was the actual duration of the film?

28. In one day, a rickshaw puller earned ₹ $137\dfrac{1}{2}$. Out of this money, he spent ₹ $56\dfrac{3}{4}$ on food. How much money is left with him?

29. A piece of wire, $2\dfrac{3}{4}$ metres long, broke into two pieces. One piece is $\dfrac{5}{8}$ metre long. How long is the other piece?

EXERCISE 5G

OBJECTIVE QUESTIONS

Mark (✓) against the correct answer in each of the following:

1. A fraction equivalent to $\dfrac{3}{5}$ is

   (a) $\dfrac{3+2}{5+2}$

   (b) $\dfrac{3-2}{5-2}$

   (c) $\dfrac{3 \times 2}{5 \times 2}$

   (d) none of these

2. A fraction equivalent to $\dfrac{8}{12}$ is

   (a) $\dfrac{8+4}{12+4}$

   (b) $\dfrac{8-4}{12-4}$

   (c) $\dfrac{8 \div 4}{12 \div 4}$

   (d) none of these

3. A fraction equivalent to $\dfrac{24}{36}$ is

(a) $\dfrac{3}{4}$ (b) $\dfrac{2}{3}$ (c) $\dfrac{8}{9}$ (d) none of these

4. If $\dfrac{3}{4}$ is equivalent to $\dfrac{x}{20}$ then the value of x is

(a) 15   (b) 18   (c) 12   (d) none of these

5. If $\dfrac{45}{60}$ is equivalent to $\dfrac{3}{x}$ then the value of x is

(a) 4   (b) 5   (c) 6   (d) 20

6. Which of the following are like fractions?

(a) $\dfrac{2}{5}, \dfrac{2}{7}, \dfrac{2}{9}, \dfrac{2}{11}$ (b) $\dfrac{2}{3}, \dfrac{3}{4}, \dfrac{4}{5}, \dfrac{5}{6}$ (c) $\dfrac{1}{8}, \dfrac{3}{8}, \dfrac{5}{8}, \dfrac{7}{8}$ (d) none of these

7. Which of the following is a proper fraction?

(a) $\dfrac{5}{3}$ (b) 5   (c) $1\dfrac{2}{5}$ (d) none of these

8. Which of the following is a proper fraction?

(a) $\dfrac{7}{8}$ (b) $1\dfrac{7}{8}$ (c) $\dfrac{8}{7}$ (d) none of these

9. Which of the following statements is correct?

(a) $\dfrac{3}{4} < \dfrac{3}{5}$ (b) $\dfrac{3}{4} > \dfrac{3}{5}$ (c) $\dfrac{3}{4}$ and $\dfrac{3}{5}$ cannot be compared

10. The smallest of the fractions $\dfrac{3}{5}, \dfrac{2}{3}, \dfrac{5}{6}, \dfrac{7}{10}$ is

(a) $\dfrac{2}{3}$ (b) $\dfrac{7}{10}$ (c) $\dfrac{3}{5}$ (d) $\dfrac{5}{6}$

11. The largest of the fractions $\dfrac{4}{5}, \dfrac{4}{7}, \dfrac{4}{9}, \dfrac{4}{11}$ is

(a) $\dfrac{4}{11}$ (b) $\dfrac{4}{5}$ (c) $\dfrac{4}{7}$ (d) $\dfrac{4}{9}$

12. The smallest of the fractions $\dfrac{6}{11}, \dfrac{7}{11}, \dfrac{8}{11}, \dfrac{9}{11}$ is

(a) $\dfrac{6}{11}$ (b) $\dfrac{7}{11}$ (c) $\dfrac{8}{11}$ (d) $\dfrac{9}{11}$

13. The smallest of the fractions $\dfrac{3}{4}, \dfrac{5}{6}, \dfrac{7}{12}, \dfrac{2}{3}$ is

(a) $\dfrac{2}{3}$ (b) $\dfrac{3}{4}$ (c) $\dfrac{5}{6}$ (d) $\dfrac{7}{12}$

14. $4\dfrac{3}{5} = ?$

(a) $\dfrac{17}{5}$ (b) $\dfrac{23}{5}$ (c) $\dfrac{17}{3}$ (d) none of these

15. $\dfrac{34}{7} = ?$

(a) $3\dfrac{4}{7}$ (b) $7\dfrac{3}{4}$ (c) $4\dfrac{6}{7}$ (d) none of these

16. $\dfrac{5}{8} + \dfrac{1}{8} = ?$

    (a) $\dfrac{3}{8}$ (b) $\dfrac{3}{4}$ (c) 6   (d) none of these

17. $\dfrac{5}{8} - \dfrac{1}{8} = ?$

    (a) $\dfrac{1}{4}$ (b) $\dfrac{1}{2}$ (c) $\dfrac{1}{16}$ (d) none of these

18. $3\dfrac{3}{4} - 2\dfrac{1}{4} = ?$

    (a) $1\dfrac{1}{2}$ (b) $1\dfrac{1}{4}$ (c) $\dfrac{1}{4}$ (d) none of these

19. $\dfrac{5}{6} + \dfrac{2}{3} - \dfrac{4}{9} = ?$

    (a) $1\dfrac{1}{3}$ (b) $1\dfrac{1}{6}$ (c) $1\dfrac{1}{9}$ (d) $1\dfrac{1}{18}$

20. Which is greater: $3\dfrac{1}{3}$ or $\dfrac{33}{10}$?

    (a) $3\dfrac{1}{3}$ (b) $\dfrac{33}{10}$ (c) both are equal

═══

Things to Remember

1. The numbers of the form $\dfrac{a}{b}$, where a and b are natural numbers, are called fractions.
2. In $\dfrac{a}{b}$, we call a the numerator and b the denominator.
3. Two or more fractions representing the same part of a whole are called equivalent fractions.
4. To get a fraction equivalent to a given fraction, we multiply or divide the numerator and the denominator of the given fraction by the same nonzero number.
5. Fractions having the same denominator are called like fractions; otherwise, they are called unlike fractions.
6. In order to convert some given fractions into like fractions, we convert each one of them into an equivalent fraction having a denominator equal to the LCM of all the denominators of the given fractions.
7. A fraction whose numerator is less than its denominator is called a proper fraction; otherwise, it is called an improper fraction.
8. A mixed fraction = A whole number + A fraction.
9. Comparison of fractions:

   Rule 1 Among two fractions with the same denominator, the one with the greater numerator is the greater of the two.

   Rule 2 Among two fractions with the same numerator, the one with the smaller denominator is the greater of the two.

   Rule 3 General Method: Let $\dfrac{a}{b}$ and $\dfrac{c}{d}$ be two given fractions.

      Step 1. Cross multiply as shown: $\dfrac{a}{b} \diagdown \dfrac{c}{d}$, and find the cross products ad and bc.

      Step 2. (i) If $ad > bc$ then $\dfrac{a}{b} > \dfrac{c}{d}$.

               (ii) If $ad < bc$ then $\dfrac{a}{b} < \dfrac{c}{d}$.

               (iii) If $ad = bc$ then $\dfrac{a}{b} = \dfrac{c}{d}$.

10. *Sum of like fractions* $= \dfrac{\text{Sum of their numerators}}{\text{Common denominator}}$.

11. *For adding unlike fractions, change them into equivalent like fractions and then add.*

12. *Difference of like fractions* $= \dfrac{\text{Difference of their numerators}}{\text{Common denominator}}$.

13. *For subtracting unlike fractions, change them into equivalent like fractions and then subtract.*

═══

CCE TEST PAPER-5

A. 1. Define a fraction. Give five examples of fractions.

2. What fraction of an hour is 35 minutes?

3. Find the equivalent fraction of 5/8 with denominator 56.

4. Represent $2\frac{3}{5}$ on the number line.

5. Find the sum $2\frac{4}{5}+1\frac{3}{10}+3\frac{1}{15}$.

6. The cost of a pen is ₹ $16\frac{2}{3}$ and that of a pencil is ₹ $4\frac{1}{6}$. Which costs more and by how much?

7. Of $\frac{3}{4}$ and $\frac{5}{7}$, which is greater and by how much?

8. Convert the fractions $\frac{1}{2}, \frac{2}{3}, \frac{4}{9}$ and $\frac{5}{6}$ into like fractions.

9. Find the equivalent fraction of $\frac{3}{5}$ having denominator 30.

10. Reduce $\frac{84}{98}$ to the simplest form.

B. *Mark (✓) against the correct answer in each of the following:*

11. $\frac{24}{11}$ is an example of

(a) a proper fraction (b) an improper fraction
(c) a mixed fraction (d) none of these

12. $\frac{3}{8}$ is an example of

(a) a proper fraction (b) an improper fraction
(c) a mixed fraction (d) none of these

13. $\frac{3}{8}$ and $\frac{5}{12}$ on comparison give

(a) $\frac{3}{8}>\frac{5}{12}$ (b) $\frac{3}{8}<\frac{5}{12}$ (c) $\frac{3}{8}=\frac{5}{12}$ (d) none of these

14. The largest of the fractions $\frac{2}{3}, \frac{5}{9}, \frac{1}{2}$ and $\frac{7}{12}$ is

(a) $\frac{2}{3}$ (b) $\frac{5}{9}$ (c) $\frac{7}{12}$ (d) $\frac{1}{2}$

15. $3\frac{3}{4}-1\frac{1}{2}=?$

(a) $2\frac{1}{2}$ (b) $2\frac{1}{4}$ (c) $1\frac{1}{2}$ (d) $1\frac{1}{4}$

16. Which of the following are like fractions?

(a) $\frac{2}{3},\frac{3}{4},\frac{4}{5},\frac{5}{6}$ (b) $\frac{2}{5},\frac{2}{7},\frac{2}{9},\frac{2}{11}$ (c) $\frac{1}{8},\frac{3}{8},\frac{5}{8},\frac{7}{8}$ (d) none of these

17. $? - \dfrac{8}{21} = \dfrac{8}{21}$

(a) 0   (b) 1   (c) $\dfrac{21}{8}$ (d) $\dfrac{16}{21}$

C. 18. *Fill in the blanks:*

(i) $9\dfrac{2}{3} + \ldots\ldots = 19$

(ii) $6\dfrac{1}{6} - ? = \dfrac{29}{30}$

(iii) $7 - 5\dfrac{2}{3} = \ldots\ldots$

(iv) $\dfrac{72}{90}$ reduced to simplest form is ....

(v) $\dfrac{42}{54} = \dfrac{7}{\square}$

D. 19. *Write 'T' for true and 'F' for false for each of the statements given below:*

(a) $3\dfrac{1}{3} > \dfrac{33}{10}$.

(b) $8 - 1\dfrac{5}{6} = 7\dfrac{1}{6}$.

(c) $\dfrac{1}{2}, \dfrac{1}{3}$ and $\dfrac{1}{4}$ are like fractions.

(d) $\dfrac{3}{5}$ lies between 3 and 5.

(e) Among $\dfrac{1}{2}, \dfrac{1}{3}, \dfrac{3}{4}, \dfrac{4}{3}$ the largest fraction is $\dfrac{4}{3}$.

6 | Simplification

Suppose we are given a numerical expression consisting of numbers with two or more of the fundamental operations. We perform these operations strictly in the following order:

(i) Division (ii) Multiplication (iii) Addition (iv) Subtraction

SOLVED EXAMPLES

EXAMPLE 1. *Simplify:* $18 - 6 \div 2 \times 3$

Solution The given expression

$= 18 - 6 \div 2 \times 3$

$= 18 - 3 \times 3$ [performing division]

$= 18 - 9$ [performing multiplication]

$= 9$ [performing subtraction].

EXAMPLE 2. *Simplify:* $15 + 24 \div 3 - 1 \times 6$

Solution The given expression

$= 15 + 24 \div 3 - 1 \times 6$

$= 15 + 8 - 1 \times 6$ [performing division]

$= 15 + 8 - 6$ [performing multiplication]

$= 23 - 6$ [performing addition]

$= 17$ [performing subtraction].

USE OF BRACKETS

We know that brackets are used to separate various parts of an expression.

There are four kinds of brackets.

  (i) *Bar, or Vinculum*   ‾

  (ii) *Round brackets, or Small brackets, or Parentheses*   ( )

  (iii) *Curly brackets, or Braces*   { }

  (iv) *Square brackets, or Big brackets*   [ ]

While simplifying expressions, the terms in brackets are taken as independent units.

The order of simplifying the brackets is:

  (i) *Bar first*   (ii) *Parentheses next*

  (iii) *Braces next*   (iv) *Square brackets in the last*

For simplifying the expressions involving brackets, we must proceed according to the letters of the word 'VBODMAS'.

Here V, B, O, D, M, A, S stand for *Vinculum, Brackets, Of, Division, Multiplication, Addition and Subtraction* respectively.

EXAMPLE 3.   *Simplify:* $16 - [11 - \{8 \div (17 + 3 \times 2 - 19)\}]$

Solution   The given expression

$$= 16 - [11 - \{8 \div (17 + 3 \times 2 - 19)\}]$$

$$= 16 - [11 - \{8 \div (17 + 6 - 19)\}]$$

$$= 16 - [11 - \{8 \div 4\}] = 16 - [11 - 2]$$

$$= 16 - 9 = 7.$$

EXAMPLE 4.   *Simplify:* $14 - [12 - \{9 - (7 - \overline{6 - 2})\}]$

Solution   The given expression

$$= 14 - [12 - \{9 - (7 - \overline{6 - 2})\}]$$

$$= 14 - [12 - \{9 - (7 - 4)\}] \quad \text{[removing vinculum]}$$

$$= 14 - [12 - \{9 - 3\}] \quad \text{[removing parentheses]}$$

$$= 14 - [12 - 6] \quad \text{[removing braces]}$$

$$= 14 - 6 \quad \text{[removing square brackets]}$$

$$= 8.$$

EXAMPLE 5.   *Simplify:* $5\frac{1}{2} \, of \left(\frac{2}{3} - \frac{3}{5} \right) + \frac{1}{2} \div \frac{5}{11}$

Solution   The given expression

$$= \frac{11}{2} \, of \left(\frac{2}{3} - \frac{3}{5} \right) + \frac{1}{2} \div \frac{5}{11}$$

$$= \frac{11}{2} \, of \left(\frac{10 - 9}{15} \right) + \frac{1}{2} \div \frac{5}{11}$$

$$= \frac{11}{2} \, of \, \frac{1}{15} + \frac{1}{2} \div \frac{5}{11} \quad \text{[removing parentheses]}$$

$$= \frac{11}{30} + \frac{1}{2} \div \frac{5}{11} \quad \text{[removing 'of']}$$

$$= \frac{11}{30} + \frac{1}{2} \times \frac{11}{5} \quad \text{[removing '$\div$']}$$

$$= \frac{11}{30} + \frac{11}{10} \quad \text{[removing '$\times$']}$$

$$= \frac{(11 + 33)}{30} = \frac{44}{30} \quad \text{[performing addition]}$$

$$= \frac{22}{15} = 1\frac{7}{15}.$$

EXAMPLE 6.   *Simplify:* $\left[3\frac{1}{4} \div \left\{ 1\frac{1}{4} - \frac{1}{2}\left(2\frac{1}{2} - \overline{\frac{1}{4} - \frac{1}{6}} \right) \right\} \right]$

Solution   We have:

$$\left[3\frac{1}{4} \div \left\{ 1\frac{1}{4} - \frac{1}{2}\left(2\frac{1}{2} - \overline{\frac{1}{4} - \frac{1}{6}} \right) \right\} \right]$$

$$= \left[\frac{13}{4} \div \left\{ \frac{5}{4} - \frac{1}{2} \left(\frac{5}{2} - \overline{\frac{1}{4} - \frac{1}{6}} \right) \right\} \right]$$

$$= \left[\frac{13}{4} \div \left\{ \frac{5}{4} - \frac{1}{2} \left(\frac{5}{2} - \frac{3-2}{12} \right) \right\} \right] \qquad \text{[removing bar]}$$

$$= \left[\frac{13}{4} \div \left\{ \frac{5}{4} - \frac{1}{2} \left(\frac{5}{2} - \frac{1}{12} \right) \right\} \right]$$

$$= \left[\frac{13}{4} \div \left\{ \frac{5}{4} - \frac{1}{2} \left(\frac{30-1}{12} \right) \right\} \right]$$

$$= \left[\frac{13}{4} \div \left\{ \frac{5}{4} - \frac{1}{2} \times \frac{29}{12} \right\} \right] \qquad \text{[removing parentheses]}$$

$$= \left[\frac{13}{4} \div \left\{ \frac{5}{4} - \frac{29}{24} \right\} \right] = \left[\frac{13}{4} \div \left\{ \frac{30-29}{24} \right\} \right]$$

$$= \left[\frac{13}{4} \div \frac{1}{24} \right] \qquad \text{[removing braces]}$$

$$= \left[\frac{13}{4} \times \frac{24}{1} \right] = 78 \qquad \text{[removing square brackets].}$$

EXERCISE 6A

Simplify:

1. $21 - 12 \div 3 \times 2$

2. $16 + 8 \div 4 - 2 \times 3$

3. $13 - (12 - 6 \div 3)$

4. $19 - [4 + \{16 - (12 - 2)\}]$

5. $36 - [18 - \{14 - (15 - 4 \div 2 \times 2)\}]$

6. $27 - [18 - \{16 - (5 - \overline{4-1})\}]$

7. $4\frac{4}{5} \div \frac{3}{5} \text{ of } 5 + \frac{4}{5} \times \frac{3}{10} - \frac{1}{5}$

8. $\left(\frac{2}{3} + \frac{4}{9} \right) \text{ of } \frac{3}{5} \div 1\frac{2}{3} \times 1\frac{1}{4} - \frac{1}{3}$

9. $7\frac{1}{3} \div \frac{2}{3} \text{ of } 2\frac{1}{5} + 1\frac{3}{8} \div 2\frac{3}{4} - 1\frac{1}{2}$

10. $5\frac{1}{7} - \left\{ 3\frac{3}{10} \div \left(2\frac{4}{5} - \frac{7}{10} \right) \right\}$

11. $9\frac{3}{4} \div \left[2\frac{1}{6} + \left\{ 4\frac{1}{3} - \left(1\frac{1}{2} + 1\frac{3}{4} \right) \right\} \right]$

12. $4\frac{1}{10} - \left[2\frac{1}{2} - \left\{ \frac{5}{6} - \left(\frac{2}{5} + \frac{3}{10} - \frac{4}{15} \right) \right\} \right]$

13. $1\frac{5}{6} + \left[2\frac{2}{3} - \left\{ 3\frac{3}{4} \left(3\frac{4}{5} \div 9\frac{1}{2} \right) \right\} \right]$

14. $4\frac{4}{5} \div \left\{ 2\frac{1}{5} - \frac{1}{2} \left(1\frac{1}{4} - \overline{\frac{1}{4} - \frac{1}{5}} \right) \right\}$

15. $7\frac{1}{2} - \left[2\frac{1}{4} \div \left\{ 1\frac{1}{4} - \frac{1}{2} \left(\frac{3}{2} - \overline{\frac{1}{3} - \frac{1}{6}} \right) \right\} \right]$

SQUARE ROOT

The square root of a given number is that number whose square is the given number.

The square root of 4 is denoted by $\sqrt{4}$, the square root of 9 will be denoted by $\sqrt{9}$, etc.

EXAMPLES
(i) Since $2 \times 2 = 4$, we have $\sqrt{4} = \sqrt{2 \times 2} = 2$.

(ii) Since $3 \times 3 = 9$, we have $\sqrt{9} = \sqrt{3 \times 3} = 3$.

METHOD   *For finding the square root of a number, express it as product of primes. Take the product of all primes, choosing one out of every pair.*

EXAMPLE   *Find (i) $\sqrt{36}$ (ii) $\sqrt{49}$ (iii) $\sqrt{64}$.*

Solution   We have

(i) $\sqrt{36} = \sqrt{(2 \times 2) \times (3 \times 3)} = (2 \times 3) = 6.$

(ii) $\sqrt{49} = \sqrt{7 \times 7} = 7.$

(iii) $\sqrt{64} = \sqrt{(2 \times 2) \times (2 \times 2) \times (2 \times 2)} = (2 \times 2 \times 2) = 8.$

Show that: (i) $\sqrt{81} = 9$ (ii) $\sqrt{100} = 10$ (iii) $\sqrt{121} = 11$ (iv) $\sqrt{144} = 12.$

EXERCISE 6B

OBJECTIVE QUESTIONS

Mark (✓) against the correct answer in each of the following:

1. $8 + 4 \div 2 \times 5 = ?$
   (a) 30   (b) 50   (c) 18   (d) none of these

2. $54 \div 3$ of $6 + 9 = ?$
   (a) 117   (b) 12   (c) $\dfrac{6}{5}$ (d) none of these

3. $13 - (12 - 6 \div 3) = ?$
   (a) 11   (b) 3   (c) $\dfrac{7}{3}$ (d) none of these

4. $1001 \div 11$ of $13 = ?$
   (a) 7   (b) 1183   (c) 847   (d) none of these

5. $133 + 28 \div 7 - 8 \times 2 = ?$
   (a) 7   (b) 121   (c) 30   (d) none of these

6. $3640 - 14 \div 7 \times 2 = ?$
   (a) 3636   (b) 1036   (c) 1819   (d) none of these

7. $100 \times 10 - 100 + 2000 \div 100 = ?$
   (a) 29   (b) 920   (c) none of these

8. $27 - [18 - \{16 - (5 - \overline{4 - 1})\}] = ?$
   (a) 25   (b) 23   (c) none of these

9. $32 - [48 \div \{36 - (27 - \overline{16 - 9})\}] = ?$
   (a) 29   (b) $\dfrac{520}{17}$ (c) none of these

10. $8 - [28 \div \{34 - (36 - 18 \div 9 \times 8)\}] = ?$
    (a) 6   (b) $6\dfrac{4}{9}$ (c) none of these

┌─────────────────────┐
│ Things to Remember │
└─────────────────────┘

1. *For simplifying a given expression, we strictly perform in the following order:*
   (i) Vinculum (ii) Brackets (iii) Of (iv) Division (v) Multiplication (vi) Addition and (vii) Subtraction.
2. *We remember the word VBODMAS, where V, B, O, D, M, A, S stand for Vinculum, Brackets, Of, Division, Multiplication, Addition and Subtraction respectively.*

CCE TEST PAPER-6

A. Simplify:

1. $16 - [11 + \{8 - (6 - \overline{4 - 2})\}]$

2. $16 + 8 \div 4 - 2 \times 3$

3. $36 - [18 - \{14 - (15 - 4 \div 2 \times 2)\}]$

B. Mark (✓) against the correct answer in each of the following:

4. $15 + 5 \div 5 \times 2 = ?$

   (a) 8   (b) 2   (c) 17   (d) none of these

5. $16 - 2 \div 7 + 6 \times 2 = ?$

   (a) 16   (b) 14   (c) $27\frac{5}{7}$ (d) none of these

6. $54 \div 3$ of $6 + 9 = ?$

   (a) 117   (b) 12   (c) $\frac{6}{5}$ (d) none of these

7 | Decimals

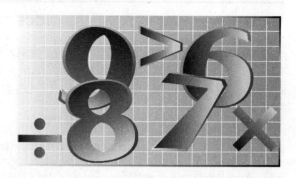

DECIMAL FRACTIONS *The fractions in which the denominators are 10, 100, 1000, etc., are known as decimal fractions.*

EXAMPLES $\dfrac{3}{10}, \dfrac{5}{100}, \dfrac{48}{1000}$, etc., are all decimal fractions.

DECIMAL FRACTIONS WITH 10 AS DENOMINATOR (TENTHS)

We know that:

$\dfrac{1}{10}, \dfrac{2}{10}, \dfrac{3}{10}, \ldots\ldots, \dfrac{9}{10}$ represent *one-tenth, two-tenths, three-tenths, ..., nine-tenths* respectively.

We write them as:

$\dfrac{1}{10} = \mathbf{.1}, \quad \dfrac{2}{10} = \mathbf{.2}, \quad \dfrac{3}{10} = \mathbf{.3}, \ldots\ldots, \dfrac{9}{10} = \mathbf{.9}.$

Here the dot (.) is called the *decimal point.*

We read them as:

point one, point two, point three, ..., point nine respectively. Note that .1 = 0.1, .3 = 0.3, .9 = 0.9, ...

DECIMAL FRACTIONS WITH 100 AS DENOMINATOR (HUNDREDTHS)

We know that:

$\dfrac{1}{100}, \dfrac{2}{100}, \dfrac{3}{100}, \ldots\ldots, \dfrac{9}{100}, \dfrac{10}{100}, \dfrac{11}{100}, \ldots\ldots, \dfrac{99}{100}$ represent

one-hundredth, two-hundredths, three-hundredths, ..., nine-hundredths, ten-hundredths, eleven-hundredths, ..., ninety-nine-hundredths respectively.

We write them as:

$\dfrac{1}{100} = \mathbf{.01}, \quad \dfrac{2}{100} = \mathbf{.02}, \quad \dfrac{3}{100} = \mathbf{.03}, \ldots\ldots, \dfrac{9}{100} = \mathbf{.09}, \quad \dfrac{10}{100} = \mathbf{.10}, \quad \dfrac{11}{10} = \mathbf{.11}, \ldots\ldots, \dfrac{99}{100} = \mathbf{.99}.$

We read them as:

point zero one, point zero two, point zero three, ..., point zero nine, point one zero, point one one, ..., point nine nine respectively. Note that .01 = 0.01, .99 = 0.99, ...

DECIMAL FRACTIONS WITH 1000 AS DENOMINATOR (THOUSANDTHS)

We know that:

$\dfrac{1}{1000}, \dfrac{2}{1000}, \ldots\ldots, \dfrac{9}{1000}, \dfrac{10}{1000}, \dfrac{11}{1000}, \ldots\ldots, \dfrac{99}{1000}, \dfrac{100}{1000}, \dfrac{101}{1000}, \ldots\ldots, \dfrac{999}{1000}$ represent

one-thousandth, two-thousandths, ..., nine-thousandths, ten-thousandths, eleven-thousandths, ..., ninety-nine-thousandths, one hundred-thousandths, one hundred one-thousandths, ... nine hundred ninety-nine-thousandths respectively.

We write them as:

$$\frac{1}{1000} = .001, \frac{2}{1000} = .002, \ldots\ldots, \frac{9}{1000} = .009, \frac{10}{1000} = .010, \frac{11}{1000} = .011, \ldots\ldots, \frac{99}{1000} = .099,$$

$$\frac{100}{1000} = .100, \frac{101}{1000} = .101, \ldots\ldots, \frac{999}{1000} = .999.$$

We read them as:

point zero zero one, point zero zero two, ..., point zero zero nine, point zero one zero, point zero one one, ..., point zero nine nine, point one zero zero, point one zero one, ..., point nine nine nine respectively. Remember that .001 = 0.001, .011 = 0.011, ...

EXAMPLES OF MIXED FRACTIONS AS DECIMALS

EXAMPLES   *Express the numbers* $2\frac{1}{10}, 6\frac{17}{100}$ *and* $18\frac{29}{1000}$ *as decimals.*

Solution   We have:

$$2\frac{1}{10} = 2 + \frac{1}{10} = 2 + 0.1 = 2.1.$$

$$6\frac{17}{100} = 6 + \frac{17}{100} = 6 + 0.17 = 6.17.$$

$$18\frac{29}{1000} = 18 + \frac{29}{1000} = 18 + 0.029 = 18.029.$$

DECIMALS

DECIMALS *The numbers expressed in decimal form are called **decimal numbers** or simply **decimals**.*

EXAMPLE   Each of the numbers 5.8, 19.63, 7.295, 0.068, etc., is a decimal.

A decimal has two parts, namely, (i) whole-number part and (ii) decimal part.

These parts are separated by a dot (.), called the *decimal point*.

The part on the left side of the decimal point is the whole-number part and that on the right side of the decimal point is the decimal part.

EXAMPLE   In 68.49, we have, whole-number part = 68 and decimal part = .49.

DECIMAL PLACES *The number of digits contained in the decimal part of a decimal gives the number of decimal places.*

EXAMPLES   4.93 has two decimal places and 7.632 has three decimal places.

LIKE AND UNLIKE DECIMALS

LIKE DECIMALS *Decimals having the same number of decimal places are called like decimals.*

EXAMPLE   9.82, 6.03, 14.58 are like decimals, each having two decimal places.

UNLIKE DECIMALS *Decimals having different number of decimal places are called unlike decimals.*

EXAMPLE   Clearly, 6.4, 8.93, 12.065 are unlike decimals.

AN IMPORTANT RESULT

We shall show that 0.6 = 0.60 = 0.600, etc.

$$0.6 = \frac{6}{10} = \frac{6 \times 10}{10 \times 10} = \frac{60}{100} = 0.60.$$

$$0.6 = \frac{6}{10} = \frac{6 \times 100}{10 \times 100} = \frac{600}{1000} = 0.600.$$

$\therefore$ 0.6 = 0.60 = 0.600, etc.

RESULT *Putting any number of zeros to the extreme right of the decimal part of a decimal does not change its value.*

Thus, we may write 2.64 = 2.640 = 2.6400, etc.

Thus, we may convert unlike decimals into like decimals by annexing the required number of zeros to the extreme right of the decimal part.

SOME EXAMPLES

EXAMPLE 1. *Convert 5.3, 7.19, 0.376 and 84 into like decimals.*

Solution In the given numbers, the maximum number of decimal places is 3. So, we convert each one of the given numbers into one having 3 decimal places by annexing suitable number of zeros to the extreme right of the decimal part.

5.3 = 5.300, 7.19 = 7.190, 0.376 = 0.376 and 84 = 84.000.

Thus, 5.300, 7.190, 0.376 and 84.000 are the required like decimals.

EXAMPLE 2. *Arrange the digits of 269.374 in the place-value chart. Write the place value of each digit. Also, write 269.374 in expanded form.*

Solution We may arrange the digits of the given number in the place-value chart as shown below.

Hundreds	Tens	Ones	Decimal point	Tenths	Hundredths	Thousandths
2	6	9	.	3	7	4

In 269.374, we have:

Place value of 2 = 2 hundreds = 200.

Place value of 6 = 6 tens = 60..

Place value of 9 = 9 ones = 9

Place value of 3 = 3 tenths = $\frac{3}{10}$.

Place value of 7 = 7 hundredths = $\frac{7}{100}$.

Place value of 4 = 4 thousandths = $\frac{4}{1000}$.

$\therefore$ 269.374 = 2 hundreds + 6 tens + 9 ones + 3 tenths + 7 hundredths

+ 4 thousandths

$$= 200 + 60 + 9 + \frac{3}{10} + \frac{7}{100} + \frac{4}{1000}.$$

COMPARING DECIMALS

Suppose we have to compare two decimals. Then, we proceed according to the following steps.

Step 1. *Convert the given decimals into like decimals.*

Step 2. *First compare the whole-number part.*

The decimal with the greater whole-number part is greater.

Step 3. *If the whole-number parts are equal, compare the tenths digits.*
The decimal with the bigger digit in the tenths place is greater.

Step 4. *If the tenths digits are also equal, compare the hundredths digits, and so on.*

The following examples will make the ideas more clear.

EXAMPLE 3. *Compare 63.84 and 57.98.*

Solution The given decimals are 63.84 and 57.98.
Let us compare their whole-number parts.
Clearly, 63 > 57.
∴ 63.84 > 57.98.

EXAMPLE 4. *Compare 24.7 and 24.58.*

Solution Converting the given decimals into like decimals, they become 24.70 and 24.58.
The whole-number parts of these numbers are equal.
So, we compare their tenths digits.
Clearly, 7 tenths > 5 tenths.
∴ 24.70 > 24.58.
Hence, 24.7 > 24.58.

EXAMPLE 5. *Write the following decimals in ascending order:*
4.83, 6.07, 0.9, 0.465 and 7.4.

Solution Converting the given decimals into like decimals, we get them as
4.830, 6.070, 0.900, 0.465 and 7.400.
Clearly, 0.465 < 0.900 < 4.830 < 6.070 < 7.400.
∴ 0.465 < 0.9 < 4.83 < 6.07 < 7.4.
Hence, the given decimals in ascending order are:
0.465, 0.9, 4.83, 6.07 and 7.4.

EXERCISE 7A

1. Write each of the following in figures:
   (i) Fifty-eight point six three
   (ii) One hundred twenty-four point four two five
   (iii) Seven point seven six
   (iv) Nineteen point eight
   (v) Four hundred four point zero four four
   (vi) Point one seven three
   (vii) Point zero one five

2. Write the place value of each digit in each of the following decimals:
   (i) 14.83   (ii) 275.269   (iii) 46.075
   (iv) 302.459   (v) 5370.34   (vi) 186.209

3. Write each of the following decimals in expanded form:
   (i) 67.83   (ii) 283.61   (iii) 24.675
   (iv) 0.294   (v) 8.006   (vi) 4615.72

4. Write each of the following in decimal form:
   (i) $40 + 6 + \dfrac{7}{10} + \dfrac{9}{100}$
   (ii) $500 + 70 + 8 + \dfrac{3}{10} + \dfrac{1}{100} + \dfrac{6}{1000}$

(iii) $700 + 30 + 1 + \dfrac{8}{10} + \dfrac{4}{100}$ (iv) $600 + 5 + \dfrac{7}{100} + \dfrac{9}{1000}$

(v) $800 + 5 + \dfrac{8}{10} + \dfrac{6}{1000}$ (vi) $30 + 9 + \dfrac{4}{100} + \dfrac{8}{1000}$

5. Convert each of the following into like decimals:
   (i) 7.5, 64.23, 0.074   (ii) 0.6, 5.937, 2.36, 4.2
   (iii) 1.6, 0.07, 3.58, 2.9   (iv) 2.5, 0.63, 14.08, 1.637

6. Fill in each of the place holders with the correct symbol > or <:
   (i) 84.23 ☐ 76.35   (ii)   7.608 ☐   7.68
   (iii) 8.34 ☐   8.43   (iv) 12.06 ☐ 12.006
   (v)   3.85 ☐   3.805   (vi) 0.97 ☐   1.07

7. Arrange the following decimals in ascending order:
   (i) 5.8, 7.2, 5.69, 7.14, 5.06   (ii) 0.6, 6.6, 6.06, 66.6, 0.06
   (iii) 6.54, 6.45, 6.4, 6.5, 6.05   (iv) 3.3, 3.303, 3.033, 0.33, 3.003

8. Arrange the following decimals in descending order:
   (i) 7.3, 8.73, 73.03, 7.33, 8.073   (ii) 3.3, 3.03, 30.3, 30.03, 3.003
   (iii) 2.7, 7.2, 2.27, 2.72, 2.02, 2.007   (iv) 8.88, 8.088, 88.8, 88.08, 8.008

═══════════

CONVERTING A DECIMAL INTO A FRACTION

METHOD: Step 1. *Write the given decimal without the decimal point as the numerator of the fraction.*

Step 2. *In the denominator, write 1 followed by as many zeros as there are decimal places in the given decimal.*

Step 3. *Convert the above fraction to the simplest form.*

The following examples will make the ideas more clear.

EXAMPLE 1. *Convert each of the following decimals into a fraction in its simplest form:*
   (i) .4   *(ii)* .25   *(iii)* 0.06   *(iv)* .075   *(v)* 0.625

Solution   We have:

(i) $.4 = \dfrac{\overset{2}{\cancel{4}}}{\underset{5}{\cancel{10}}} = \dfrac{2}{5}$.   (ii) $.25 = \dfrac{\overset{1}{\cancel{25}}}{\underset{4}{\cancel{100}}} = \dfrac{1}{4}$.

(iii) $0.06 = \dfrac{\overset{3}{\cancel{6}}}{\underset{50}{\cancel{100}}} = \dfrac{3}{50}$.   (iv) $.075 = \dfrac{\overset{3}{\cancel{75}}}{\underset{40}{\cancel{1000}}} = \dfrac{3}{40}$.

(v) $0.625 = \dfrac{\overset{\overset{5}{25}}{\cancel{625}}}{\underset{\underset{8}{40}}{\cancel{1000}}} = \dfrac{5}{8}$.

EXAMPLE 2. *Convert each of the following decimals as a mixed fraction:*
   (i) 7.5   *(ii)* 24.8   *(iii)* 13.25   *(iv)* 6.375

Solution   We have:

(i) $7.5 = \dfrac{\cancel{75}^{15}}{\cancel{10}_2} = \dfrac{15}{2} = 7\dfrac{1}{2}.$

(ii) $24.8 = \dfrac{\cancel{248}^{124}}{\cancel{10}_5} = \dfrac{124}{5} = 24\dfrac{4}{5}.$

(iii) $13.25 = \dfrac{\cancel{1325}^{53}}{\cancel{100}_4} = \dfrac{53}{4} = 13\dfrac{1}{4}.$

(iv) $6.375 = \dfrac{\cancel{6375}^{255^{51}}}{\cancel{1000}_{40_8}} = \dfrac{51}{8} = 6\dfrac{3}{8}.$

CONVERTING A FRACTION INTO A DECIMAL

When the denominator of a fraction is a power of 10
then we can convert the fraction into a decimal, as shown below:

EXAMPLE 3.   *Convert each of the following fractions into a decimal:*

(i) $\dfrac{17}{10}$ (ii) $\dfrac{239}{100}$ (iii) $\dfrac{2103}{100}$ (iv) $\dfrac{3001}{1000}$

Solution   We have:

(i) $\dfrac{17}{10} = 1\dfrac{7}{10} = 1 + \dfrac{7}{10} = 1 + 0.7 = 1.7.$

(ii) $\dfrac{239}{100} = 2\dfrac{39}{100} = 2 + \dfrac{39}{100} = 2 + 0.39 = 2.39.$

(iii) $\dfrac{2103}{100} = 21\dfrac{3}{100} = 21 + \dfrac{3}{100} = 21 + 0.03 = 21.03.$

(iv) $\dfrac{3001}{1000} = 3\dfrac{1}{1000} = 3 + \dfrac{1}{1000} = 3 + 0.001 = 3.001.$

GENERAL METHOD OF CONVERTING A FRACTION INTO A DECIMAL

Step 1.   *Divide the numerator by the denominator till a nonzero remainder is obtained.*

Step 2.   *Put a decimal point in the dividend as well as in the quotient.*

Step 3.   *Put a zero on the right of the decimal point in the dividend as well as on the right of the remainder.*

Step 4.   *Divide again just as we do in whole numbers.*

Step 5.   *Repeat step 4 till the remainder is zero.*

SOME MORE EXAMPLES

EXAMPLE 4.   *Convert $\dfrac{29}{4}$ into a decimal fraction.*

Solution   On dividing, we get:

```
        7.25
  4 ) 29.00 (
      - 28
        10
       - 8
        20
       - 20
         ×
```

$\therefore \dfrac{29}{4} = 7.25.$

EXAMPLE 5. *Convert $4\frac{7}{8}$ into a decimal fraction.*

Solution   We have: $4\frac{7}{8} = \frac{4 \times 8 + 7}{8} = \frac{39}{8}$.

By actual division, we get:

$$\begin{array}{r} 4.875 \\ 8\,\overline{)\,39.000\,(} \\ \underline{-32} \\ 70 \\ \underline{-64} \\ 60 \\ \underline{-56} \\ 40 \\ \underline{-40} \\ \times \end{array}$$

$\therefore \quad 4\frac{7}{8} = 4.875.$

EXAMPLE 6. *Convert $15\frac{17}{40}$ into a decimal fraction.*

Solution   We have:

$$15\frac{17}{40} = \frac{15 \times 40 + 17}{40} = \frac{617}{40}.$$

By actual division, we get:

$$\begin{array}{r} 15.425 \\ 40\,\overline{)\,617.000\,(} \\ \underline{-40} \\ 217 \\ \underline{-200} \\ 170 \\ \underline{-160} \\ 100 \\ \underline{-80} \\ 200 \\ \underline{-200} \\ \times \end{array}$$

$\therefore \quad 15\frac{17}{40} = 15.425.$

EXAMPLE 7. *Convert $\frac{6}{25}$ into a decimal fraction.*

Solution   By actual division, we get:

$$\begin{array}{r} 0.24 \\ 25\,\overline{)\,6.00\,(} \\ \underline{-0} \\ 60 \\ \underline{-50} \\ 100 \\ \underline{-100} \\ \times \end{array}$$

$\therefore \quad \frac{6}{25} = 0.24.$

EXAMPLE 8.   *Express in kilograms, using decimals:*
   (i) 2 kg 348 g   *(ii)* 5 kg 35 g   *(iii)* 78 g   *(iv)* 5 g

Solution   (i) 2 kg 348 g = 2 kg + 348 g = 2 kg + $\dfrac{348}{1000}$ kg

$$= 2 \text{ kg} + 0.348 \text{ kg} = 2.348 \text{ kg}.$$

(ii) 5 kg 35 kg = 5 kg + 35 kg = 5 kg + $\dfrac{35}{1000}$ kg

$$= 5 \text{ kg} + 0.035 \text{ kg} = 5.035 \text{ kg}.$$

(iii) 78 g = $\dfrac{78}{1000}$ kg = 0.078 kg.

(iv) 5 g = $\dfrac{5}{1000}$ kg = 0.005 kg.

EXAMPLE 9.   *Express in kilometres, using decimals:*
   (i) 5 km 245 m   *(ii)* 9 km 46 m   *(iii)* 435 m   *(iv)* 56 m   *(v)* 4 m

Solution   (i) 5 km 245 m = 5 km + 245 m

$$= 5 \text{ km} + \frac{245}{1000} \text{ km} = 5 \text{ km} + .245 \text{ km}$$

$$= 5.245 \text{ km}.$$

(ii) 9 km 46 m = 9 km + 46 m

$$= 9 \text{ km} + \frac{46}{1000} \text{ km} = 9 \text{ km} + .046 \text{ km}$$

$$= 9.046 \text{ km}.$$

(iii) 435 m = $\dfrac{435}{1000}$ km = 0.435 km.

(iv) 56 m = $\dfrac{56}{1000}$ km = 0.056 km.

(v) 4 m = $\dfrac{4}{1000}$ km = 0.004 km.

EXAMPLE 10.   *Express in rupees, using decimals:*
   (i) ₹ 26 *and* 75 *paise*   *(ii)* ₹ 35 *and* 8 *paise*   *(iii)* ₹ 6 *and* 9 *paise*
   (iv) 38 *paise*   *(v)* 9 *paise*   *(vi)* 104 *paise*

Solution   (i) ₹ 26 and 75 paise = ₹ 26 + ₹ $\dfrac{75}{100}$

$$= ₹\ 26 + ₹\ 0.75 = ₹\ 26.75.$$

(ii) ₹ 35 and 8 paise = ₹ 35 + ₹ $\dfrac{8}{100}$

$$= ₹\ 35 + ₹\ 0.08 = ₹\ 35.08.$$

(iii) ₹ 6 and 9 paise = ₹ 6 + ₹ $\dfrac{9}{100}$

$$= ₹\ 6 + ₹\ 0.09 = ₹\ 6.09.$$

(iv) 38 paise = ₹ $\dfrac{38}{100}$ = ₹ 0.38.

(v) 9 paise = ₹ $\dfrac{9}{100}$ = ₹ 0.09.

(vi) 104 paise = ₹ $\dfrac{104}{100}$ = ₹ 1.04.

EXERCISE 7B

Convert each of the following into a fraction in its simplest form:

1. .9
2. 0.6
3. .08
4. 0.15
5. 0.48
6. .053
7. 0.125
8. .224

Convert each of the following as a mixed fraction:

9. 6.4
10. 16.5
11. 8.36
12. 4.275
13. 25.06
14. 7.004
15. 2.052
16. 3.108

Convert each of the following into a decimal:

17. $\dfrac{23}{10}$
18. $\dfrac{167}{100}$
19. $\dfrac{1589}{100}$
20. $\dfrac{5413}{1000}$

21. $\dfrac{21415}{1000}$
22. $\dfrac{25}{4}$
23. $3\dfrac{3}{5}$
24. $1\dfrac{4}{25}$

25. $5\dfrac{17}{50}$
26. $12\dfrac{3}{8}$
27. $2\dfrac{19}{40}$
28. $\dfrac{19}{20}$

29. $\dfrac{37}{50}$
30. $\dfrac{107}{250}$
31. $\dfrac{3}{40}$
32. $\dfrac{7}{8}$

33. Using decimals, express
    (i) 8 kg 640 g in kilograms
    (ii) 9 kg 37 g in kilograms
    (iii) 6 kg 8 g in kilograms

34. Using decimals, express
    (i) 4 km 365 m in kilometres
    (ii) 5 km 87 m in kilometres
    (iii) 3 km 6 m in kilometres
    (iv) 270 m in kilometres
    (v) 35 m in kilometres
    (vi) 6 m in kilometres

35. Using decimals, express
    (i) 15 kg 850 g in kilograms
    (ii) 8 kg 96 g in kilograms
    (iii) 540 g in kilograms
    (iv) 8 g in kilograms

36. Using decimals, express
    (i) ₹ 18 and 25 paise in rupees
    (ii) ₹ 9 and 8 paise in rupees
    (iii) 32 paise in rupees
    (iv) 5 paise in rupees

OPERATIONS ON DECIMALS

ADDITION OF DECIMALS

METHOD: Step 1. *Convert the given decimals into like decimals.*

Step 2. *Write the addends one under the other in column form, keeping the decimal points of all the addends in the same column and the digits of the same place in the same column.*

Step 3. *Add as in the case of whole numbers.*

Step 4. *In the sum, put the decimal point directly under decimal points in the addends.*

The following examples will make the ideas more clear.

EXAMPLE 1.   *Add:* 27.8, 46, 175.09 *and* 685.7

Solution   Converting the given decimals into like decimals, we get
27.80, 46.00, 175.09 and 685.70.

Writing these decimals in column form and adding, we get:

$$\begin{array}{r} 27.80 \\ 46.00 \\ 175.09 \\ 685.70 \\ \hline 934.59 \end{array}$$

Hence, the sum of the given decimals is 934.59.

EXAMPLE 2.   *Add:* 67.25, 249, 8.785, 9.8 *and* 0.23

Solution   Converting the given decimals into like decimals, we get
67.250, 249.000, 8.785, 9.800 and 0.230.

Writing these decimals in column form and adding, we get:

$$\begin{array}{r} 67.250 \\ 249.000 \\ 8.785 \\ 9.800 \\ 0.230 \\ \hline 335.065 \end{array}$$

Hence, the sum of the given decimals is 335.065.

EXAMPLE 3.   *A man covers a journey by car in 3 hours. He covers a distance of 64 km 324 m during the first hour, 58 km 56 m during the second hour and 62 km 8 m during the third hour. What is the length of his journey?*

Solution   We have:

distance covered during the first hour	=	64.324 km
distance covered during the second hour	=	58.056 km
distance covered during the third hour	=	62.008 km
Total distance covered in 3 hours	=	184.388 km

Hence, the length of his journey = 184.388 km
= 184 km 388 m.

EXAMPLE 4. *Ramesh purchased a book, a pen and a notebook for ₹165.35, ₹72 and ₹14.85 respectively. How much money will he have to pay to the shopkeeper for these items?*

Solution
Cost of a book   = ₹165.35
Cost of a pen   = ₹ 72.00
Cost of a notebook = ₹ 14.85
Total cost   = ₹ 252.20
Total money to be paid by Ramesh = ₹ 252.20.

EXAMPLE 5. *The weight of an empty gas cylinder is 18 kg 75 g. The weight of the gas contained in it is 12 kg 350 g. What is the total weight of the cylinder filled with gas?*

Solution
Weight of an empty cylinder = 18.075 kg
Weight of the gas filled in it = 12.350 kg
Total weight   = 30.425 kg
Hence, the total weight of the cylinder filled with gas = 30.425 kg = 30 kg 425 g.

EXERCISE 7C

Add the following decimals:

1. 9.6, 14.8, 37 and 5.9
2. 23.7, 106.94, 68.9 and 29.5
3. 72.8, 7.68, 16.23 and 0.7
4. 18.6, 84.75, 8.345 and 9.7
5. 8.236, 16.064, 63.8 and 27.53
6. 28.9, 19.64, 123.697 and 0.354
7. 4.37, 9.638, 17.007 and 6.8
8. 14.5, 0.038, 118.573 and 6.84
9. During three days of a week, a rickshaw puller earns ₹32.60, ₹56.80 and ₹72 respectively. What is his total earning during these days?
10. A man purchases an almirah for ₹11025, gives ₹172.50 as its cartage and spends ₹64.80 on its repair. How much does the almirah cost him?
11. Ramesh covers 36 km 235 m by taxi, 4 km 85 m by rickshaw and 1 km 80 m on foot. What is the total distance covered by him?
12. A bag contains 45 kg 80 g of sugar and the mass of the empty bag is 950 g. What is the mass of the bag containing this much of sugar?
13. Ramu bought 2 m 70 cm cloth for his shirt and 2 m 60 cm cloth for his pyjamas. Find the total length of cloth bought by him.
14. Radhika bought 2 m 5 cm cloth for her salwar and 3 m 35 cm cloth for her shirt. Find the total length of cloth bought by her.

SUBTRACTION OF DECIMALS

METHOD: Step 1. *Convert the given decimals into like decimals.*
Step 2. *Write the smaller number under the larger one in column form in such a way that the decimal points of both the numbers are in the same column and the digits of the same place lie in the same column.*
Step 3. *Subtract as we do in case of whole numbers.*
Step 4. *In the difference, put the decimal point directly under the decimal points of the given numbers.*

The following examples will make the ideas more clear.

EXAMPLE 1. *Subtract 35.87 from 63.2.*

Solution   Converting the given decimals into like decimals, we get 35.87 and 63.20.

Writing them in column form with the larger one at the top and subtracting, we get:

$$\begin{array}{r} 63.20 \\ -\ 35.87 \\ \hline 27.33 \\ \hline \end{array}$$

Hence, $63.2 - 35.87 = 27.33$.

EXAMPLE 2. *Subtract 28.65 from 73.*

Solution Converting the given decimals into like decimals, we get 28.65 and 73.00.
Writing them in column form with the larger one at the top and subtracting, we get:

$$\begin{array}{r} 73.00 \\ -\ 28.65 \\ \hline 44.35 \\ \hline \end{array}$$

Hence, $73 - 28.65 = 44.35$.

EXAMPLE 3. *Simplify:* $53.5 - 34.68 + 64.75 - 28.9$

Solution Converting the given decimals into like decimals, and adding and subtracting as shown alongside, the given expression

$\begin{array}{r} 53.50 \\ +\ 64.75 \\ \hline 118.25 \\ \hline \end{array}$ and $\begin{array}{r} 34.68 \\ +\ 28.90 \\ \hline 63.58 \\ \hline \end{array}$

$= 53.50 - 34.68 + 64.75 - 28.90$

$= (53.50 + 64.75) - (34.68 + 28.90)$

$= 118.25 - 63.58$

$= 54.67$.

$$\begin{array}{r} 118.25 \\ -\ 63.58 \\ \hline 54.67 \\ \hline \end{array}$$

EXAMPLE 4. *Ramesh purchased a book worth ₹ 146.75 from a bookseller and gave him a 500-rupee note. How much balance did he get back?*

Solution
Total money paid = ₹ 500.00
Cost of the book = – ₹ 146.75
Balance = ₹ 353.25

Hence, the balance received by Ramesh = ₹ 353.25.

EXAMPLE 5. *The weight of a cylinder filled with gas is 30 kg. If the weight of the empty cylinder is 14 kg 80 g, find the weight of the gas contained in it.*

Solution
Weight of the cylinder filled with gas = 30.000 kg
Weight of the empty cylinder = – 14.080 kg
Weight of the gas in the cylinder = 15.920 kg

Hence, the weight of the gas = 15.920 kg.

EXAMPLE 6. *Monika went to the market with ₹ 3000 in cash. Out of this money she purchased one frock, one toy and one bag costing ₹ 578.75, ₹ 309 and ₹ 1862.85 respectively. How much money is left with her?*

Solution
Cost of one frock = ₹ 578.75
Cost of one toy = ₹ 309.00
Cost of one bag = ₹ 1862.85
Total cost = ₹ 2750.60
Total cash in hand = ₹ 3000.00
Total money spent = – ₹ 2750.60
Balance = ₹ 249.40

Hence, the money left with Monika = ₹ 249.40.

EXAMPLE 7. *The distance between Richa's house and her school hostel is 61 km. For reaching her house from the hostel, she covers 54 km 860 m by taxi, 5 km 65 m by tonga and the rest of the distance by rickshaw. How much distance did Richa cover by rickshaw?*

Solution

Distance covered by taxi	=	54.860 km
Distance covered by tonga	=	+ 5.065 km
Total distance covered by taxi and tonga	=	59.925 km
Total distance to be covered by Richa	=	61.000 km
Distance covered by taxi and tonga	=	− 59.925 km
∴ distance covered by rickshaw	=	1.075 km

Hence, the distance covered by rickshaw = 1.075 km
= 1 km 75 m.

EXAMPLE 8. *The total weight of a bag containing 13 kg 750 g of potatoes and 8 kg 80 g of tomatoes is 22 kg 200 g. How much is the weight of the empty bag?*

Solution

Weight of potatoes = 13 kg 750 g	=	13.750 kg
Weight of tomatoes = 8 kg 80 g	=	+ 8.080 kg
Total weight of vegetables	=	21.830 kg
Total weight of the bag and vegetables	=	22.200 kg
Total weight of vegetables in it	=	− 21.830 kg
Weight of the empty bag	=	0.370 kg

Hence, the weight of the empty bag = 0.370 kg
= 370 g.

EXERCISE 7D

Subtract:

1. 27.86 from 53.74
2. 64.98 from 103.87
3. 59.63 from 92.4
4. 56.8 from 204
5. 127.38 from 216.2
6. 39.875 from 70.68
7. 348.237 from 523.12
8. 458.573 from 600
9. 149.456 from 206.321
10. 0.612 from 3.4

Simplify:

11. 37.6 + 72.85 − 58.678 − 6.09
12. 75.3 − 104.645 + 178.96 − 47.9
13. 213.4 − 56.84 − 11.87 − 16.087
14. 76.3 − 7.666 − 6.77
15. What is to be added to 74.5 to get 91?
16. What is to be subtracted from 7.3 to get 0.862?
17. By how much should 23.754 be increased to get 50?
18. By how much should 84.5 be decreased to get 27.84?
19. If the school bags of Neelam and Garima weigh 6 kg 80 g and 5 kg 265 g respectively, whose bag is heavier and by how much?
20. Kunal purchased a notebook for ₹ 19.75, a pencil for ₹ 3.85 and a pen for ₹ 8.35 from a book shop. He gave a 50-rupee note to the shopkeeper. What amount did he get back?
21. Sunita purchased 5 kg 75 g of fruits and 3 kg 465 g of vegetables, and put them in a bag. If this bag with these contents weighs 9 kg, find the weight of the empty bag.

22. The distance between Reeta's house and her office is 14 km. She covers 10 km 65 m by scooter, 3 km 75 m by bus and the rest on foot. How much distance does she cover by walking?

≡≡≡

EXERCISE 7E

OBJECTIVE QUESTIONS

Mark (✓) against the correct answer in each of the following:

1. $\dfrac{7}{10} = ?$

   (a) 7.1   (b) 1.7   (c) 0.7   (d) 0.07

2. $\dfrac{5}{100} = ?$

   (a) 5.1   (b) 5.01   (c) 0.5   (d) 0.05

3. $\dfrac{9}{1000} = ?$

   (a) 0.0009   (b) 0.009   (c) 9.001   (d) none of these

4. $\dfrac{16}{1000} = ?$

   (a) 0.016   (b) 0.16   (c) 0.0016   (d) 1.006

5. $\dfrac{134}{1000} = ?$

   (a) 13.4   (b) 1.34   (c) 0.134   (d) 0.0134

6. $2\dfrac{17}{100} = ?$

   (a) 2.17   (b) 2.017   (c) 0.217   (d) 21.7

7. $4\dfrac{3}{100} = ?$

   (a) 4.3   (b) 4.03   (c) 4.003   (d) 43.10

8. 6.25 = ?

   (a) $6\dfrac{1}{2}$ (b) $6\dfrac{1}{4}$ (c) $62\dfrac{1}{2}$ (d) none of these

9. $\dfrac{6}{25} = ?$

   (a) 2.4   (b) 0.24   (c) 0.024   (d) none of these

10. $4\dfrac{7}{8} = ?$

    (a) 4.78   (b) 4.87   (c) 4.875   (d) none of these

11. 24.8 = ?

    (a) $24\dfrac{4}{5}$ (b) $24\dfrac{2}{5}$ (c) $24\dfrac{1}{5}$ (d) none of these

12. $2\dfrac{1}{25} = ?$

(a) 2.4   (b) 2.04   (c) 2.004   (d) none of these

13. $2 + \dfrac{3}{10} + \dfrac{4}{100} = ?$

(a) 2.304   (b) 2.403   (c) 2.34   (d) none of these

14. $2 + \dfrac{6}{100} = ?$

(a) 2.006   (b) 2.06   (c) 2.6   (d) none of these

15. $\dfrac{4}{100} + \dfrac{7}{10000} = ?$

(a) 0.47   (b) 0.407   (c) 0.0407   (d) none of these

   Hint. *Given exp.* = 0.04 + 0.0007.

16. The correct expanded form of 2.06 is

(a) $(2 \times 10) + \left(6 \times \dfrac{1}{10}\right)$ (b) $(2 \times 1) + \left(6 \times \dfrac{1}{10}\right)$

(c) $(2 \times 1) + \left(6 \times \dfrac{1}{100}\right)$ (d) none of these

17. Among 2.6, 2.006, 2.66 and 2.08, the largest number is

(a) 2.006   (b) 2.08   (c) 2.6   (d) 2.66

18. Which of the following is the correct order?

(a) 2.2 < 2.02 < 2.002 < 2.222   (b) 2.002 < 2.02 < 2.2 < 2.222

(c) 2.02 < 2.22 < 2.002 < 2.222   (d) none of these

19. Which is larger: 2.1 or 2.055?

(a) 2.1   (b) 2.055   (c) cannot be compared

20. 1 cm = ?

(a) 0.1 m   (b) 0.01 m   (c) 0.001 m   (d) none of these

21. 2 m 5 cm = ?

(a) 2.5 m   (b) 2.05 m   (c) 2.005 m   (d) 0.25 m

22. 2 kg 8 g = ?

(a) 2.8 kg   (b) 2.08 kg   (c) 2.008 kg   (d) none of these

23. 2 kg 56 g = ?

(a) 2.56 kg   (b) 2.056 kg   (c) 2.560 kg   (d) none of these

24. 2 km 35 m = ?

(a) 2.35 km   (b) 2.350 km   (c) 2.035 km   (d) none of these

25. 0.4 + 0.004 + 4.4 = ?

(a) 4.444   (b) 5.2   (c) 4.804   (d) 5.404

26. 3.5 + 4.05 − 6.005 = ?

(a) 1.545   (b) 1.095   (c) 1.6   (d) none of these

27. 6.3 − 2.8 = ?

(a) 0.35   (b) 3.5   (c) 3.035   (d) none of these

28. 5.01 − 3.6 = ?

(a) 4.65   (b) 1.95   (c) 1.41   (d) none of these

29. $2 - 0.7 = ?$

    (a) 1.3   (b) 1.5   (c) 2.03   (d) none of these

30. $1.1 - 0.3 = ?$

    (a) 0.8   (b) 0.08   (c) 8   (d) none of these

Things to Remember

1. *The fractions in which the denominators are 10, 100, 1000, etc., are known as decimal fractions.*
2. *Numbers written in decimal form are called decimals.*
3. *A decimal has two parts, namely, the whole-number part and the decimal part.*
4. *The number of digits contained in the decimal part of a decimal is called the number of its decimal places.*
5. *Decimals having the same number of decimal places are called like decimals; otherwise, they are known as unlike decimals.*
6. *We have $0.1 = 0.10 = 0.100$, etc., $0.2 = 0.20 = 0.200$, etc., and so on.*
7. *We may convert unlike decimals into like decimals by annexing the requisite number of zeros at the end of the decimal part.*
8. *Comparing decimals:*
   Step 1. *Convert the given decimals into like decimals.*
   Step 2. *First compare the whole-number parts. The decimal having larger whole-number part is larger than the other.*
   Step 3. *If the whole-number parts are equal, compare the tenths digits. The decimal having bigger digit in the tenths place is the larger one.*
   If the tenths digits are equal, compare the hundredths digits, and so on.
9. *Addition of decimals:*
   Step 1. *Convert the given decimals into like decimals.*
   Step 2. *Write the addends one under the other so that the decimal points of all the addends are in the same column.*
   Step 3. *Add as in case of whole numbers.*
   Step 4. *In the sum, put the decimal point directly under the decimal points in the addends.*
10. *Subtraction of decimals:*
    Step 1. *Convert the given decimals into like decimals.*
    Step 2. *Write the smaller number under the larger one so that their decimal points are in the same column.*
    Step 3. *Subtract as in the case of whole numbers.*
    Step 4. *In the difference, put the decimal point directly under the decimal points of the given numbers.*

CCE TEST PAPER-7

A. 1. Convert $4\frac{5}{8}$ into a decimal fraction.

2. Express 105 cm into metres using decimals.

3. Express 6 km 5 m as km using decimals.

4. Express 8 m as kilometre using decimals.

5. Add 26.4, 163.05, 8.75 and 5.6.

6. Subtract 0.528 from 3.2.

7. What is to be added to 63.5 to get 71?

8. What is to be subtracted from 13 to get 5.4?

9. Arrange the following decimals in descending order:
6.5, 6.05, 6.54, 6.4 and 6.45

10. Convert each of the following into a fraction in simplest form:

(i) .4   (ii) .35   (iii) 0.08   (iv) 0.075

B. *Mark (✓) against the correct answer in each of the following:*

11. $\frac{3}{25} = ?$

(a) 1.2   (b) 0.12   (c) 0.012   (d) none of these

12. $\frac{6}{1000} = ?$

(a) 6.001   (b) 0.0006   (c) 0.006   (d) 0.06

13. $2\frac{3}{100} = ?$

(a) 2.003   (b) 2.03   (c) 2.3   (d) none of these

14. The place value of 3 in 16.534 is

(a) $\frac{3}{10}$ (b) $\frac{3}{100}$ (c) $\frac{3}{1000}$ (d) 3

15. $4\frac{7}{8} = ?$

(a) 4.78   (b) 4.87   (c) 4.875   (d) none of these

16. $5.01 - 3.6 = ?$

(a) 4.65   (b) 1.95   (c) 1.41   (d) none of these

17. $3.5 + 4.05 - 6.005 = ?$

(a) 1.545   (b) 1.095   (c) 1.6   (d) none of these

18. $\frac{4}{100} + \frac{7}{10000} = ?$

(a) 0.47   (b) 0.407   (c) 0.0407   (d) none of these

19. Among 2.6, 2.006, 2.66 and 2.08, the largest number is

(a) 2.006   (b) 2.08   (c) 2.6   (d) 2.66

C. 20. *Fill in the blanks.*

(i) 1 m = ... km   (ii) 10 ml = ... l

(iii) 16 kg 5 g = ... kg
(iv) 2 m 8 cm = ... m

(v) 3.02, 4.75, 1.63 are examples of ...... decimals.

D. 21. Write 'T' for true and 'F' for false for each of the statements given below:

(i) 3.02 < 3.2.

(ii) 3 g = 0.003 kg.

(iii) $\dfrac{341}{1000}$ = 3.410.

(iv) 6.2 and 6.200 are equivalent decimals.

(v) 2.3, 3.41, 4.53, 5.61 are examples of like decimals.

8

Algebraic Expressions

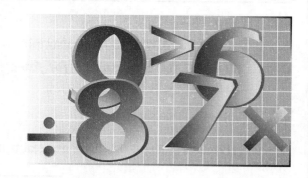

INTRODUCTION

In arithmetic, we deal with *specific numbers* and use the symbols 0, 1, 2, 3, 4, 5, 6, 7, 8, 9 to represent them. We use the four fundamental operations, namely, addition (+), subtraction (−), multiplication (×) and division (÷) on specific numbers and obtain *number expressions.*

On the basis of certain observations, we obtain a general result, called a *formula.*

Consider the following example:

The perimeter of a square is given by *perimeter = 4 × side.*

If we represent the perimeter by the letter *p* and the length of the side by the letter *s*, we can write $p = 4 \times s$.

This rule is true for all systems of units and for all possible values of the length of the side of the square.

When $s = 2$, we get $p = 4 \times 2 = 8$.

When $s = 3$, we get $p = 4 \times 3 = 12$, and so on.

Clearly, *p* and *s* represent numbers.

Thus, the generalized results of arithmetic are known as formulae.

In a formula, *we use letters to represent numbers.*

Such letters are known as literal numbers.

ALGEBRA

Algebra is generalized arithmetic in which numbers are represented by letters, known as **literal numbers** *or simply* **literals.**

Since literals are also numbers, they obey all the rules of addition, subtraction, multiplication and division.

OPERATIONS ON LITERALS AND NUMBERS

1. ADDITION
   (i) The sum of a literal x and a number 5 is $x + 5$.
   (ii) y more than x is written as $x + y$.
   (iii) For any literals a, b, c, we have:
   $$a + b = b + a; \quad a + 0 = 0 + a = a; \text{ and } (a + b) + c = a + (b + c).$$

2. SUBTRACTION
   (i) 5 less than a literal x is $x - 5$.
   (ii) y less than x is $x - y$.

3. MULTIPLICATION
   (i) 4 times x is $4 \times x$, written as $4x$.

(ii) The product of x and y is $x \times y$, written as $x \cdot y$ or xy.

(iii) For any literals a, b, c we have:
$$a \times 0 = 0 \times a = 0; \qquad a \times 1 = 1 \times a = a; \qquad a \times b = b \times a;$$
$$(ab)c = a(bc); \qquad a(b + c) = ab + ac.$$

4. DIVISION

(i) x divided by y is written as $\dfrac{x}{y}$.

(ii) x divided by 7 is $\dfrac{x}{7}$.

(ii) 30 divided by x is $\dfrac{30}{x}$.

5. POWERS OF A LITERAL

$x \times x$ is written as x^2, called x squared;

$x \times x \times x$ is written as x^3, called x cubed;

$x \times x \times x \times x$ is written as x^4, called x raised to the power 4;

$x \times x \times x \times x \times x$ is written as x^5, called x raised to the power 5, and so on.

Instead of writing x^1, we write x only.

In x^5, we call x the *base* and 5, the *exponent* or *index*.

Similarly, in y^7 the base is y and the exponent is 7.

EXAMPLE 1. *Write the following using numbers, literals and signs of basic operations:*

  (i) 3 more than a number x

  (ii) y less than 6

  (iii) One-third of the sum of x and y

  (iv) 5 less than the quotient of x by y

  (v) The quotient of x by y added to the product of x and y

  (vi) 7 taken away from the sum of x and y

Solution   (i) $x + 3$ (ii) $6 - y$ (iii) $\dfrac{1}{3}(x + y)$ (iv) $\dfrac{x}{y} - 5$

       (v) $xy + \dfrac{x}{y}$ (vi) $x + y - 7$

EXAMPLE 2. *Write the following statement using numbers, literals and signs of basic operations: '7 times a number x is y less than a number z'.*

Solution   The given statement can be written as $7x = z - y$.

EXAMPLE 3. *Write the following in the exponential form:*

  (i) $a \times a \times a \times \ldots 12$ times   *(ii) $5 \times x \times x \times x \times x \times y \times y$*

Solution   We can write:

   (i) $a \times a \times a \times \ldots 12$ times $= a^{12}$.

   (ii) $5 \times x \times x \times x \times x \times y \times y = 5x^3 y^2$.

EXAMPLE 4. *Write down each of the following in the product form:*

  (i) $a^2 b^7$ *(ii) $9b^3 c$*   *(iii) $6a^2 b^3 c^4$*

Solution   We can write:

   (i) $a^2 b^7 = a \times a \times b \times b \times b \times b \times b \times b \times b$.

   (ii) $9b^3 c = 9 \times b \times b \times b \times c$.

   (iii) $6a^2 b^3 c^4 = 6 \times a \times a \times b \times b \times b \times c \times c \times c \times c$.

EXERCISE 8A

1. Write the following using literals, numbers and signs of basic operations:
   (i) x increased by 12   (ii) y decreased by 7
   (iii) The difference of a and b, when $a > b$
   (iv) The product of x and y added to their sum
   (v) One-third of x multiplied by the sum of a and b
   (vi) 5 times x added to 7 times y
   (vii) Sum of x and the quotient of y by 5
   (viii) x taken away from 4
   (ix) 2 less than the quotient of x by y
   (x) x multiplied by itself   (xi) Twice x increased by y
   (xii) Thrice x added to y squared   (xiii) x minus twice y
   (xiv) x cubed less than y cubed   (xv) The quotient of x by 8 is multiplied by y

2. Ranjit scores 80 marks in English and x marks in Hindi. What is his total score in the two subjects?

3. Write the following in the exponential form:
   (i) $b \times b \times b \times \ldots 15$ times   (ii) $y \times y \times y \times \ldots 20$ times
   (iii) $14 \times a \times a \times a \times a \times b \times b \times b$ (iv) $6 \times x \times x \times x \times y \times y$
   (v) $3 \times z \times z \times z \times y \times y \times x$

4. Write down the following in the product form:
   (i) $x^2 y^4$ (ii) $6y^5$ (iii) $9xy^2 z$ (iv) $10a^3 b^3 c^3$

═══════

ALGEBRAIC EXPRESSIONS

VARIABLES AND CONSTANTS In algebra, we come across two types of symbols, namely, constants and variables.

A symbol having a fixed numerical value is called a **constant.** *And, a symbol which takes on various numerical values is known as a* **variable.**

Consider the following examples:

The diameter d of a circle of radius r is given by the formula $d = 2r$.

Here, 2 is a fixed number and, therefore, a constant, whereas the literal numbers d and r depend upon the size of the circle and, therefore, they may take on various values. So, d and r are variables.

Similarly, the perimeter p of a square of side s is given by the formula $p = 4s$.

Here 4 is a constant, whereas p and s are variables.

REMARK   In some situations literal numbers are also treated as constants. In such situations, it is presumed that the particular literal number will only take a fixed value.

ALGEBRAIC EXPRESSION *A combination of constants and variables connected by any one or more of the symbols* $+, -, \times$ *and* $\div$ *is called an algebraic expression.*
The several parts of the expression, separated by the sign + *or* −, *are called the terms of the expression.*

Thus, (i) the expression $3x + 5y - 2xyz$ has three terms, namely, $3x$, $5y$ and $-2xyz$,
   (ii) the expression $5x^2 - 6x^3 y + 8xy^3 z - 9$ has four terms, namely, $5x^2$, $-6x^3 y$, $8xy^3 z$ and -9.

Various types of algebraic expressions are as follows:

(I) MONOMIALS: An expression which contains only one term is known as a monomial.

Thus, $3x, 5xy^2, -2abc, -8$, etc., are all monomials.

(II) BINOMIALS: An expression containing two terms is called a binomial.

Thus, $6 - y, 2x + 3y, x^2 - 5xy^2z$ are all binomials.

(III) TRINOMIALS: An expression containing three terms is called a trinomial.

Thus, $2 + x - y, a + b + c, x^3 - y^3 + z^3, 6 + xyz + x^2$, etc., are all trinomials.

(IV) QUADRINOMIALS: An expression containing four terms is called a quadrinomial.

Thus, $x^2 + y^2 + z^2 - xyz, x^3 + y^3 + z^3 + 3xyz$, etc., are quadrinomials.

(V) POLYNOMIALS: An expression containing two or more terms is known as a polynomial.

FACTORS *When two or more numbers and literals are multiplied then each one of them is called a factor of the product.*

A constant factor is called a numerical factor, while a literal one is known as a literal factor.

(i) In $5x^2y$, we have 5 as the numerical factor, whereas x^2 and y are the literal factors.

(ii) In $-xy$, the numerical factor is -1 while x and y are literal factors.

COEFFICIENTS *In a product of numbers and literals, any of the factors is called the coefficient of the product of other factors.*

EXAMPLES (i) In $5xy$, the coefficient of y is $5x$, and the coefficient of x is $5y$.

(ii) In $-7xy^2$, the coefficient of x is $-7y^2$, and the coefficient of y^2 is $-7x$.

(iii) In $-x$, the coefficient of x is -1.

CONSTANT TERM *A term of the expression having no literal factor is called a constant term.*

(i) In the expression $3x + 5$, the constant term is 5.

(ii) In the expression $x^2 + y^2 - \frac{4}{5}$, the constant term is $-\frac{4}{5}$.

LIKE TERMS *The terms having the same literal factors are called like or similar terms.*

UNLIKE TERMS *The terms not having the same literal factors are called unlike or dissimilar terms.*

EXAMPLES (i) In the expression $6x^2y + 5xy^2 - 8xy - 7yx^2$ we have $6x^2y$ and $-7yx^2$ as like terms, whereas $5xy^2$ and $-8xy$ are unlike terms.

(ii) $3y^2, -5y^2, 80y^2$ are like terms.

(iii) $5xy^2$ and $5x^2y$ are unlike terms.

FINDING THE VALUE OF AN ALGEBRAIC EXPRESSION *If the values of all literal numbers appearing in a given expression are known, on replacing these literals by their numerical values we obtain an arithmetic expression which can be evaluated.*

Thus, for the given numerical values of the literals, we obtain the corresponding value of the algebraic expression.

The process of replacing the literals by their numerical values is called *substitution*.

EXAMPLE 1. *If $x = 1, y = -2$ and $z = 3$, find the value of*

(i) $x^3 + y^3 + z^3 - 3xyz$ (ii) $3xy^4 - 15x^2y + 4z$

Solution   (i) Substituting $x = 1$, $y = -2$ and $z = 3$ in the given expression, we get:

$$x^3 + y^3 + z^3 - 3xyz = (1)^3 + (-2)^3 + (3)^3 - 3 \times 1 \times (-2) \times 3$$
$$= 1 - 8 + 27 + 18 = 38.$$

(ii) Substituting $x = 1$, $y = -2$ and $z = 3$ in the given expression, we get:

$$3xy^4 - 15x^2y + 4z = 3 \times 1 \times (-2)^4 - 15 \times (1)^2 \times (-2) + 4 \times 3$$
$$= 3 \times 1 \times 16 + 30 + 12 = 48 + 30 + 12 = 90.$$

EXAMPLE 2. *Identify monomials, binomials and trinomials from the following expressions:*

(i) $-3xyz$ (ii) $4x^2yz + 9 - 5x^3$ (iii) -7

(iv) $x^2 + y^2 + z^2 - p^2$ (v) $x + 5$ (vi) $6a^3b$

Solution   Clearly, each of the expressions given in (i), (iii) and (vi) contains only one term. So, each one of them is a monomial.
The expression given in (v) contains two terms, and therefore, it is a binomial.
The expression given in (ii) contains three terms, and therefore, it is a trinomial.
The expression given in (iv) contains four terms, so it is none of the given type.

EXAMPLE 3. *Write down the coefficient of*

(i) x in $9xy$ (ii) a in $-7abc$ (iii) xyz in $-xyz$ (iv) b in $-abc$

Solution   (i) The coefficient of x in $9xy$ is $9y$.
(ii) The coefficient of a in $-7abc$ is $-7bc$.
(iii) The coefficient of xyz in $-xyz$ is -1.
(iv) The coefficient of b in $-abc$ is $-ac$.

EXERCISE 8B

1. If $a = 2$ and $b = 3$, find the value of
(i) $a + b$ (ii) $a^2 + ab$ (iii) $ab - a^2$
(iv) $2a - 3b$ (v) $5a^2 - 2ab$ (vi) $a^3 - b^3$

2. If $x = 1$, $y = 2$ and $z = 5$, find the value of
(i) $3x - 2y + 4z$ (ii) $x^2 + y^2 + z^2$ (iii) $2x^2 - 3y^2 + z^2$
(iv) $xy + yz - zx$ (v) $2x^2y - 5yz + xy^2$ (vi) $x^3 - y^3 - z^3$

3. If $p = -2$, $q = -1$ and $r = 3$, find the value of
(i) $p^2 + q^2 - r^2$ (ii) $2p^2 - q^2 + 3r^2$ (iii) $p - q - r$
(iv) $p^3 + q^3 + r^3 + 3pqr$ (v) $3p^2q + 5pq^2 + 2pqr$ (vi) $p^4 + q^4 - r^4$

4. Write the coefficient of
(i) x in $13x$ (ii) y in $-5y$ (iii) a in $6ab$ (iv) z in $-7xz$
(v) p in $-2pqr$ (vi) y^2 in $8xy^2z$ (vii) x^3 in x^3 (viii) x^2 in $-x^2$

5. Write the numerical coefficient of
(i) ab (ii) $-6bc$ (iii) $7xyz$ (iv) $-2x^3y^2z$

6. Write the constant term of
(i) $3x^2 + 5x + 8$ (ii) $2x^2 - 9$ (iii) $4y^2 - 5y + \dfrac{3}{5}$ (iv) $z^3 - 2z^2 + z - \dfrac{8}{3}$

7. Identify the monomials, binomials and trinomials in the following:
(i) $-2xyz$ (ii) $5 + 7x^3y^3z^3$ (iii) $-5x^3$
(iv) $a + b - 2c$ (v) $xy + yz - zx$ (vi) x^5
(vii) $ax^3 + bx^2 + cx + d$ (viii) -14 (ix) $2x + 1$

8. Write all the terms of the algebraic expressions:

(i) $4x^5 - 6y^4 + 7x^2y - 9$

(ii) $9x^3 - 5z^4 + 7x^3y - xyz$

9. Identify the like terms in the following:

(i) $a^2, b^2, -2a^2, c^2, 4a$

(ii) $3x, 4xy, -yz, \frac{1}{2}zy$

(iii) $-2xy^2, x^2y, 5y^2x, x^2z$

(iv) $abc, ab^2c, acb^2, c^2ab, b^2ac, a^2bc, cab^2$

OPERATIONS ON ALGEBRAIC EXPRESSIONS

ADDITION OF ALGEBRAIC EXPRESSIONS

The basic principle of addition of algebraic expressions is that only like terms can be added.

We know that 5 tables + 7 tables = 12 tables.

But, '5 tables + 7 chairs' does not form 12 tables or 12 chairs.

Thus, the sum of two unlike terms can only be indicated.

RULE OF ADDITION *The sum of several like terms is another like term whose coefficient is the sum of the coefficients of the like terms.*

EXAMPLE 1. Add $6xy^2, -4xy^2, xy^2, 5xy^2$.

Solution The required sum $= 6xy^2 + (-4)xy^2 + xy^2 + 5xy^2$
$$= (6 - 4 + 1 + 5)xy^2 = 8xy^2.$$

EXAMPLE 2. *Collect the like terms and simplify:*
$$5x^2 - 2x + 7 - 9 + 7x - 3x^2 + 4x^2 - x + 1$$

Solution Rearranging and collecting the like terms, we get:
$$5x^2 - 2x + 7 - 9 + 7x - 3x^2 + 4x^2 - x + 1$$
$$= 5x^2 - 3x^2 + 4x^2 - 2x + 7x - x + 7 - 9 + 1$$
$$= (5 - 3 + 4)x^2 + (-2 + 7 - 1)x + (7 - 9 + 1)$$
$$= 6x^2 + 4x - 1.$$

COLUMN METHOD *In this method, each expression is written in a separate row such that their like terms are arranged one below the other in a column. Then, addition or subtraction of the terms is done columnwise.*

EXAMPLE 3. *Add the following expressions:*
$$5x^2 + 7y - 6z^2, \ 4y + 3x^2, \ 9x^2 + 2z^2 - 9y \text{ and } 2y - 2x^2$$

Solution Column method: We write the expressions so that the like terms are in a column as shown below and add columnwise.

$$5x^2 + 7y - 6z^2$$
$$+ 3x^2 + 4y$$
$$+ 9x^2 - 9y + 2z^2$$
$$- 2x^2 + 2y$$
$$\overline{15x^2 + 4y - 4z^2}$$

Alternative method The sum of the given expressions
$$= (5x^2 + 7y - 6z^2) + (4y + 3x^2) + (9x^2 + 2z^2 - 9y) + (2y - 2x^2)$$
$$= (5x^2 + 3x^2 + 9x^2 - 2x^2) + (7y + 4y - 9y + 2y) + (-6z^2 + 2z^2)$$
$$= (5 + 3 + 9 - 2)x^2 + (7 + 4 - 9 + 2)y + (-6 + 2)z^2 = 15x^2 + 4y - 4z^2.$$

SUBTRACTION OF ALGEBRAIC EXPRESSIONS

Rule   *Change the sign of each term of the expression to be subtracted and add it to the expression from which subtraction is to be made.*

EXAMPLE 4.   Subtract $6xy - 4x^2 - y^2 - 2$ from $x^2 - 3xy + 7y^2 + 5$.

Solution   Arranging the like terms columnwise, changing the sign of each term of the expression to be subtracted and then adding, we get:

$$x^2 - 3xy + 7y^2 + 5$$
$$-4x^2 + 6xy - y^2 - 2 \quad \text{(change the sign of each term and add)}$$
$$+ \quad\quad - \quad\quad + \quad\quad +$$
$$\overline{5x^2 - 9xy + 8y^2 + 7}$$

EXAMPLE 5.   From the sum of $6x^4 - 3x^3 + 7x^2 - 5x + 1$ and $-3x^4 + 5x^3 - 9x^2 + 7x - 2$ subtract $2x^4 - 5x^3 + 2x^2 - 6x - 8$.

Solution   We have:

$$6x^4 - 3x^3 + 7x^2 - 5x + 1$$
Plus $\quad -3x^4 + 5x^3 - 9x^2 + 7x - 2$
$$\overline{3x^4 + 2x^3 - 2x^2 + 2x - 1}$$
Minus $\quad 2x^4 - 5x^3 + 2x^2 - 6x - 8$
$$- \quad + \quad - \quad + \quad +$$
$$\overline{x^4 + 7x^3 - 4x^2 + 8x + 7}$$

EXERCISE 8C

1. Add:
 (i) $3x, 7x$
 (ii) $7y, -9y$
 (iii) $2xy, 5xy, -xy$
 (iv) $3x, 2y$
 (v) $2x^2, -3x^2, 7x^2$
 (vi) $7xyz, -5xyz, 9xyz, -8xyz$
 (vii) $6a^3, -4a^3, 10a^3, -8a^3$
 (viii) $x^2 - a^2, -5x^2 + 2a^2, -4x^2 + 4a^2$

2. Add the following:

(i)
$$x - 3y - 2z$$
$$5x + 7y - z$$
$$-7x - 2y + 4z$$

(ii)
$$m^2 - 4m + 5$$
$$-2m^2 + 6m - 6$$
$$-m^2 - 2m - 7$$

(iii)
$$2x^2 - 3xy + y^2$$
$$-7x^2 - 5xy - 2y^2$$
$$4x^2 + xy - 6y^2$$

(iv)
$$4xy - 5yz - 7zx$$
$$-5xy + 2yz + zx$$
$$-2xy - 3yz + 3zx$$

3. Add:
 (i) $3a - 2b + 5c, 2a + 5b - 7c, -a - b + c$
 (ii) $8a - 6ab + 5b, -6a - ab - 8b, -4a + 2ab + 3b$

(iii) $2x^3 - 3x^2 + 7x - 8$, $-5x^3 + 2x^2 - 4x + 1$, $3 - 6x + 5x^2 - x^3$

(iv) $2x^2 - 8xy + 7y^2 - 8xy^2$, $2xy^2 + 6xy - y^2 + 3x^2$, $4y^2 - xy - x^2 + xy^2$

(v) $x^3 + y^3 - z^3 + 3xyz$, $-x^3 + y^3 + z^3 - 6xyz$, $x^3 - y^3 - z^3 - 8xyz$

(vi) $2 + x - x^2 + 6x^3$, $-6 - 2x + 4x^2 - 3x^3$, $2 + x^2$, $3 - x^3 + 4x - 2x^2$

4. Subtract:

  (i) $5x$ from $2x$ (ii) $-xy$ from $6xy$ (iii) $3a$ from $5b$

  (iv) $-7x$ from $9y$ (v) $10x^2$ from $-7x^2$ (vi) $a^2 - b^2$ from $b^2 - a^2$

5. Subtract:

  (i) $5a + 7b - 2c$ from $3a - 7b + 4c$

  (ii) $a - 2b - 3c$ from $-2a + 5b - 4c$

  (iii) $5x^2 - 3xy + y^2$ from $7x^2 - 2xy - 4y^2$

  (iv) $6x^3 - 7x^2 + 5x - 3$ from $4 - 5x + 6x^2 - 8x^3$

  (v) $x^3 + 2x^2y + 6xy^2 - y^3$ from $y^3 - 3xy^2 - 4x^2y$

  (vi) $-11x^2y^2 + 7xy - 6$ from $9x^2y^2 - 6xy + 9$

  (vii) $-2a + b + 6d$ from $5a - 2b - 3c$

6. Simplify:

  (i) $2p^3 - 3p^2 + 4p - 5 - 6p^3 + 2p^2 - 8p - 2 + 6p + 8$

  (ii) $2x^2 - xy + 6x - 4y + 5xy - 4x + 6x^2 + 3y$

  (iii) $x^4 - 6x^3 + 2x - 7 + 7x^3 - x + 5x^2 + 2 - x^4$

7. From the sum of $3x^2 - 5x + 2$ and $-5x^2 - 8x + 6$, subtract $4x^2 - 9x + 7$.

8. If $A = 7x^2 + 5xy - 9y^2$, $B = -4x^2 + xy + 5y^2$ and $C = 4y^2 - 3x^2 - 6xy$ then show that $A + B + C = 0$.

9. What must be added to $5x^3 - 2x^2 + 6x + 7$ to make the sum $x^3 + 3x^2 - x + 1$?

10. Let $P = a^2 - b^2 + 2ab$, $Q = a^2 + 4b^2 - 6ab$, $R = b^2 + 6$, $S = a^2 - 4ab$ and $T = -2a^2 + b^2 - ab + a$. Find $P + Q + R + S - T$.

11. What must be subtracted from $a^3 - 4a^2 + 5a - 6$ to obtain $a^2 - 2a + 1$?

12. How much is $a + 2b - 3c$ greater than $2a - 3b + c$?

13. How much less than $x - 2y + 3z$ is $2x - 4y - z$?

14. By how much does $3x^2 - 5x + 6$ exceed $x^3 - x^2 + 4x - 1$?

15. Subtract the sum of $5x - 4y + 6z$ and $-8x + y - 2z$ from the sum of $12x - y + 3z$ and $-3x + 5y - 8z$.

16. By how much is $2x - 3y + 4z$ greater than $2x + 5y - 6z + 2$?

17. By how much does 1 exceed $2x - 3y - 4$?

USE OF GROUPING SYMBOLS

When we make operations on two or more algebraic expressions, we separate them by the symbols of groupings, namely, parentheses ( ), braces { } and brackets [ ].

In simplifying such expressions, we first remove the grouping symbols, using the laws given below:

(i) If a '+' sign precedes a symbol of grouping, the grouping symbol may be removed without any change in the sign of the terms.

(ii) If a '−' sign precedes a symbol of grouping, the grouping symbol may be removed and the sign of each term is changed.

(iii) If more than one grouping symbol is present in an expression, we remove the innermost grouping symbol first and combine the like terms, if any. We continue the process outwards until all the grouping symbols have been removed.

EXAMPLE 1. *Simplify:* $(a^2 - 8ab - 5) + (3ab - 4a^2 + 8)$

Solution Clearly, a '+' sign precedes the second parenthesis, so we remove it without changing the signs of the terms within it.

$\therefore\ (a^2 - 8ab - 5) + (3ab - 4a^2 + 8)$
$= a^2 - 8ab - 5 + 3ab - 4a^2 + 8$
$= (1 - 4)a^2 + (-8 + 3)ab + (-5 + 8)$
$= -3a^2 - 5ab + 3.$

EXAMPLE 2. *Simplify:* $(x^2 - y^2 + 2xy + 1) - (x^2 + y^2 + 4xy - 5)$

Solution Here, a '−' sign precedes the second parenthesis, so we remove it and change the sign of each term within.

$\therefore\ (x^2 - y^2 + 2xy + 1) - (x^2 + y^2 + 4xy - 5)$
$= x^2 - y^2 + 2xy + 1 - x^2 - y^2 - 4xy + 5$
$= (1 - 1)x^2 - 2y^2 + (2 - 4)xy + 6$
$= -2y^2 - 2xy + 6.$

EXAMPLE 3. *Simplify:* $2x - [3y - \{2x - (y - x)\}]$

Solution We first remove the innermost grouping symbol ( ), then { }, and then [ ]. Thus, we have:

$2x - [3y - \{2x - (y - x)\}]$
$= 2x - [3y - \{2x - y + x\}]$
$= 2x - [3y - \{3x - y\}]$
$= 2x - [3y - 3x + y]$
$= 2x - [4y - 3x]$
$= 2x - 4y + 3x$
$= 5x - 4y.$

EXAMPLE 4. *Simplify:* $2a - [3b - \{a - (2c - 3b) + 4c - 3(a - b - 2c)\}]$

Solution We first remove the innermost grouping symbol ( ), then { }, and then [ ]. Thus, we have:

$2a - \left[3b - \{a - (2c - 3b) + 4c - 3(a - b - 2c)\}\right]$
$= 2a - [3b - \{a - 2c + 3b + 4c - 3a + 3b + 6c\}]$
$= 2a - [3b - \{-2a + 6b + 8c\}]$
$= 2a - [3b + 2a - 6b - 8c]$
$= 2a - [-3b + 2a - 8c]$
$= 2a + 3b - 2a + 8c$
$= 3b + 8c.$

EXERCISE 8D

Simplify:

1. $a - (b - 2a)$
2. $4x - (3y - x + 2z)$
3. $(a^2 + b^2 + 2ab) - (a^2 + b^2 - 2ab)$
4. $-3(a + b) + 4(2a - 3b) - (2a - b)$
5. $-4x^2 + \{(2x^2 - 3) - (4 - 3x^2)\}$
6. $-2(x^2 - y^2 + xy) - 3(x^2 + y^2 - xy)$
7. $a - [2b - \{3a - (2b - 3c)\}]$
8. $-x + [5y - \{x - (5y - 2x)\}]$

9. $86 - [15x - 7(6x - 9) - 2\{10x - 5(2 - 3x)\}]$

10. $12x - [3x^3 + 5x^2 - \{7x^2 - (4 - 3x - x^3) + 6x^3\} - 3x]$

11. $5a - [a^2 - \{2a(1 - a + 4a^2) - 3a(a^2 - 5a - 3)\}] - 8a$

12. $3 - [x - \{2y - (5x + y - 3) + 2x^2\} - (x^2 - 3y)]$

13. $xy - [yz - zx - \{yx - (3y - xz) - (xy - zy)\}]$

14. $2a - 3b - [3a - 2b - \{a - c - (a - 2b)\}]$

15. $-a - [a + \{a + b - 2a - (a - 2b)\} - b]$

16. $2a - [4b - \{4a - (3b - \overline{2a + 2b})\}]$

17. $5x - [4y - \{7x - (3z - 2y) + 4z - 3(x + 3y - 2z)\}]$

═══

Things to Remember

1. *Algebra is generalized arithmetic.*
2. *Letters used to represent numbers are called literals.*
3. *The literals obey all the rules and signs of addition, subtraction, multiplication and division.*
4. $3 \times x = 3x, 1 \times x = x, x \times y = xy, x \times 5 = 5x$, *etc.*
5. $x \times x \times \ldots\ldots 5\ times = x^5, \quad y \times y \times y \times \ldots\ldots 10\ times = y^{10}$.
6. *In* x^4, *we call 4 the exponent or index, and x is called the base.*
7. *A symbol having a fixed numerical value is called a constant.*
8. *A symbol which takes on various numerical values is called a variable.*
9. *A combination of constants and variables using any of the signs + and –, or a combination of the signs +, –, × and ÷, is called an algebraic expression.*
10. *'+' or '–' signs separate the expression into various parts, each part is known as a term.*
11. *An expression is called a monomial, a binomial, a trinomial or a quadrinomial if it contains one term, two terms, three terms or four terms respectively.*
12. *In 4x, we have 4 as the numerical factor and x as the literal factor.*
13. *The terms having the same literal factors are called like terms; otherwise they are called unlike terms.*
14. *The sum of several like terms is another like term whose coefficient is the sum of the coefficients of the like terms.*
15. *To subtract an expression from another we change the sign of each term of the expression to be subtracted and then add the two expressions.*
16. *When a grouping symbol preceded by a '–' sign is removed, the sign of each term in the grouping is changed.*

9 | Linear Equations in One Variable

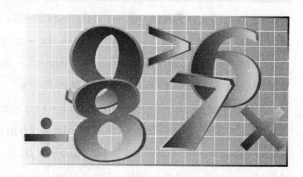

In arithmetic, we usually come across statements of the following type:

(i) $16 + 5 = 21$

(ii) $7 \times (5 + 4) = 7 \times 5 + 7 \times 4$, etc.

Such a statement involving the symbol '=' is called *a statement of equality or simply an equality.*

Clearly, none of the above statements involves a variable.

EQUATION *A statement of equality which involves one or more variables is called an equation.*

Consider the following statements:

(i) A number x increased by 7 is 15.

(ii) 9 exceeds a number x by 3.

(iii) 4 times a number x is 24.

(iv) A number y divided by 5 is 7.

(v) The sum of the number x and twice the number y is 12.

We can write the above statements as under:

(i) $x + 7 = 15$ (ii) $9 - x = 3$ (iii) $4x = 24$

(iv) $\dfrac{y}{5} = 7$ (v) $x + 2y = 12$

Clearly, each one of the above statements is a statement of equality, containing one or more variables. Thus, each one of them is an equation.

Each of the equations through (i) to (iv) involves only one unknown (i.e., variable), while the equation (v) contains two unknowns, namely, x and y.

LINEAR EQUATION *An equation in which the highest power of the variables involved is 1 is called a linear equation.*

In this chapter, we shall discuss the linear equations in one variable only.

Clearly, the sign of equality in an equation divides it into two sides, namely, the left-hand side and the right-hand side, written as LHS and RHS respectively.

SOLUTION OF AN EQUATION *A number which makes LHS = RHS when it is substituted for the variable in an equation is said to satisfy the equation and is called a **solution** or **root** of the equation.*

Solving an equation is finding the roots of the equation.

SOLVING A LINEAR EQUATION BY THE TRIAL-AND-ERROR METHOD In this method, we often make a guess of the root of the equation. We try several values of the variables and find the values of the LHS and the RHS in each case. When LHS = RHS for a particular value of the variable, we say that it is a root of the equation.

EXAMPLE 1.   *Find the solution of the equation $4x = 12$ by the trial-and-error method.*

Solution   We try several values of x and find the values of the LHS and the RHS. We stop when for a particular value of x, LHS = RHS.

x	LHS	RHS
1	$4 \times 1 = 4$	12
2	$4 \times 2 = 8$	12
3	$4 \times 3 = 12$	12

∴ $x = 3$ is the solution of the given equation.

EXAMPLE 2.   *Solve the equation $3x - 5 = 7 - x$ by the trial-and-error method.*

Solution   We try several values of x and find the values of the LHS and the RHS. We stop when for a particular value of x, LHS = RHS.

x	LHS	RHS
1	$3 \times 1 - 5 = -2$	$7 - 1 = 6$
2	$3 \times 2 - 5 = 1$	$7 - 2 = 5$
3	$3 \times 3 - 5 = 4$	$7 - 3 = 4$

∴ $x = 3$ is the solution of the given equation.

EXAMPLE 3.   *Solve the equation $\dfrac{1}{3}y + 5 = 8$ by the trial-and-error method.*

Solution   We make a guess and try several values of y, and find the values of the LHS as well as the RHS in each case. We stop when for a particular value of y, LHS = RHS.

y	LHS	RHS
3	$\dfrac{1}{3} \times 3 + 5 = 6$	8
6	$\dfrac{1}{3} \times 6 + 5 = 7$	8
9	$\dfrac{1}{3} \times 9 + 5 = 8$	8

Thus, when $y = 9$, we have: LHS = RHS.

∴ $y = 9$ is the solution of the given equation.

EXERCISE 9A

1. Write each of the following statements as an equation:
   (i) 5 times a number equals 40.
   (ii) A number increased by 8 equals 15.
   (iii) 25 exceeds a number by 7.
   (iv) A number exceeds 5 by 3.
   (v) 5 subtracted from thrice a number is 16.
   (vi) If 12 is subtracted from a number, the result is 24.
   (vii) Twice a number subtracted from 19 is 11.
   (viii) A number divided by 8 gives 7.
   (ix) 3 less than 4 times a number is 17.
   (x) 6 times a number is 5 more than the number.

2. Write a statement for each of the equations, given below:

    (i) $x - 7 = 14$ (ii) $2y = 18$ (iii) $11 + 3x = 17$

    (iv) $2x - 3 = 13$ (v) $12y - 30 = 6$ (vi) $\dfrac{2z}{3} = 8$

3. Verify by substitution that

    (i) the root of $3x - 5 = 7$ is $x = 4$ (ii) the root of $3 + 2x = 9$ is $x = 3$

    (iii) the root of $5x - 8 = 2x - 2$ is $x = 2$ (iv) the root of $8 - 7y = 1$ is $y = 1$

    (v) the root of $\dfrac{z}{7} = 8$ is $z = 56$

4. Solve each of the following equations by the trial-and-error method:

    (i) $y + 9 = 13$ (ii) $x - 7 = 10$ (iii) $4x = 28$ (iv) $3y = 36$

    (v) $11 + x = 19$ (vi) $\dfrac{x}{3} = 4$ (vii) $2x - 3 = 9$ (viii) $\dfrac{1}{2}x + 7 = 11$

    (ix) $2y + 4 = 3y$ (x) $z - 3 = 2z - 5$

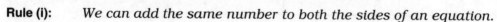

SYSTEMATIC METHOD FOR SOLVING AN EQUATION

We can compare an equation with a balance.

If equal weights are put in the two pans, we find that the two pans remain in balance.

If we remove equal weights from the two pans, we find that the two pans remain in balance.

Thus, we can add (and, therefore, multiply) equal weights or amounts to both the pans to keep them in balance.

Also, we can lessen (and, therefore, divide) equal amounts from both pans to keep the pans in balance.

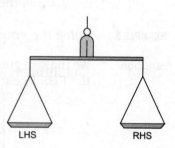

LHS   RHS

Similarly, in the case of an equation, we have the following rules.

Rule (i):   *We can add the same number to both the sides of an equation.*

Rule (ii):   *We can subtract the same number from both the sides of an equation.*

Rule (iii): *We can multiply both the sides of an equation by the same nonzero number.*

Rule (iv): *We can divide both the sides of an equation by the same nonzero number.*

Using these rules, we can solve linear equations easily.

EXAMPLE 1.   *Solve the equation $x - 5 = 7$ and check the result.*

Solution $x - 5 = 7$

           $\Rightarrow x - 5 + 5 = 7 + 5$ [adding 5 to both sides]

           $\Rightarrow x = 12.$

        So, $x = 12$ is the solution of the given equation.

CHECK   Substituting $x = 12$ in the given equation, we get

           LHS $= 12 - 5 = 7$ and RHS $= 7$.

          $\therefore$ when $x = 12$, we have: LHS $=$ RHS.

EXAMPLE 2.   *Solve the equation $8 + x = 3$ and check the result.*

Solution $8 + x = 3$

           $\Rightarrow 8 + x - 8 = 3 - 8$ [subtracting 8 from both sides]

$\Rightarrow x + 8 - 8 = 3 - 8 \quad [\because 8 + x = x + 8]$

$\Rightarrow x = -5.$

So, $x = -5$ is the solution of the given equation.

CHECK   Substituting $x = -5$ in the given equation, we get LHS $= 8 - 5 = 3$ and RHS $= 3$.

$\therefore$ when $x = -5$, we have: LHS = RHS.

EXAMPLE 3. *Solve the equation $8x = 24$ and check the result.*

Solution $8x = 24$

$\Rightarrow \dfrac{8x}{8} = \dfrac{24}{8}$ [dividing both sides by 8]

$\Rightarrow x = 3.$

$\Rightarrow x = 3$ is the solution of the given equation.

CHECK   Substituting $x = 3$ in the given equation, we get

LHS $= 8 \times 3 = 24$ and RHS $= 24$.

$\therefore$ when $x = 3$, we have: LHS = RHS.

EXAMPLE 4. *Solve the equation $\dfrac{2}{3}x = 18$ and check the result.*

Solution $\dfrac{2}{3}x = 18 \Rightarrow \dfrac{2}{3}x \times \dfrac{3}{2} = 18 \times \dfrac{3}{2}$ [multiplying both sides by $\dfrac{3}{2}$]

$\Rightarrow \dfrac{2}{3} \times \dfrac{3}{2} \times x = 27 \Rightarrow x = 27.$

$\therefore x = 27$ is the solution of the given equation.

CHECK   Substituting $x = 27$ in the given equation, we get

LHS $= \dfrac{2}{3} \times 27 = 18$ and RHS $= 18$.

$\therefore$ when $x = 27$, we have: LHS = RHS.

TRANSPOSITION You know that one can add or subtract a number from both sides of the equation. So, for the equation $x - 4 = 5$, we can write

$x - 4 + 4 = 5 + 4 \Rightarrow x = 5 + 4.$

Similarly, for the equation $x + 5 = 3$, we can write

$x + 5 - 5 = 3 - 5 \Rightarrow x = 3 - 5.$

In both these cases you will notice that after this operation, the number appears on the other side of the equation, but with the opposite sign. So, you can straightaway change the sign of a term and transfer it from one side of an equation to the other side. This is called *transposition* .

EXAMPLE 5. *Solve : $3x + 5 = 13 - x$. Check the result.*

Solution $3x + 5 = 13 - x$

$\Rightarrow 3x + x = 13 - 5$ [transposing $-x$ to LHS and $+5$ to RHS]

$\Rightarrow 4x = 8$

$\Rightarrow \dfrac{4x}{4} = \dfrac{8}{4}$ [dividing both sides by 4]

$\Rightarrow x = 2.$

$\therefore x = 2$ is the solution of the given equation.

CHECK   Substituting $x = 2$ in the given equation, we get

LHS $= 3 \times 2 + 5 = 11$ and RHS $= 13 - 2 = 11$.

$\therefore$ LHS = RHS, when $x = 2$.

EXAMPLE 6.   Solve: $x - 7 = 5 + \dfrac{x}{2}$. *Check the result.*

Solution $x - 7 = 5 + \dfrac{x}{2}$

$\Rightarrow x - \dfrac{x}{2} = 5 + 7$ [transposing $\dfrac{x}{2}$ to LHS and -7 to RHS]

$\Rightarrow \dfrac{x}{2} = 12$

$\Rightarrow \dfrac{x}{2} \times 2 = 12 \times 2$ [multiplying both sides by 2]

$\Rightarrow x = 24.$

$\therefore$ $x = 24$ is the solution of the given equation.

CHECK   Substituting $x = 24$ in the given equation, we get

LHS $= (24 - 7) = 17$ and RHS $= \left(5 + \dfrac{1}{2} \times 24\right) = 17.$

$\therefore$ LHS = RHS, when $x = 24$.

EXAMPLE 7.   Solve: $3(x + 3) - 2(x - 1) = 5(x - 5)$. *Check the result.*

Solution $3(x + 3) - 2(x - 1) = 5(x - 5)$

$\Rightarrow 3x + 9 - 2x + 2 = 5x - 25$ [removing parentheses]

$\Rightarrow x + 11 = 5x - 25$

$\Rightarrow x - 5x = -25 - 11$ [transposing $5x$ to LHS and 11 to RHS]

$\Rightarrow -4x = -36$

$\Rightarrow x = 9$ [dividing both sides by -4]

$\therefore$ $x = 9$ is the solution of the given equation.

CHECK   Substituting $x = 9$ in the given equation, we get

LHS $= 3(9 + 3) - 2(9 - 1) = (3 \times 12 - 2 \times 8) = 36 - 16 = 20,$

RHS $= 5(9 - 5) = 5 \times 4 = 20.$

$\therefore$ LHS = RHS, when $x = 9$.

EXAMPLE 8.   Solve: $\dfrac{x}{8} - \dfrac{1}{2} = \dfrac{x}{6} - 2.$ *Check the result.*

Solution   Multiplying each term by 24, the LCM of 8, 2 and 6, the given equation becomes:

$3x - 12 = 4x - 48$

$\Rightarrow 3x - 4x = -48 + 12$ [transposing $4x$ to LHS and -12 to RHS]

$\Rightarrow -x = -36$

$\Rightarrow x = 36.$

$\therefore$ $x = 36$ is the solution of the given equation.

CHECK   Substituting $x = 36$ in the given equation, we get

LHS $= \left(\dfrac{36}{8} - \dfrac{1}{2}\right) = \left(\dfrac{36 - 4}{8}\right) = \dfrac{32}{8} = 4$

and RHS $= \left(\dfrac{36}{6} - 2\right) = (6 - 2) = 4.$

$\therefore$ LHS = RHS, when $x = 36.$

EXERCISE 9B

Solve each of the following equations and verify the answer in each case:

1. $x + 5 = 12$
2. $x + 3 = -2$
3. $x - 7 = 6$
4. $x - 2 = -5$

5. $3x - 5 = 13$
6. $4x + 7 = 15$
7. $\dfrac{x}{5} = 12$
8. $\dfrac{3x}{5} = 15$

9. $5x - 3 = x + 17$
10. $2x - \dfrac{1}{2} = 3$
11. $3(x + 6) = 24$
12. $6x + 5 = 2x + 17$

13. $\dfrac{x}{4} - 8 = 1$
14. $\dfrac{x}{2} = \dfrac{x}{3} + 1$
15. $3(x + 2) - 2(x - 1) = 7$

16. $5(x - 1) + 2(x + 3) + 6 = 0$
17. $6(1 - 4x) + 7(2 + 5x) = 53$

18. $16(3x - 5) - 10(4x - 8) = 40$
19. $3(x + 6) + 2(x + 3) = 64$

20. $3(2 - 5x) - 2(1 - 6x) = 1$

21. $\dfrac{n}{4} - 5 = \dfrac{n}{6} + \dfrac{1}{2}$
22. $\dfrac{2m}{3} + 8 = \dfrac{m}{2} - 1$
23. $\dfrac{2x}{5} - \dfrac{3}{2} = \dfrac{x}{2} + 1$
24. $\dfrac{x - 3}{5} - 2 = \dfrac{2x}{5}$

25. $\dfrac{3x}{10} - 4 = 14$
26. $\dfrac{3}{4}(x - 1) = x - 3$

APPLICATIONS OF EQUATIONS

We have learnt how to translate word statements about numbers in the form of equations. If a problem on numbers is given, we shall first translate it in the form of an equation and then solve it. The ideas will be clear from the examples given below.

EXAMPLE 1.   *If 5 is subtracted from three times a number, the result is 16. Find the number.*

Solution   Let the required number be x. Then,
$3x - 5 = 16$
$\Rightarrow 3x = 16 + 5$ [on transposing -5 to RHS]
$\Rightarrow 3x = 21$
$\Rightarrow x = 7$ [dividing both sides by 3].
Hence, the required number is 7.

EXAMPLE 2.   *Find two numbers such that one of them exceeds the other by 9 and their sum is 81.*

Solution   Let the smaller number be x.
Then, the other number $= (x + 9)$.
$\therefore$ $x + (x + 9) = 81$ $\Rightarrow$ $2x + 9 = 81$
$\Rightarrow 2x = 81 - 9$ [on transposing 9 to RHS]
$\Rightarrow 2x = 72$
$\Rightarrow x = 36$ [dividing both sides by 2].
Hence, one number = 36, and
    the other number $= (36 + 9) = 45.$

EXAMPLE 3. *The length of a rectangular field is twice its breadth. If the perimeter of the field is 228 metres, find the dimensions of the field.*

Solution   Let the breadth of the field be x metres. Then, its length = $2x$ metres.

∴ perimeter of the field = 2(length + breadth) = 2($2x + x$) metres = $6x$ metres.

So, $6x = 228 \Rightarrow x = \dfrac{228}{6}$ [dividing both sides by 6]

$\Rightarrow x = 38$.

Hence, breadth of the field = 38 metres, and

length of the field = (2 × 38) metres = 76 metres.

EXAMPLE 4. *Mona's father is thrice as old as Mona. After 12 years, his age will be twice that of his daughter. Find their present ages.*

Solution   Let Mona's present age be x years.

Then, her father's present age = $3x$ years.

Mona's age after 12 years = ($x + 12$) years.

Mona's father's age after 12 years = ($3x + 12$) years.

∴ $3x + 12 = 2(x + 12)$

$\Rightarrow 3x + 12 = 2x + 24$

$\Rightarrow 3x - 2x = 24 - 12$ [transposing $2x$ to LHS and 12 to RHS]

$\Rightarrow x = 12$.

∴   Mona's present age = 12 years.

And, her father's present age = (3 × 12) years = 36 years.

EXERCISE 9C

1. If 9 is added to a certain number, the result is 36. Find the number.

2. If 11 is subtracted from 4 times a number, the result is 89. Find the number.

3. Find a number which when multiplied by 5 is increased by 80.

4. The sum of three consecutive natural numbers is 114. Find the numbers.

5. When Raju multiplies a certain number by 17 and adds 4 to the product, he gets 225. Find that number.

6. If a number is tripled and the result is increased by 5, we get 50. Find the number.

7. Find two numbers such that one of them exceeds the other by 18 and their sum is 92.

8. One out of two numbers is thrice the other. If their sum is 124, find the numbers.

9. Find two numbers such that one of them is five times the other and their difference is 132.

10. The sum of two consecutive even numbers is 74. Find the numbers.

11. The sum of three consecutive odd numbers is 21. Find the numbers.

12. Reena is 6 years older than her brother Ajay. If the sum of their ages is 28 years, what are their present ages ?

13. Deepak is twice as old as his brother Vikas. If the difference of their ages be 11 years, find their present ages.

14. Mrs Goel is 27 years older than her daughter Rekha. After 8 years she will be twice as old as Rekha. Find their present ages.

15. A man is 4 times as old as his son. After 16 years he will be only twice as old as his son. Find their present ages.

16. A man is thrice as old as his son. Five years ago the man was four times as old as his son. Find their present ages.

17. After 16 years, Fatima will be three times as old as she is now. Find her present age.

18. After 32 years, Rahim will be 5 times as old as he was 8 years ago. How old is Rahim today?

19. A bag contains 25-paisa and 50-paisa coins whose total value is ₹ 30. If the number of 25-paisa coins is four times that of 50-paisa coins, find the number of each type of coins.

20. Five times the price of a pen is ₹ 17 more than three times its price. Find the price of the pen.

21. The number of boys in a school is 334 more than the number of girls. If the total strength of the school is 572, find the number of girls in the school.

22. The length of a rectangular park is thrice its breadth. If the perimeter of the park is 168 metres, find its dimensions.

23. The length of a rectangular hall is 5 metres more than its breadth. If the perimeter of the hall is 74 metres, find its length and breadth.

24. A wire of length 86 cm is bent in the form of a rectangle such that its length is 7 cm more than its breadth. Find the length and the breadth of the rectangle so formed.

═══

Things to Remember

1. A statement of equality which involves one or more variables is called an equation.
2. An equation involving only one variable with its highest power 1 is called a linear equation in one variable.
3. While solving an equation we can
   (i) add the same number to both sides of the equation;
   (ii) subtract the same number from both sides of the equation;
   (iii) multiply both sides of the equation by the same nonzero number; and
   (iv) divide both sides of the equation by the same nonzero number.
4. In an equation, we can drop a term from one side and put it on the other side with the opposite sign. This process is known as transposition.

═══

CCE TEST PAPER-9

A. 1. A man earns ₹ 25 per hour. How much does he earn in x hours?

2. The cost of 1 pen is ₹ 16 and the cost of 1 pencil is ₹ 5. What is the total cost of x pens and y pencils.

3. Lalit earns ₹ x per day and spends ₹ y per day. How much does he save in 30 days?

4. Three times a number added to 8 gives 20. Find the number.

5. If $x = 1$, $y = 2$ and $z = 3$, find the value of $x^2 + y^2 + 2xyz$.

6. Solve: $4x + 9 = 17$.

7. Solve: $3(x + 2) - 2(x - 1) = 7$.

8. Solve: $\dfrac{2x}{5} - \dfrac{x}{2} = \dfrac{5}{2}$.

9. The sum of three consecutive natural numbers is 51. Find the numbers.

10. After 16 years, Seema will be three times as old as she is now. Find her present age.

B. *Mark (✓) against the correct answer in each of the following:*

11. By how much does 1 exceed $2x - 3y - 4$?

　(a) $2x - 3y - 5$　　(b) $2x - 3y - 3$　　(c) $5 - 2x + 3y$　　(d) none of these

12. What must be added to $5x^3 - 2x^2 + 6x + 7$ to make the sum $x^3 + 3x^2 - x + 1$?

　(a) $4x^3 - 5x^2 + 7x + 6$　　　　　(b) $-4x^3 + 5x^2 - 7x - 6$

　(c) $4x^3 + 5x^2 - 7x + 6$　　　　　(d) none of these

13. $2x - [3y - \{2x - (y - x)\}] = ?$

　(a) $5x - 4y$　　(b) $4y - 5x$　　(c) $5y - 4x$　　(d) $4x - 5y$

14. The coefficient of x in $-5xyz$ is

　(a) -5　　(b) $5yz$　　(c) $-5yz$　　(d) yz

15. $\dfrac{1}{3}(x + y + z)$ is a

　(a) monomial　　(b) binomial　　(c) trinomial　　(d) quadrinomial

16. If $\dfrac{x}{5} = 1$, then

　(a) $x = \dfrac{1}{5}$　　(b) $x = 5$　　(c) $x = (5 + 1)$　　(d) none of these

17. If $x = 1$, $y = 2$ and $z = 3$ then $(x^2 + y^2 + z^2) = ?$

　(a) 6　　(b) 12　　(c) 14　　(d) 15

18. If $\dfrac{1}{3}x + 5 = 8$, then $x = ?$

　(a) 3　　(b) 6　　(c) 9　　(d) 12

C. 19. *Fill in the blanks.*

　(i) An expression having one term is called a ....

　(ii) An expression having two terms is called a ....

　(iii) An expression having three terms is called a ....

　(iv) $3x - 5 = 7 - x \Rightarrow x = ...$

　(v) $(b^2 - a^2) - (a^2 - b^2) = ...$

D. 20. ***Write 'T' for true and 'F' for false for each of the statements given below:***

(i) $-3xy^2z$ is a monomial.

(ii) $x = \dfrac{2}{3}$ is a solution of $2x + 5 = 8$.

(iii) $2x + 3 = 5$ is a linear equation.

(iv) The coefficient of x in $5xy$ is 5.

(v) $8 - x = 5 \Rightarrow x = 3$.

10 | Ratio, Proportion and Unitary Method

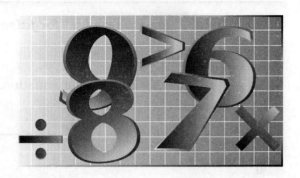

RATIO OF NUMBERS *The ratio of two nonzero numbers a and b is the fraction $\dfrac{a}{b}$ and we write it as $\boldsymbol{a : b}$ read as 'a is to b'.*

In the ratio $\boldsymbol{a : b}$ we call a the **first term** or **antecedent** and b the **second term** or **consequent**.

EXAMPLE 3 : 5 is a ratio in which first term is 3 and the second term is 5 and we define 3 : 5 as $\dfrac{3}{5}$.

AN IMPORTANT RESULT

We know that a fraction does not change when its numerator and denominator are multiplied or divided by the same nonzero number.

So, *a ratio does not change when its first and second terms are multiplied or divided by the same nonzero number.*

EXAMPLES (i) $2 : 3 = \dfrac{2}{3} = \dfrac{2 \times 4}{3 \times 4} = \dfrac{8}{12} = 8 : 12.$

(ii) $60 : 45 = \dfrac{60}{45} = \dfrac{60 \div 5}{45 \div 5} = \dfrac{12}{9} = 12 : 9.$

EQUIVALENT RATIOS *On multiplying (or dividing) each term of a ratio by the same nonzero number we get a ratio equivalent to the given ratio.*

EXAMPLES (i) As shown above, 2 : 3 and 8 : 12 are equivalent ratios.

(ii) As shown above, 60 : 45 and 12 : 9 are equivalent ratios.

RATIO IN SIMPLEST FORM *The ratio a : b is said to be in the simplest form if the HCF of a and b is 1.*

EXAMPLES (i) The ratio 11 : 15 is in the simplest form since the HCF of 11 and 15 is 1.

(ii) The ratio 15 : 20 is not in the simplest form since the HCF of 15 and 20 is 5, not 1.

TO CONVERT A GIVEN RATIO TO ITS SIMPLEST FORM *To convert a given ratio a : b to its simplest form, we divide each term by the HCF of a and b.*

EXAMPLE 1. *Convert the ratio 40 : 25 in its simplest form.*

Solution HCF of 40 and 25 is 5.

$\therefore$ $40 : 25 = \dfrac{40}{25} = \dfrac{40 \div 5}{25 \div 5} = \dfrac{8}{5} = 8 : 5.$

Hence, the simplest form of 40 : 25 is 8 : 5.

EXAMPLE 2. *Express the ratio* 87 : 58 *in simplest form.*

Solution   HCF of 87 and 58 is 29.

$$\therefore \quad 87:58 = \frac{87}{58} = \frac{87 \div 29}{58 \div 29} = \frac{3}{2} = 3:2.$$

RATIO OF TWO QUANTITIES IN SAME UNITS

NOTE   The ratio of two quantities is defined only when they are in the same unit.

EXAMPLE 1.   Suppose that Kunal's weight is 28 kg and Tanvy's weight is 32 kg. Then,

(Kunal's weight) : (Tanvy's weight) = 28 kg : 32 kg = 28 : 32

$$= \frac{28}{32} = \frac{28 \div 4}{32 \div 4} = \frac{7}{8} = 7:8.$$

$\therefore$ ratio of Kunal's weight to Tanvy's weight is 7 : 8.

EXAMPLE 2. *Find the ratio of* 40 cm *to* 1.5 m.

Solution   1.5 m = (1.5 × 100) cm = 150 cm

40 cm : 1.5 m = 40 cm : 150 cm

$$= 40:150 = \frac{40}{150} = \frac{40 \div 10}{150 \div 10} = \frac{4}{15} = 4:15.$$

Hence, the required ratio is 4 : 15.

SOLVED EXAMPLES

EXAMPLE 1. *The length and the breadth of a rectangular park are* 75 m *and* 60 m *respectively. What is the ratio of the length to the breadth of the park?*

Solution   Length of the park = 75 m.

Breadth of the park = 60 m.

$\therefore$ length : breadth = 75 m : 60 m = 75 : 60

$$= \frac{75}{60} = \frac{75 \div 15}{60 \div 15} = \frac{5}{4} = 5:4 \quad [\because \text{ the HCF of 75 and 60 is 15}].$$

Hence, the required ratio is 5 : 4.

EXAMPLE 2. *The length of a pencil is* 16 cm *and its diameter is* 6 mm. *What is the ratio of the diameter of the pencil to that of its length?*

Solution   Taking both the quantities in the same unit, we get

diameter of the pencil = 6 mm,

length of the pencil = 16 cm = (16 × 10) mm = 160 mm.

$\therefore$ (diameter of pencil) : (length of pencil) = 6 : 160 $= \dfrac{6}{160} = \dfrac{6 \div 2}{160 \div 2} = \dfrac{3}{80} = 3:80.$

Hence, the required ratio is 3 : 80.

EXAMPLE 3. *Find the ratio of* 90 cm *to* 1.5 m.

Solution   Taking both the quantities in the same unit, we have:

given ratio = 90 cm : (1.5 × 100) cm = 90 cm : 150 cm = 90 : 150

$$= \frac{90}{150} = \frac{90 \div 30}{150 \div 30} \quad [\because \text{ the HCF of 90 and 150 is 30}]$$

$$= \frac{3}{5} = 3:5.$$

Hence, the given ratio is 3 : 5.

EXAMPLE 4.   *Find the ratio of*
   (i) 36 minutes to an hour   *(ii) 40 paise to ₹ 3*
   (iii) 125 mL to 2 L   *(iv) a dozen to a score*

Solution   Taking both the quantities in the same unit, we have:

(i) 36 minutes : 1 hour = 36 minutes : (1×60) minutes

$$= 36 \text{ minutes} : 60 \text{ minutes} = 36 : 60$$

$$= \frac{36}{60} = \frac{36 \div 12}{60 \div 12} \quad [\because \text{ the HCF of 36 and 60 is 12}]$$

$$= \frac{3}{5} = 3 : 5.$$

(ii) 40 paise : ₹ 3 = 40 paise : (3×100) paise = 40 paise : 300 paise

$$= \frac{40}{300} = \frac{40 \div 20}{300 \div 20} \quad [\because \text{ the HCF of 40 and 300 is 20}]$$

$$= \frac{2}{15} = 2 : 15.$$

(iii) 125 mL : 2 L = 125 mL : (2×1000) mL = 125 mL : 2000 mL = 125 : 2000

$$= \frac{125}{2000} = \frac{125 \div 125}{2000 \div 125} \quad [\because \text{ the HCF of 125 and 2000 is 125}]$$

$$= \frac{1}{16} = 1 : 16.$$

(iv) (a dozen) : (a score) = 12 : 20

$$= \frac{12}{20} = \frac{12 \div 4}{20 \div 4} \quad [\because \text{ the HCF of 12 and 20 is 4}]$$

$$= \frac{3}{5} = 3 : 5.$$

EXAMPLE 5.   *Find two equivalent ratios of* 3 : 4.

Solution   We have:

$$3 : 4 = \frac{3}{4} = \frac{3 \times 2}{4 \times 2} = \frac{3 \times 3}{4 \times 3}$$

$$\Rightarrow \quad 3 : 4 = \frac{3}{4} = \frac{6}{8} = \frac{9}{12}$$

$$\Rightarrow \quad 3 : 4 = 6 : 8 = 9 : 12.$$

Hence, each one of 6 : 8 and 9 : 12 is equivalent to 3 : 4.

EXAMPLE 6.   *Fill in the blank boxes:*

$$\frac{14}{21} = \frac{\Box}{3} = \frac{6}{\Box}$$

Solution   Let $\dfrac{14}{21} = \dfrac{x}{3}$. Then, $21x = (14 \times 3) \Rightarrow x = \dfrac{14 \times 3}{21} = 2.$

$$\therefore \quad \frac{14}{21} = \frac{2}{3}.$$

Again, let $\dfrac{2}{3} = \dfrac{6}{y}$. Then, $2y = (3 \times 6) = 18 \Rightarrow y = 9.$

$$\therefore \quad \frac{2}{3} = \frac{6}{9}.$$

Hence, $\dfrac{14}{21} = \dfrac{2}{3} = \dfrac{6}{9}.$

EXAMPLE 7. *Two numbers are in the ratio 5 : 4 and their sum is 162. Find the numbers.*

Solution   Let the required numbers be $5x$ and $4x$. Then,

$$5x + 4x = 162 \implies 9x = 162$$
$$\implies x = \frac{162}{9} = 18.$$

So, the numbers are (5×18) and (4×18), i.e., 90 and 72.

EXAMPLE 8. *Divide ₹ 1250 between Mayank and Ishita in the ratio 3 : 2.*

Solution   Total money = ₹ 1250 and given ratio = 3 : 2.

Sum of ratio terms = (3 + 2) = 5.

Mayank's share $= \left(\dfrac{3}{5} \text{ of } ₹\, 1250\right) = ₹\left(1250 \times \dfrac{3}{5}\right) = ₹\, 750.$

Ishita's share $= \left(\dfrac{2}{5} \text{ of } ₹\, 1250\right) = ₹\left(1250 \times \dfrac{2}{5}\right) = ₹\, 500.$

EXAMPLE 9. *Divide ₹ 1200 among A, B and C in the ratio 2 : 3 : 5.*

Solution   Total money = ₹ 1200.

Sum of ratio terms = (2 + 3 + 5) = 10.

A's share $= ₹\left(1200 \times \dfrac{2}{10}\right) = ₹\, 240.$

B's share $= ₹\left(1200 \times \dfrac{3}{10}\right) = ₹\, 360.$

C's share $= ₹\left(1200 \times \dfrac{5}{10}\right) = ₹\, 600.$

COMPARISON OF RATIOS

Suppose we want to compare two given ratios. Then, we express each one of them as a fraction in the simplest form. Now, compare these fractions by making their denominators equal.

EXAMPLE 10. *Compare the ratios (5 : 6) and (3 : 4).*

Solution   We can write:

$$(5 : 6) = \frac{5}{6} \text{ and } (3 : 4) = \frac{3}{4}.$$

Now, let us compare $\dfrac{5}{6}$ and $\dfrac{3}{4}$.

The LCM of 6 and 4 is 12.

Making the denominator of each fraction equal to 12, we have:

$$\frac{5}{6} = \frac{5 \times 2}{6 \times 2} = \frac{10}{12} \text{ and } \frac{3}{4} = \frac{3 \times 3}{4 \times 3} = \frac{9}{12}.$$

Clearly, $\dfrac{10}{12} > \dfrac{9}{12} \implies \dfrac{5}{6} > \dfrac{3}{4}.$

Hence, (5 : 6) > (3 : 4).

EXAMPLE 11. *The ratio of copper and zinc in an alloy is 5 : 3. If the weight of copper in the alloy is 30.5 g, find the weight of zinc in it.*

Solution   Ratio of copper and zinc in the alloy = 5 : 3.

Let the weight of copper and zinc in it be $(5x)$ g and $(3x)$ g respectively.

Now, weight of copper = (30.5) g   (given).

$\therefore \quad 5x = 30.5 \implies x = \dfrac{30.5}{5} = 6.1.$

$\therefore \quad$ weight of zinc = $(3x)$ g = (3×6.1) g = 18.3 g.

EXERCISE 10A

1. Find each of the following ratios in the simplest form:
    (i) 24 to 56   (ii) 84 paise to ₹ 3   (iii) 4 kg to 750 g
    (iv) 1.8 kg to 6 kg   (v) 48 minutes to 1 hour   (vi) 2.4 km to 900 m

2. Express each of the following ratios in the simplest form:
    (i) 36 : 90   (ii) 324 : 144   (iii) 85 : 561
    (iv) 480 : 384   (v) 186 : 403   (vi) 777 : 1147

3. Write each of the following ratios in the simplest form:
    (i) ₹ 6.30 : ₹ 16.80   (ii) 3 weeks : 30 days   (iii) 3 m 5 cm : 35 cm
    (iv) 48 min : 2 hours 40 min (v) 1 L 35 mL : 270 mL   (vi) 4 kg : 2 kg 500 g

4. Mr Sahai and his wife are both school teachers and earn ₹ 16800 and ₹ 10500 per month respectively. Find the ratio of
    (i) Mr Sahai's income to his wife's income;
    (ii) Mrs Sahai's income to her husband's income;
    (iii) Mr Sahai's income to the total income of the two.

5. Rohit earns ₹ 15300 and saves ₹ 1224 per month. Find the ratio of
    (i) his income and savings;   (ii) his income and expenditure;
    (iii) his expenditure and savings.

6. The ratio of the number of male and female workers in a textile mill is 5 : 3. If there are 115 male workers, what is the number of female workers in the mill?

7. The boys and the girls in a school are in the ratio 9 : 5. If the total strength of the school is 448, find the number of girls.

8. Divide ₹ 1575 between Kamal and Madhu in the ratio 7 : 2.

9. Divide ₹ 3450 among A, B and C in the ratio 3 : 5 : 7.

10. Two numbers are in the ratio 11 : 12 and their sum is 460. Find the numbers.

11. A 35-cm line segment is divided into two parts in the ratio 4 : 3. Find the length of each part.

12. A factory produces electric bulbs. If 1 out of every 10 bulbs is defective and the factory produces 630 bulbs per day, find the number of defective bulbs produced each day.

13. Find the ratio of the price of a pencil to that of a ball pen if pencils cost ₹ 96 per score and ball pens cost ₹ 50.40 per dozen.

14. The ratio of the length of a field to its width is 5 : 3. Find its length if the width is 42 metres.

15. The ratio of income to savings of a family is 11 : 2. Find the expenditure if the savings is ₹ 1520.

16. The ratio of income to expenditure of a family is 7 : 6. Find the savings if the income is ₹ 14000.

17. The ratio of zinc and copper in an alloy is 7 : 9. If the weight of copper in the alloy is 11.7 kg, find the weight of zinc in it.

18. A bus covers 128 km in 2 hours and a train covers 240 km in 3 hours. Find the ratio of their speeds.

19. From each of the given pairs, find which ratio is larger:
     (i) (3 : 4) or (9 : 16)   (ii) (5 : 12) or (17 : 30)   (iii) (3 : 7) or (4 : 9)
     (iv) (1 : 2) or (13 : 27)

20. Fill in the place holders:

(i) $\dfrac{24}{40} = \dfrac{\square}{5} = \dfrac{12}{\square}$ (ii) $\dfrac{36}{63} = \dfrac{4}{\square} = \dfrac{\square}{21}$ (iii) $\dfrac{5}{7} = \dfrac{\square}{28} = \dfrac{35}{\square}$

PROPORTION

PROPORTION *If two ratios are equal, we say that they are in proportion and use the symbol ': :' or '=' to equate the two ratios.*

EXAMPLE It is given that the weights of 150 litres and 100 litres of kerosene oil are 135 kg and 90 kg respectively.

Then, the ratio of volumes = 150 litres : 100 litres

$$= 150 : 100 = \frac{150}{100} = \frac{3}{2} = 3 : 2.$$

And, the ratio of weights = 135 kg : 90 kg

$$= 135 : 90 = \frac{135}{90} = \frac{3}{2} = 3 : 2.$$

Thus, (150 litres) : (100 litres) = (135 kg) : (90 kg)
⇒ 150 : 100 = 135 : 90
⇒ 150 : 100 : : 135 : 90.

FOUR NUMBERS IN PROPORTION

Four numbers a, b, c, d are said to be in proportion if a : b = c : d and we write, ***a : b :: c : d.***

We read it as ***'a is to b as c is to d'.***

Here *a, b, c, d* are respectively known as *first, second, third* and *fourth term* of the given proportion.

The **1st** and **4th** terms are called the **extreme terms** or **extremes**.

The **2nd** and **3rd** terms are called the **middle terms** or **means**.

In a proportion *a : b :: c : d*, we always have **(a × d) = (b × c)**,

i.e., ***product of extremes = product of means.***

EXAMPLE In 45 : 90 : : 3 : 6, we have:
      product of extremes = (45 × 6) = 270,
      product of means = (90 × 3) = 270.
      ∴ product of extremes = product of means.

SOLVED EXAMPLES

EXAMPLE 1. *Are the ratios 45 g : 60 g and 36 kg : 48 kg in proportion?*

Solution We have:

$$45 \text{ g} : 60 \text{ g} = 45 : 60 = \frac{45}{60} = \frac{3}{4} = 3 : 4.$$

$$36 \text{ kg} : 48 \text{ kg} = 36 : 48 = \frac{36}{48} = \frac{3}{4} = 3 : 4.$$

∴ the ratios 45 g : 60 g and 36 kg : 48 kg are in proportion.

EXAMPLE 2. *Are 30, 40, 45, 60 in proportion?*

Solution   We have: $30 : 40 = \dfrac{30}{40} = \dfrac{3}{4}$. And, $45 : 60 = \dfrac{45}{60} = \dfrac{3}{4}$.

∴ 30 : 40 = 45 : 60.

Hence, 30, 40, 45, 60 are in proportion.

Alternative method   Product of extremes = $(30 \times 60) = 1800$.

Product of means = $(40 \times 45) = 1800$.

∴ product of extremes = product of means.

Hence, 30 : 40 : : 45 : 60.

EXAMPLE 3. *Are 20, 18, 5, 6 in proportion?*

Solution   We have: $20 : 18 = \dfrac{20}{18} = \dfrac{10}{9}$. And, $5 : 6 = \dfrac{5}{6}$.

∴ 20 : 18 ≠ 5 : 6.

Hence, 20, 18, 5, 6 are not in proportion.

Alternative method   Product of extremes = $(20 \times 6) = 120$.

Product of means = $(18 \times 5) = 90$.

∴ product of extremes ≠ product of means.

Hence, 20, 18, 5, 6 are not in proportion.

EXAMPLE 4. *If 36 : 81 : : x : 63, find the value of x.*

Solution   Clearly, product of means = product of extremes.

∴ $81 \times x = 36 \times 63 \Rightarrow x = \dfrac{36 \times 63}{81} = 28.$

Hence, $x = 28$.

EXAMPLE 5. *If 36 : x : : x : 16, find the value of x.*

Solution   Clearly, product of means = product of extremes.

∴ $x \times x = 36 \times 16 \Rightarrow x^2 = (6 \times 6) \times (4 \times 4) = (6 \times 4)^2 = (24)^2$

$\Rightarrow x = 24.$

Hence, $x = 24$.

THREE NUMBERS IN PROPORTION

Three numbers a, b, c are said to be in proportion if a, b, b, c are in proportion.

∴ a, b, c are in proportion

$\Rightarrow$ a, b, b, c are in proportion

$\Rightarrow$ $a : b : : b : c$

$\Rightarrow$ $b^2 = ac$.

EXAMPLE 6.   *If 25, 35, x are in proportion, find the value of x.*

Solution   25, 35, x are in proportion

$\Rightarrow$ 25, 35, 35, x are in proportion

$\Rightarrow$ $25 : 35 :: 35 : x$

$\Rightarrow$ $25 \times x = 35 \times 35$ [product of extremes = product of means]

$\Rightarrow$ $x = \dfrac{35 \times 35}{25} = 49.$

Hence, $x = 49.$

EXERCISE 10B

1. Determine if the following numbers are in proportion:

   (i) 4, 6, 8, 12   (ii) 7, 42, 13, 78   (iii) 33, 121, 9, 96

   (iv) 22, 33, 42, 63   (v) 32, 48, 70, 210   (vi) 150, 200, 250, 300

2. Verify the following:

   (i) $60 : 105 :: 84 : 147$ (ii) $91 : 104 :: 119 : 136$

   (iii) $108 : 72 :: 129 : 86$ (iv) $39 : 65 :: 141 : 235$

3. Find the value of x in each of the following proportions:

   (i) $55 : 11 :: x : 6$ (ii) $27 : x :: 63 : 84$

   (iii) $51 : 85 :: 57 : x$ (iv) $x : 92 :: 87 : 116$

4. Write (T) for true and (F) for false in case of each of the following:

   (i) $51 : 68 :: 85 : 102$ (ii) $36 : 45 :: 80 : 100$

   (iii) 30 bags : 18 bags :: ₹ 450 : ₹ 270   (iv) 81 kg : 45 kg :: 18 men : 10 men

   (v) 45 km : 60 km :: 12 h : 15 h   (vi) 32 kg : ₹ 36 :: 8 kg : ₹ 9

5. Determine if the following ratios form a proportion:

   (i) 25 cm : 1 m and ₹ 40 : ₹ 160

   (ii) 39 litres : 65 litres and 6 bottles : 10 bottles

   (iii) 200 mL : 2.5 L and ₹ 4 : ₹ 50

   (iv) 2 kg : 80 kg and 25 g : 625 kg

6. In a proportion, the 1st, 2nd and 4th terms are 51, 68 and 108 respectively. Find the 3rd term.

7. The 1st, 3rd and 4th terms of a proportion are 12, 8 and 14 respectively. Find the 2nd term.

8. Show that the following numbers are in continued proportion:

   (i) 48, 60, 75   (ii) 36, 90, 225   (iii) 16, 84, 441

9. If 9, x, x, 49 are in proportion, find the value of x.

   Hint. $x^2 = (9 \times 49) = (3^2 \times 7^2) = (3 \times 7)^2 = (21)^2.$

10. An electric pole casts a shadow of length 20 m at a time when a tree 6 m high casts a shadow of length 8 m. Find the height of the pole.

    Hint. *(height of the tree) : (length of its shadow)*

    = *(height of the pole) : (length of its shadow).*

11. Find the value of x if $5 : 3 :: x : 6.$

UNITARY METHOD

*The method in which first we find the value of one unit and then the value of required number of units is known as **unitary method**.*

The simple rules used in this method are:

(i) *to get more, we multiply*

(ii) *to get less, we divide*

The following examples will make the ideas more clear.

SOLVED EXAMPLES

EXAMPLE 1. *If 15 oranges cost ₹ 70, what is the cost of 39 oranges?*

Solution Cost of 15 oranges = ₹ 70.

Cost of 1 orange = $₹\left(\dfrac{70}{15}\right)$ [less oranges, less cost].

Cost of 39 oranges = $₹\left(\dfrac{70}{15}\times 39\right)$ = ₹ 182 [more oranges, more cost].

Hence, the cost of 39 oranges is ₹ 182.

EXAMPLE 2. *A truck runs 492 km on 36 L of diesel. How many kilometres can it run on 33 L of diesel?*

Solution Distance covered on 36 L of diesel = 492 km.

Distance covered on 1 L of diesel = $\left(\dfrac{492}{36}\right)$ km [less diesel, less distance].

Distance covered on 33 L of diesel = $\left(\dfrac{492}{36}\times 33\right)$ km = 451 km

[more diesel, more distance].

Hence, on 33 L of diesel the truck can run 451 km.

EXAMPLE 3. *25 bags of wheat, each weighing 50 kg, cost ₹ 10000. Find the cost of 35 bags of wheat each weighing 40 kg.*

Solution Total weight of 25 bags of 50 kg each = (50 × 25) kg = 1250 kg.

Total weight of 35 bags of 40 kg each = (40 × 35) kg = 1400 kg.

Cost of 1250 kg of wheat = ₹ 10000.

Cost of 1 kg of wheat = $₹\left(\dfrac{10000}{1250}\right)$ [less wheat, less cost].

Cost of 1400 kg of wheat = $₹\left(\dfrac{10000}{1250}\times 1400\right)$ [more wheat, more cost]

= ₹ 11200.

Hence, the cost of 35 bags of 40 kg each is ₹ 11200.

EXAMPLE 4. *12 men can reap a field in 25 days. In how many days can 20 men reap the same field?*

Solution Clearly, *less men will take more days.*

And, *more men will take less days.*

12 men can reap the field in 25 days,

$\Rightarrow$ 1 man can reap the field in (25×12) days   [less men, more days]

$\Rightarrow$ 20 men can reap the field in $\dfrac{(25 \times 12)}{20}$ days   [more men, less days]

= 15 days.

Hence, 20 men can reap the field in 15 days.

EXAMPLE 5. *In an army camp, there were provisions for 425 men for 30 days. However, 375 men attended the camp. How long did the provisions last?*

Solution Clearly, *less men will take more days to consume the same food.*

More men will take less days to consume the same food.

425 men have provisions for 30 days.

1 man has provisions for (425×30) days   [less men, more days].

375 men have provisions for $\dfrac{(425 \times 30)}{375}$ days   [more men, less days]

= 34 days.

Hence, 375 men have provisions for 34 days.

EXAMPLE 6. *Find the ratio of price of coffee to that of tea when coffee costs ₹ 24 per 100 g and tea costs ₹ 180 per kilogram.*

Solution For comparing the price of coffee with that of tea, we have to find the cost of same quantity of each of them, say 1 kg.

Cost of 100 g of coffee = ₹ 24

$\Rightarrow$ cost of 1 g of coffee = ₹$\left(\dfrac{24}{100}\right)$

$\Rightarrow$ cost of 1000 g of coffee = ₹$\left(\dfrac{24}{100} \times 1000\right)$ = ₹ 240

$\Rightarrow$ cost of 1 kg of coffee = ₹ 240.

Also, cost of 1 kg of tea = ₹ 180.

(cost of 1 kg of coffee) : (cost of 1 kg of tea)

= ₹ 240 : ₹ 180

= 240 : 180 = $\dfrac{240}{180} = \dfrac{240 \div 60}{180 \div 60} = \dfrac{4}{3}$ = 4 : 3.

Hence, the required ratio is 4 : 3.

EXERCISE 10C

1. If the cost of 14 m of cloth is ₹ 1890, find the cost of 6 m of cloth.
2. If the cost of a dozen soaps is ₹ 285.60, what will be the cost of 15 such soaps?
3. If 9 kg of rice costs ₹ 327.60, what will be the cost of 50 kg of rice?
4. If 22.5 m of a uniform iron rod weighs 85.5 kg, what will be the weight of 5 m of the same rod?
5. If 15 tins of the same size contain 234 kg of oil, how much oil will there be in 10 such tins?
6. If 12 L of diesel is consumed by a car in covering a distance of 222 km, how many kilometres will it go in 22 L of diesel?
7. A transport company charges ₹ 540 to carry 25 tonnes of weight. What will it charge to carry 35 tonnes?

8. 4.5 g of an alloy of copper and zinc contains 3.5 g of copper. What weight of copper will there be in 18.9 g of the alloy?

9. 35 inland letters cost ₹ 87.50. How many such letters can we buy for ₹ 315?

10. Cost of 4 dozen bananas is ₹ 104. How many bananas can be purchased for ₹ 6.50?

11. The cost of 18 chairs is ₹ 22770. How many such chairs can be bought for ₹ 10120?

12. A car travels 195 km in 3 hours.
    (i) How long will it take to travel 520 km?
    (ii) How far will it travel in 7 hours with the same speed?

13. A labourer earns ₹ 1980 in 12 days.
    (i) How much does he earn in 7 days?
    (ii) In how many days will he earn ₹ 2640?

14. The weight of 65 books is 13 kg.
    (i) What is the weight of 80 such books?
    (ii) How many such books weigh 6.4 kg?

15. If 48 boxes contain 6000 pens, how many such boxes will be needed for 1875 pens?

16. 24 workers can build a wall in 15 days. How many days will 9 workers take to build a similar wall?

17. 40 men can finish a piece of work in 26 days. How many men will be needed to finish it in 16 days?

18. In an army camp, there were provisions for 550 men for 28 days. But, 700 men attended the camp. How long did the provisions last?

19. A given quantity of rice is sufficient for 60 persons for 3 days. How many days would the rice last for 18 persons?

═══════

EXERCISE 10D

OBJECTIVE QUESTIONS

Mark (✓) against the correct answer in each of the following:

1. The ratio 92 : 115 in its simplest form is
   (a) 23 : 25   (b) 18 : 23   (c) 3 : 5   (d) 4 : 5

2. If $57 : x :: 51 : 85$, then the value of x is
   (a) 95   (b) 76   (c) 114   (d) none of these

3. If $25 : 35 :: 45 : x$, then the value of x is
   (a) 63   (b) 72   (c) 54   (d) none of these

4. If $4 : 5 :: x : 35$, then the value of x is
   (a) 42   (b) 32   (c) 28   (d) none of these

5. If a, b, c, d are in proportion, then
   (a) $ac = bd$ (b) $ad = bc$ (c) $ab = cd$ (d) none of these

6. If a, b, c are in proportion, then
   (a) $a^2 = bc$ (b) $b^2 = ac$ (c) $c^2 = ab$ (d) none of these

7. Choose the correct statement:
   (a) $(5 : 8) > (3 : 4)$ (b) $(5 : 8) < (3 : 4)$ (c) two ratios cannot be compared

8. If ₹ 760 is divided between A and B in the ratio 8 : 11, then B's share is
   (a) ₹ 440   (b) ₹ 320   (c) ₹ 430   (d) ₹ 330

9. Two numbers are in the ratio 5 : 7 and the sum of these numbers is 252. The larger of these numbers is
   (a) 85   (b) 119   (c) 105   (d) 147

10. The sides of a triangle are in the ratio 1 : 3 : 5 and its perimeter is 90 cm. The length of its largest side is
    (a) 40 cm   (b) 50 cm   (c) 36 cm   (d) 54 cm

11. The ratio of boys and girls in a school is 12 : 5. If the number of girls is 840, the total strength of the school is
    (a) 1190   (b) 2380   (c) 2856   (d) 2142

12. If the cost of 12 pens is ₹ 138, then the cost of 14 such pens is
    (a) ₹ 164   (b) ₹ 161   (c) ₹ 118.30   (d) ₹ 123.50

13. If 24 workers can build a wall in 15 days, how many days will 8 workers take to build a similar wall?
    (a) 42 days   (b) 45 days   (c) 48 days   (d) none of these

14. If 40 men can finish a piece of work in 26 days, how many men will be required to finish it in 20 days?
    (a) 52   (b) 31   (c) 13   (d) 65

15. In covering 111 km, a car consumes 6 L of petrol. How many kilometres will it go in 10 L of petrol?
    (a) 172 km   (b) 185 km   (c) 205 km   (d) 266.4 km

16. In a fort, 550 men had provisions for 28 days. How many days will it last for 700 men?
    (a) 22 days   (b) $35\frac{7}{11}$ days   (c) 34 days   (d) none of these

17. The angles of a triangle are in the ratio 3 : 1 : 2. The measure of the largest angle is
    (a) 30°   (b) 60°   (c) 90°   (d) 120°

18. Length and breadth of a rectangular field are in the ratio 5 : 4. If the width of the field is 36 m, what is its length?
    (a) 40 m   (b) 45 m   (c) 54 m   (d) 50 m

19. If a bus covers 195 km in 3 hours and a train covers 300 km in 4 hours, then the ratio of their speeds is
    (a) 13 : 15   (b) 15 : 13   (c) 13 : 12   (d) 12 : 13

20. If the cost of 5 bars of soap is ₹ 82.50, then the cost of one dozen such bars is
    (a) ₹ 208   (b) ₹ 192   (c) ₹ 198   (d) ₹ 204

21. If the cost of 30 packets of 8 pencils each is ₹ 600, what is the cost of 25 packets of 12 pencils each?
    (a) ₹ 725   (b) ₹ 750   (c) ₹ 480   (d) ₹ 720

22. A rail journey of 75 km costs ₹ 215. How much will a journey of 120 km cost?
    (a) ₹ 344   (b) ₹ 324   (c) ₹ 268.75   (d) none of these

23. The 1st, 2nd and 4th terms of a proportion are 12, 21 and 14 respectively. Its third term is
    (a) 16   (b) 18   (c) 21   (d) 8

24. 10 boys can dig a pitch in 12 hours. How long will 8 boys take to do it?
    (a) 9 h 36 min   (b) 15 h   (c) 6 h 40 min   (d) 13 h 20 min

Things to Remember

1. *The more the number of articles, the more is the cost.*
   ∴ *cost of any number of articles = (cost of 1 article) × (number of articles).*
2. *Less is the number of articles then less is the cost.*
   ∴ *cost of 1 article =* $\left(\dfrac{\text{cost of a given number of articles}}{\text{number of articles}}\right).$
3. *The method of finding first the value of one quantity from the value of some given quantities and then finding the value of the required quantities is called the unitary method.*
4. *The ratio of two quantities in the same unit is a fraction that one quantity is of the other.*
5. *a to b is a ratio* $\dfrac{a}{b}$, *written as a : b.*
6. *In the ratio a : b, the first term is a and the second term is b.*
7. *A ratio is said to be in its simplest form if the first and second terms have no common factor other than 1.*
8. *The ratio of two numbers is usually expressed in its simplest form.*
9. *A ratio has no units in itself.*
10. *An equality of two ratios is called a proportion.*
    If a : b = c : d, we write a : b :: c : d.
11. *The numbers a, b, c, d are said to be in proportion if a : b = c : d.*
12. *In the proportion a : b :: c : d, we call a, b, c, d as the first, second, third and fourth term respectively.*
13. *The first and fourth terms of a proportion are called the extreme terms or the extremes.*
    Also, the second and third terms are called the middle terms or means.
14. *Product of means = product of extremes.*
15. *Three numbers a, b, c are said to be in proportion if a : b :: b : c.*
16. *If a : b :: c : d then we have three more proportions, namely:*
    (i) *a : c :: b : d*   (ii) *b : a :: d : c*   (iii) *c : a :: d : b.*

CCE TEST PAPER-10

A. 1. Find the ratio of:

   (a) 90 cm to 1.05 m

   (b) 35 minutes to an hour

   (c) 150 mL to 2 L

   (d) 2 dozens to a score

2. The ratio of zinc and copper in an alloy is 7 : 9. If the weight of copper in the alloy is 12.6 kg, find the weight of zinc in it.

3. Divide ₹ 1400 among A, B and C in the ratio 2 : 3 : 5.

4. Prove that (5 : 6) > (3 : 4).

5. 40 men can finish a piece of work in 26 days. How many men will be needed to finish it in 16 days?

6. In an army camp, there were provisions for 425 men for 30 days. How long did the provisions last for 375 men?

7. Find the value of x when $36 : x :: x : 16$.

8. Show that 48, 60, 75 are in continued proportion.

B. *Mark (✓) against the correct answer in each of the following:*

9. Two numbers are in the ratio 3 : 5 and their sum is 96. The larger number is

   (a) 36   (b) 42   (c) 60   (d) 70

10. A car travels 288 km is 4 hours and a train travels 540 km in 6 hours. The ratio of their speeds is

   (a) 5 : 4   (b) 4 : 5   (c) 5 : 6   (d) 3 : 5

11. The first three terms of a proportion are 12, 21 and 8 respectively. The 4th term is

   (a) 18   (b) 16   (c) 14   (d) 20

12. The ratio 92 : 115 in simplest form is

   (a) 23 : 25   (b) 18 : 23   (c) 3 : 5   (d) 4 : 5

13. If $57 : x :: 51 : 85$, then the value of x is

   (a) 95   (b) 76   (c) 114   (d) none of these

14. If $4 : 5 :: x : 45$, then the value of x is

   (a) 54   (b) 60   (c) 36   (d) 30

15. If a, b, c are in proportion, then

   (a) $a^2 = bc$ (b) $b^2 = ac$ (c) $c^2 = ab$ (d) none of these

16. 10 boys can dig a pitch in 12 hours. How long will 8 boys take to do it?

   (a) 9 hrs 36 min   (b) 15 hrs   (c) 6 hrs 40 min   (d) 13 hrs 10 min

17. In covering 148 km, a car consumes 8 litres of petrol. How many kilometres will it go in 10 litres of petrol?

   (a) 172 km   (b) 185 km   (c) 205 km   (d) 266.4 km

C. 18. *Fill in the blanks.*

   (i) $\dfrac{14}{21} = \dfrac{\square}{3} = \dfrac{6}{\square}$

   (ii) 90 cm : 1.5 m = ...

   (iii) If $36 : 81 :: x : 63$, then $x =$ ....

   (iv) If 25, 35, x are in proportion, then $x =$ ....

(v) If 9, x, x, 49 are in proportion, then x = ...

D. 19. ***Write 'T' for true and 'F' for false for each of the statements given below:***

   (i) 30, 40, 45, 60 are in proportion.

  (ii) 6 : 8 and 9 : 12 are equivalent ratios of 3 : 4.

 (iii) a dozen : a score = 5 : 3.

 (iv) 60 p : ₹ 3 = 1 : 5.

11 | Line Segment, Ray and Line

BASIC CONCEPTS

Three geometrical terms, namely, *point, line* and *plane*, form the foundation of geometry. These terms cannot be precisely defined. However, we give examples to illustrate the meaning of these terms.

PLANE

A solid has a surface which may be flat or curved. For example, the surface of a wall is flat and the surface of a ball is curved.

Flat surfaces are known as plane surfaces.

In mathematics, a smooth flat surface which extends endlessly in all the directions is called a plane.

A plane has no boundary.

The surface of a smooth wall, the surface of the top of a table, the surface of a smooth black-board, the surface of a sheet of paper, the surface of calm water in a pool are all examples of a portion of a plane.

We draw figures such as a triangle, a rectangle, a circle, etc., in a plane. We call them plane figures.

POINT

POINT *A point is a mark of position.*

A small dot made by a sharp pencil on a plane paper represents a point.   • A

We name a point by a capital letter of the English alphabet.

In the given figure, A is a point.

A point has no length, breadth or thickness.

LINE SEGMENT

LINE SEGMENT *Let A and B be two points on a plane. Then, the straight path from A to B is called the line segment AB. This is denoted by* $\overline{AB}$.

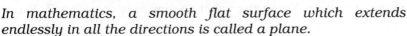

A   Line segment   B

Thus, a line segment has a definite length, which can be measured.

The line segment $\overline{AB}$ is the same thing as the line segment $\overline{BA}$.

MEASURING LINE SEGMENTS

To measure a line segment, we need a *ruler*. One edge of a ruler is marked in centimetres (cm). Each cm is divided into 10 equal small divisions, called millimetres (mm).

How to measure a line segment

EXAMPLE.   *Measure the length of a given line segment $\overline{AB}$.*

Method   Let $\overline{AB}$ be the given line segment. Place the ruler with its edge along the segment $\overline{AB}$ such that the zero mark of the ruler coincides with the point A. Now, we read the mark on the ruler which is against the point B.

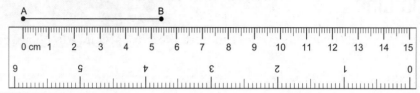

We see that the mark on the ruler against B indicates 5 big divisions (cm) and 4 small divisions (mm).

Hence, the length of $\overline{AB}$ is 5 cm 4 mm, that is, 5.4 cm.

How to construct a line segment

EXAMPLE.   *Draw a line segment of length 6.8 cm.*

Method   Place the ruler on the plane of the paper and hold it firmly.
Mark a point with a fine pencil against the zero cm mark of the ruler. Name it point A. By sliding the pencil gently along the edge of the ruler, draw a line segment up to the 6 cm 8 mm mark on the ruler. Name the point against this mark as B. Then, $\overline{AB}$ = 6.8 cm.

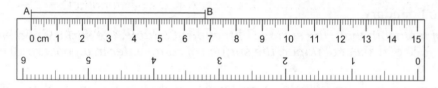

RAY

RAY *A line segment extended endlessly in one direction is called a ray.*

Thus, a line segment $\overline{AB}$, extended endlessly in the direction from A to B, is a ray, denoted by $\overrightarrow{AB}$

The arrow indicates that the ray $\overrightarrow{AB}$ is endless in the direction from A to B.

The ray $\overrightarrow{AB}$ has one end point, namely A, called its *initial point.*

Clearly, *a ray has no definite length.*

Note that $\overrightarrow{BA}$ is a ray with initial point B and extending endlessly in the direction from B to A, as shown alongside.

Clearly, $\overrightarrow{AB}$ and $\overrightarrow{BA}$ are two different rays.

An unlimited number of rays can be drawn in different directions with a given point O as the initial point, as shown in the figure given below.

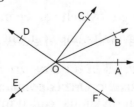

LINE

LINE *A line segment extended endlessly on both sides is called a line.*

Thus, a line segment $\overline{AB}$ extended on both sides and marked by arrows at the two ends, represents a line, denoted by $\overleftrightarrow{AB}$ or $\overleftrightarrow{BA}$.

(Line $\overleftrightarrow{AB}$)

These arrows indicate that the line is endless in both directions. Sometimes, we represent a line by a small letter *l, m, n*, etc.

In the adjoining figure, *l* is a line.

These arrows indicate that the line is endless in both directions. Sometimes, we represent a line by a small letter *l, m, n*, etc.

In the adjoining figure, *l* is a line. ⟷ *l*

Two intersecting planes intersect in a line.

A line has no end points.

RESULT 1. *An unlimited number of lines can be drawn passing through a given point, as shown below.*

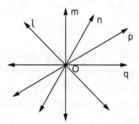

In the above figure, lines *l, m, n, p* and *q* all pass through a given point *O*.

RESULT 2. *If two different points A and B are given in a plane then exactly one line can be drawn passing through these points.*

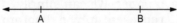

INTERSECTING LINES *If there is a point P common to two lines l and m, we say that the two lines intersect at the point P and this point P is called the point of intersection of the given lines.*

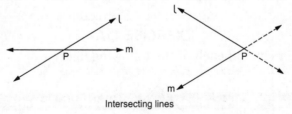

Intersecting lines

PARALLEL LINES If no point is common to two given lines, it would mean that the lines do not intersect. Such lines are known as *parallel lines*.

The rails of a railway line, opposite edges of a ruler and the opposite sides of a rectangle are examples of parallel lines.

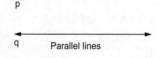

Parallel lines

It is clear that either one point is common to two given lines or no point is common to them.

So, we obtain the following result.

RESULT 3. *Two lines in a plane either intersect at exactly one point or are parallel.*

CONCURRENT LINES *Three or more lines in a plane are said to be concurrent if all of them pass through the same point and this point is called the point of concurrence of the given lines.*

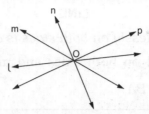

In the above figure, the lines *l, m, n, p* are concurrent lines, since all these lines pass through the same point *O*.

COLLINEAR POINTS   *Three or more points in a plane are said to be collinear if they all lie on the same line and this line is called the line of collinearity for the given points.*

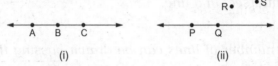

In the figure (i) given above, the three points *A, B, C* are collinear, while in the figure (ii), the points *P, Q, R* and *S* are noncollinear.

DISTINCTION BETWEEN A LINE SEGMENT, A RAY AND A LINE

Line segment	Ray	Line
1. A line segment has two end points.	1. A ray has only one end point.	1. A line has no end point.
2. A line segment has a definite length.	2. A ray does not have a definite length.	2. A line does not have a definite length.
3. A line segment can be drawn on a paper.	3. We cannot draw a ray on a paper. We can simply represent it by a diagram.	3. We cannot draw a line on a paper. We can simply represent it by a diagram.

4. •——————• is a line
  A   B
segment $\overline{AB}$.
	4. ———————→ represents
	  A B
	a ray $\overrightarrow{AB}$.
		4. ←———————→ represents
		  A B
		a line $\overleftrightarrow{AB}$

EXERCISE 11A

1. Name all the line segments in each of the following figures:

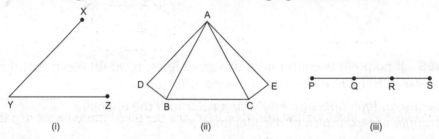

(i)   (ii)   (iii)

2. Identify and name the line segments and rays in each of the following figures:

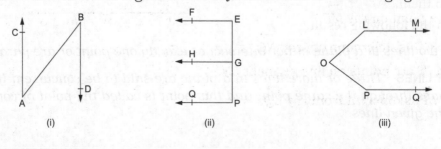

(i)   (ii)   (iii)

3. In the adjoining figure, name
   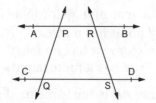
   (i) four line segments;
   (ii) four rays;
   (iii) two non-intersecting line segments.

4. What do you mean by collinear points?
   (i) How many lines can you draw passing through three collinear points?
   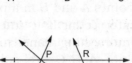
   (ii) Given three collinear points *A, B, C.* How many line segments do they determine? Name them.

5. In the adjoining figure, name:
   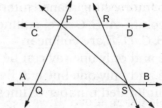
   (i) four pairs of intersecting lines
   (ii) four collinear points
   (iii) three noncollinear points
   (iv) three concurrent lines
   (v) three lines whose point of intersection is *P*

6. Mark three noncollinear points *A, B, C,* as shown. Draw lines through these points taking two at a time. Name the lines. How many such different lines can be drawn?

7. Count the number of line segments drawn in each of the following figures and name them.

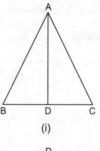

(i)

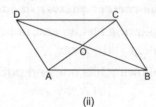

(ii)

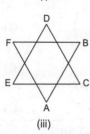

(iii)

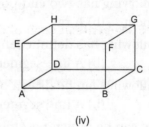

(iv)

8. Consider the line $\overleftrightarrow{PQ}$ given below and find whether the given statements are true or false:
   (i) *M* is a point on ray $\overrightarrow{NQ}$.
   (ii) *L* is a point on ray $\overrightarrow{MP}$.

   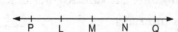

   (iii) Ray $\overrightarrow{MQ}$ is different from ray $\overrightarrow{NQ}$.
   (iv) *L, M, N* are points on line segment $\overline{LN}$.
   (v) Ray $\overrightarrow{LP}$ is different from ray $\overrightarrow{LQ}$.

9. Write 'T' for true and 'F' for false in case of each of the following statements:
   (i) Every point has a size.
   (ii) A line segment has no length.
   (iii) Every ray has a finite length.
   (iv) The ray $\overrightarrow{AB}$ is the same as the ray $\overrightarrow{BA}$.
   (v) The line segment $\overline{AB}$ is the same as the line segment $\overline{BA}$.
   (vi) The line $\overleftrightarrow{AB}$ is the same as the line $\overleftrightarrow{BA}$.
   (vii) Two points A and B in a plane determine a unique line segment.
   (viii) Two intersecting lines intersect at a point.
   (ix) Two intersecting planes intersect at a point.
   (x) If points A, B, C are collinear and points C, D, E are collinear then the points A, B, C, D, E are collinear.
   (xi) One and only one ray can be drawn with a given end point.
   (xii) One and only one line can be drawn to pass through two given points.
   (xiii) An unlimited number of lines can be drawn to pass through a given point.

10. Fill in the blanks:
   (i) A line segment has a .... length. (ii) A ray has .... end point.
   (iii) A line has .... end point.   (iv) A ray has no .... length.
   (v) A line .... be drawn on a paper.

EXERCISE 11B

OBJECTIVE QUESTIONS

Mark (✓) against the correct answer in each of the following:

1. Which of the following has no end points?
   (a) A line segment   (b) A ray   (c) A line   (d) None of these

2. Which of the following has one end point?
   (a) A line   (b) A ray   (c) A line segment (d) None of these

3. Which of the following has two end points?
   (a) A line segment   (b) A ray   (c) A line   (d) None of these

4. Which of the following has definite length?
   (a) A line   (b) A line segment (c) A ray   (d) None of these

5. Which of the following can be drawn on a piece of paper?
   (a) A line   (b) A line segment (c) A ray   (d) A plane

6. How many lines can be drawn passing through a given point?
   (a) One only   (b) Two   (c) Three   (d) Unlimited number

7. How many lines can be drawn passing through two given points?
   (a) One only   (b) Two   (c) Three   (d) Unlimited number

8. Two planes intersect
   (a) at a point   (b) in a plane   (c) in a line   (d) none of these

9. Two lines intersect
   (a) at a point   (b) at two points
   (c) at an infinite number of points   (d) in a line

10. Two points in a plane determine
    (a) exactly one line segment   (b) exactly two line segments
    (c) an infinite number of line segments   (d) none of these

11. The minimum number of points of intersection of three lines in a plane is
    (a) 1   (b) 2   (c) 3   (d) 0

12. The maximum number of points of intersection of three lines in a plane is
    (a) 0   (b) 1   (c) 2   (d) 3

13. Choose the correct statement:
    (a) every line has a definite length   (b) every ray has a definite length
    (c) every line segment has a definite length   (d) none of these

14. Choose the false statement:
    (a) Line $\overleftrightarrow{AB}$ is the same as line $\overleftrightarrow{BA}$
    (b) Ray $\overrightarrow{AB}$ is the same as ray $\overrightarrow{BA}$
    (c) Line segment $\overline{AB}$ is the same as the line segment $\overline{BA}$
    (d) None of these

15. How many rays can be drawn with a given point as the initial point?
    (a) One   (b) Two
    (c) An unlimited number   (d) A limited number only

Things to Remember

1. *Flat surfaces are known as plane surfaces.*
2. *A point is a mark of position.*
3. *A point has no length, breadth or thickness.*
4. *A plane is a flat surface which extends indefinitely in all directions.*
5. *If A and B are any two points in a plane then the straight path from A to B is called the line segment AB, denoted by $\overline{AB}$.*
6. *A line segment has a definite length, which can be measured.*
7. *The line segment $\overline{AB}$ is the same as the line segment $\overline{BA}$.*
8. *A line segment extended endlessly in one direction is called a ray.*
9. *A line segment $\overline{AB}$ extended endlessly in the direction from A to B, is the ray $\overrightarrow{AB}$.*
10. *A ray has no definite length.*
11. *Ray $\overrightarrow{AB}$ is different from ray $\overrightarrow{BA}$.*
12. *An unlimited number of rays can be drawn in different directions with a given point as the initial point.*
13. *A line segment $\overline{AB}$ extended endlessly on both sides is the line $\overleftrightarrow{AB}$.*
14. *A line has no end points.*
15. *A line has no definite length.*
16. *Two intersecting planes intersect in a line.*
17. *An unlimited number of lines can be drawn, passing through a given point.*
18. *One and only one line can be drawn to pass through two given points.*
19. *If there is a point common to two lines, we say that the two lines intersect at that point.*
20. *If no point is common to two given lines then they are said to be parallel.*
21. *Two lines in a plane either intersect or they are parallel.*
22. *Three or more lines in a plane are said to be concurrent if all of them pass through the same point.*
23. *Three or more points in a plane are said to be collinear if they all lie on the same line.*

12 | Parallel Lines

Let us draw two straight lines *AB* and *CD*, as shown in the figure (i). We find that these lines when produced towards the left, meet at a point *O*.

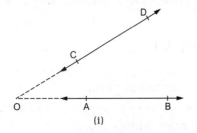

(i)

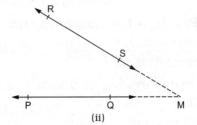

(ii)

Again, let us draw straight lines *PQ* and *RS*, as shown in the figure (ii). These lines, when produced towards the right, meet at a point *M*.

However, there are examples of lines which when produced indefinitely in either direction, do not meet. Such lines are known as *parallel lines*.

The opposite edges of a blackboard, the opposite edges of a ruler, railway lines, etc., are all examples of *parallel lines*.

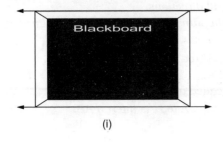

(i)

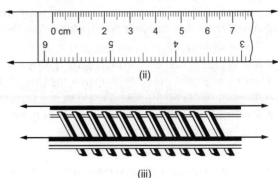

(ii)

(iii)

PARALLEL LINES *Two lines in a plane which do not meet even when produced indefinitely in either direction, are known as parallel lines.*

If *l* and *m* are two parallel lines, we write $l \parallel m$ and read it as *l* is parallel to *m*.

Clearly, when $l \parallel m$, we have, $m \parallel l$.

DISTANCE BETWEEN TWO PARALLEL LINES Let us draw two lines *l* and m such that $l \parallel m$. Take any point *A* on one of these lines, say *l*. At *A*, draw *AD* perpendicular to *l*, meeting *m* at *D*.

Measure the length of the line segment *AD*.

This length *AD* is called the *perpendicular distance* between *l* and *m* at the point *A*.

Let us take any other point B on l. From B, draw BC perpendicular to l, meeting m at C. Measure the length of the line segment BC.

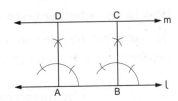

We find that $AD = BC$.

Thus, the perpendicular distance between l and m at the point A is the same as that at B.

Actually speaking, *the perpendicular distance between two parallel lines is the same throughout*. This distance is called *the distance between two parallel lines.*

Thus, parallel lines are the same distance apart throughout.

Why railway lines are made parallel

The wheels of a railway engine and those of the bogies are attached by axles of a fixed length. So, the distance between each pair of opposite wheels remains fixed.

Therefore, the rails on which these wheels roll, must be at a constant distance from each other.

Hence, the opposite rails must be parallel.

Parallel segments and parallel rays

  (i) Two segments are parallel, if the corresponding lines determined by them are parallel [figure (i)].

  (ii) Two rays are parallel, if the corresponding lines determined by them are parallel [figure (ii)].

  (iii) One segment and one ray are parallel, if the corresponding lines determined by them are parallel [figure (iii)].

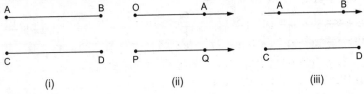

Now, consider the following questions:

  (i) If two segments do not intersect, are they parallel?

  (ii) If two rays do not intersect, are they parallel?

  (iii) If a ray and a segment do not intersect, are they parallel?

See the figures given below.

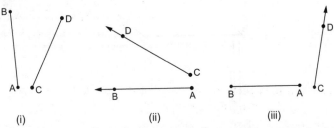

In the figure (i), we observe that the segments AB and CD do not intersect. But, the corresponding lines determined by them will clearly intersect. So, the segments AB and CD are not parallel.

Similarly, in the figure (ii), the rays AB and CD do not intersect and yet they are not parallel.

And, in the figure (iii), the segment AB and the ray CD do not intersect. But, they are not parallel.

Thus, we conclude that *if two segments do not intersect, we cannot say that they are parallel.*

The same is true for two rays as well as for one ray and one segment.

How to test whether given lines are parallel

By using set squares we can test whether the given lines *AB* and *CD* are parallel or not. We proceed in the manner given below:

Method   Place the ruler so that one of its measuring edges lies along the line *AB*. Hold it firmly with one hand. Now place a set square with one arm of the right angle coinciding with the edge of the ruler. Draw the line segment *PQ* along the edge of the set square as shown in the figure.

Slide the set square along the ruler and draw some more segments *RS* and *LM*, as shown in the figure.

If *PQ* = *RS* = *LM* then *AB* || *CD*, otherwise *AB* is not parallel to *CD*.

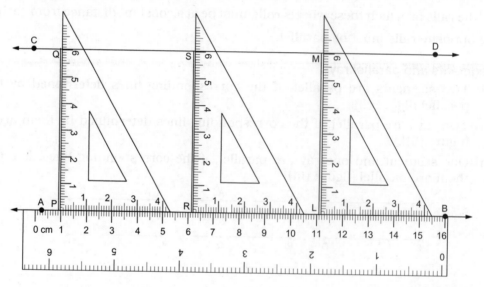

EXERCISE 12

1. In the figure of a table given below, name the pairs of parallel edges of the top.

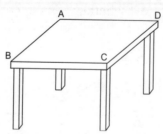

2. Name the groups of all possible parallel edges of the box whose figure is shown below.

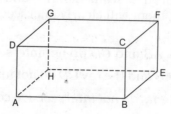

3. Identify parallel line segments in each of the figures given below:

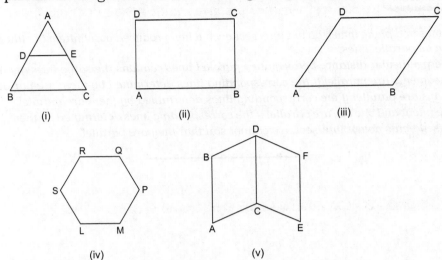

4. Find the distance between the parallel lines l and m, using a set square.

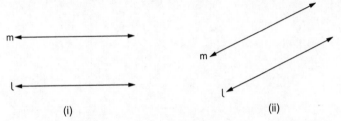

5. In the figure, $l \parallel m$. If $AB \perp l$, $CD \perp l$ and $AB = 2.3$ cm , find CD.

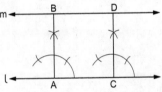

6. In the figure, do the segments AB and CD intersect? Are they parallel? Give reasons for your answer.

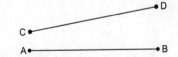

7. Using a set square and a ruler, test whether $l \parallel m$ in each of the following cases:

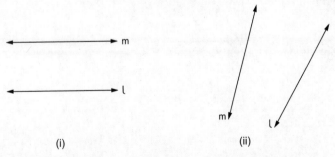

8. Which of the following statements are true and which are false?
  (i) Two lines are parallel if they do not meet, even when produced.
  (ii) Two parallel lines are everywhere the same distance apart.
  (iii) If two line segments do not intersect, they are parallel.
  (iv) If two rays do not intersect, they are parallel.

Things to Remember

1. *Two lines in a plane which do not intersect even when produced indefinitely in either direction, are known as parallel lines.*
2. *The perpendicular distance between two parallel lines remains the same throughout.*
3. *Two segments are parallel if the corresponding lines determined by them are parallel.*
4. *Two rays are parallel if the corresponding lines determined by them are parallel.*
5. *One segment and one ray are parallel if the corresponding lines determined by them are parallel.*
6. *If two segments do not intersect, we cannot say that they are parallel.*

13 | Angles and Their Measurement

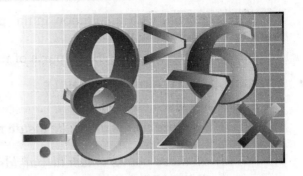

In our daily life, we come across physical objects having two arms, joined together at a common point. For example, the hands of a clock and the two arms of a divider.

These arms are hinged at a point, as shown in the figures given below.

Clock

(i)

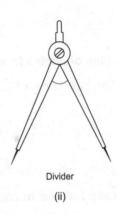

Divider

(ii)

It can be said that each pair of arms forms an angle at its joint.

In geometry, we define the angle as under.

ANGLE *The figure formed by two rays with the same initial point is called an angle.*

The common initial point is known as the *vertex* of the angle, and the rays forming the angle are called its *arms* or *sides*.

In the figure given below, two rays $\overrightarrow{OA}$ and $\overrightarrow{OB}$ with a common initial point O form an angle. We name this angle as $\angle AOB$ or $\angle BOA$, keeping the name of the vertex in the middle.

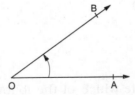

We read it as angle AOB or angle BOA. The symbol $\angle$ stands for angle.

We can simply call it $\angle O$.

When there are more than one angle in a figure, we label them 1, 2, 3, etc., and call them $\angle 1$, $\angle 2$, $\angle 3$, etc.

Thus, in the adjoining figure, $\angle ABC = \angle 1$ and $\angle BAD = \angle 2$.

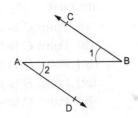

Two line segments with a common initial point also form an angle, as shown in the adjoining figure.

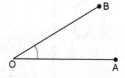

Actually speaking, *OA* and *OB* are parts of the rays *OA* and *OB*.

INTERIOR AND EXTERIOR OF AN ANGLE

Let ∠*AOB* be a given angle. Then,

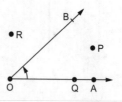

    (i) *all those points which lie inside the angle form the interior of the angle,*

    (ii) *all those points which lie outside the angle form the exterior of the angle,*

    (iii) *every point of each of the arms of the angle is said to lie on the angle.*

In the adjoining figure, the point *P* lies in the interior of ∠*AOB*, the point *R* lies in the exterior of ∠*AOB* and the points *A*, *O*, *B*, *Q* all lie on ∠*AOB*.

EXERCISE 13A

1. Name three examples of angles from your daily life.

2. Name the vertex and the arms of ∠*ABC*, given in the figure below.

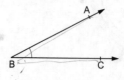

3. How many angles are formed in each of the figures given below? Name them.

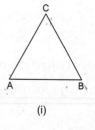
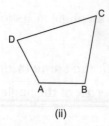
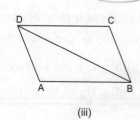

           (i)   (ii)   (iii)

4. In the given figure, list the points which
    (i) are in the interior of ∠*AOB*
    (ii) are in the exterior of ∠*AOB*
    (iii) lie on ∠*AOB*

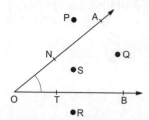

5. See the adjacent figure and state which of the following statements are true and which are false.
    (i) Point *C* is in the interior of ∠*AOC*.
    (ii) Point *C* is in the interior of ∠*AOD*.
    (iii) Point *D* is in the interior of ∠*AOC*.
    (iv) Point *B* is in the exterior of ∠*AOD*.
    (v) Point *C* lies on ∠*AOB*.

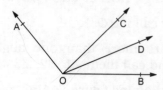

6. In the adjoining figure, write another name for:

   (i) ∠1   (ii) ∠2   (iii) ∠3

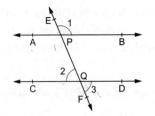

MAGNITUDE OF AN ANGLE AND ITS MEASUREMENT

ANGLE AS ROTATION OF A RAY Suppose a ray after starting from its initial position $\overrightarrow{OA}$ rotates about the point O and takes the final position $\overrightarrow{OB}$. Then, we say that an angle ∠AOB has been described by the rotating ray with O as vertex, and OA and OB as its arms.

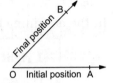

MAGNITUDE OF AN ANGLE *The magnitude of an angle is the amount of rotation through which one of the arms must be rotated about the vertex to bring it to the position of the other.*

COMPARING TWO ANGLES We say that ∠1 is greater than ∠2 if the magnitude of ∠1 is greater than that of ∠2. Also, in other words, we say that ∠2 is smaller than ∠1.

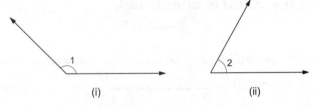

COMPARISON BY INSPECTION Clearly, the more is the opening between two arms, the greater will be the magnitude of an angle. So, sometimes we may compare two angles simply by looking at them.

In the figures (i) and (ii) given above, we can clearly say that ∠1 is greater than ∠2.

COMPARING ANGLES BY USING TRACING PAPER Suppose we have to compare two angles ∠ABC and ∠DEF. We place a tracing paper on one of the angles, say ∠DEF and copy this angle on the tracing paper. Now, place the traced angle ∠DEF on ∠ABC such that the point E lies on the point B and the ray EF lies along the ray BC.

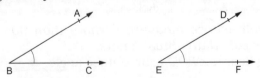

Now, there are the following possibilities:

   (i) If ray ED lies between ray BA and ray BC, as shown in the figure (i), we say that ∠DEF is smaller than ∠ABC and we write, ∠DEF < ∠ABC.

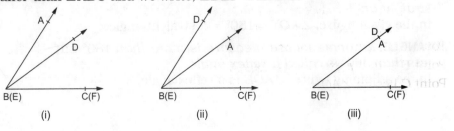

(ii) If ray *ED* lies beyond ray *BA*, as shown in the figure (ii), we say that ∠*DEF* is larger than ∠*ABC* and we write, ∠*DEF* > ∠*ABC*.

(iii) If ray *ED* lies along ray *BA*, we say that ∠*DEF* is congruent to ∠*ABC* and we write, ∠*DEF* = ∠*ABC*. See the figure (iii) above.

UNITS OF MEASURING AN ANGLE

The standard unit of measuring an angle is degree, to be denoted by '°'.

RIGHT ANGLE

A quarter turn of a ray $\overrightarrow{OA}$ about O describes an angle called a right angle.

The measure of a right angle is 90°.

In the adjoining figure, ∠*AOB* = 90°.

> **1 right angle = 90°.**
>
> **1° = 60 minutes, written as 60'.**
>
> **1' = 60 seconds, written as 60".**

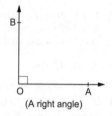
(A right angle)

VARIOUS TYPES OF ANGLES

(i) **ACUTE ANGLE** *An angle whose measure is more than 0° but less than 90° is called an acute angle.*

In the given figure, ∠*AOB* is an acute angle.

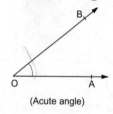
(Acute angle)

(ii) **RIGHT ANGLE** *An angle whose measure is 90° is called a right angle.*

In the given figure, ∠*LOM* = 90° = 1 right angle.

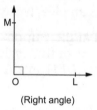
(Right angle)

(iii) **OBTUSE ANGLE** *An angle whose measure is more than 90° but less than 180° is called an obtuse angle.*

In the adjoining figure, ∠*POQ* is an obtuse angle.

(iv) **STRAIGHT ANGLE** *An angle whose measure is 180° is called a straight angle.*

In the given figure, ∠*XOY* = 180° = a straight angle.

(v) **REFLEX ANGLE** *An angle whose measure is more than 180° but less than 360° is called a reflex angle.*

In the adjoining figure, ∠*AOB* is a reflex angle.

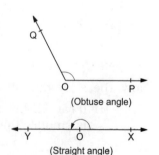
(Obtuse angle)

(Straight angle)

(Reflex angle)

(vi) COMPLETE ANGLE *An angle whose measure is 360° is called a complete angle.*

In the adjoining figure, ∠AOA = 360°.

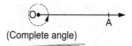

(Complete angle)

(vii) ZERO ANGLE *The angle whose masure is 0° is caled a zero angle.*

In the given figure, ∠AOA = 0°.

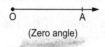

(Zero angle)

EXERCISE 13B

1. State the type of each of the following angles:

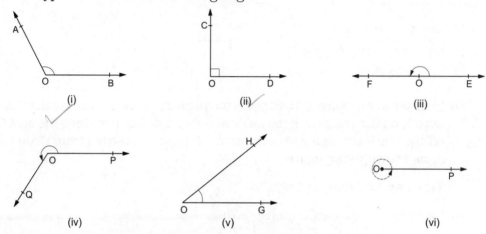

2. Classify the angles whose magnitudes are given below:
   (i) 30°   (ii) 91°   (iii) 179°   (iv) 90°
   (v) 181°   (vi) 360°   (vii) 128°   (viii) (90.5)°
   (ix) (38.3)°   (x) 80°   (xi) 0°   (xii) 15°

3. How many degrees are there in
   (i) one right angle?   (ii) two right angles?
   (iii) three right angles?   (iv) four right angles?
   (v) $\frac{2}{3}$ right angle?   (vi) $1\frac{1}{2}$ right angles?

4. How many degrees are there in the angle between the hour hand and the minute hand of a clock, when it is
   (i) 3 o'clock?   (ii) 6 o'clock?   (iii) 12 o'clock?   (iv) 9 o'clock?

5. Using only a ruler, draw an acute angle, an obtuse angle and a straight angle.

MEASURING AN ANGLE BY A PROTRACTOR

PROTRACTOR It is an instrument for measuring or constructing an angle of a given measure. It is a semicircular piece of metal or plastic, which is marked in degrees from 0° to 180° from left to right as well as from right to left, as shown in the figure.

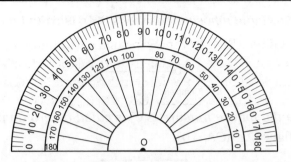

The centre *O* of this piece is also the midpoint of its base line.

EXAMPLE 1.   *Find the measure of each one of the angles given below by using a protractor.*

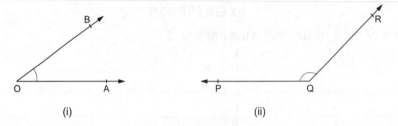

(i)   (ii)

Method   (i) In order to measure ∠*AOB*, place the protractor in such a way that its centre is exactly on the vertex *O* of the angle and the base line lies along the arm *OA*. Read off the mark through which the arm *OB* passes, starting from 0° on the side of *A*, as shown in the figure.

Thus, we find that ∠*AOB* = 38°.

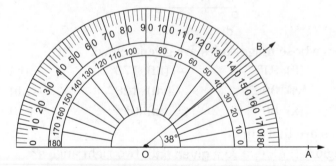

(ii) In order to measure ∠*PQR*, place the protractor in such a way that its centre is exactly on the vertex *Q* of the angle and the base line lies along the arm *PQ*. Read off the mark through which the arm *QR* passes, starting from 0° on the side of *P*, as shown in the figure.

Thus, we find that ∠*PQR* = 127°.

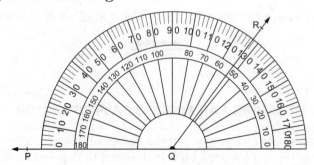

EXAMPLE 2.   *Construct an angle of 105° with the help of a protractor.*

Method   Draw a ray OA. Place the protractor in such a way that its centre lies exactly at O and the base line lies along OA. Starting from 0° on the side of A, move the eyes and look for the 105° mark on the protractor. Mark a point B against this 105° mark. Remove the protractor and draw the ray OB. Then, ∠AOB is the required angle whose measure is 105°.

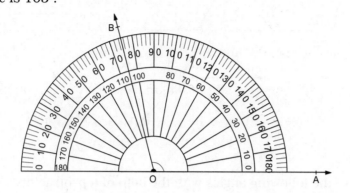

PERPENDICULAR LINES

PERPENDICULAR LINES   *Two lines l and m are said to be perpendicular to each other if one of the angles formed by them is a right angle,* and we write *l ⊥ m* (read as *l* is perpendicular to *m*).

Two rays are said to be perpendicular to each other if the corresponding lines determined by them are perpendicular to each other.

Two segments are said to be perpendicular to each other if the corresponding lines determined by them are perpendicular to each other.

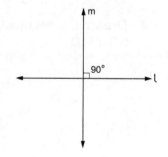

A ray and a segment are said to be perpendicular to each other if the corresponding lines determined by them are perpendicular to each other.

Construction of a line perpendicular to a given line

EXAMPLE 1.   *Draw a line l and mark a point A on it. Construct a line perpendicular to the line l at the point A, using a protractor.*

Method   Let *l* be the given line and *A* be the given point on it.

Place the protractor on *l* in such a way that its centre is exactly on the point *A* and its base line lies along *l*.

Holding the protractor fixed, mark with a pencil a point *B* on the paper against the 90° mark of the protractor.

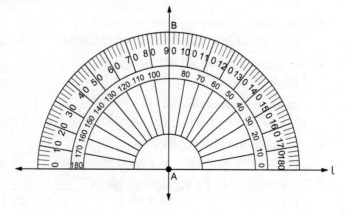

Remove the protractor and with a ruler draw a line passing through *A* and *B*.

Then, *AB ⊥ l* at *A*.

EXERCISE 13C

1. Measure each of the following angles with the help of a protractor and write the measure in degrees:

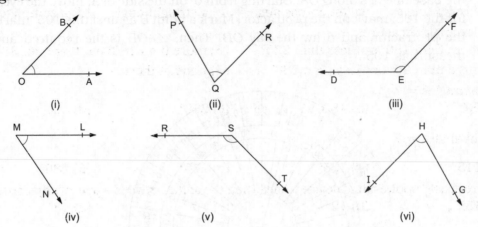

(i)   (ii)   (iii)

(iv)   (v)   (vi)

2. Construct each of the following angles with the help of a protractor:
   (i) 25°   (ii) 72°   (iii) 90°   (iv) 117°
   (v) 165°   (vi) 23°   (vii) 180°   (viii) 48°

3. Measure ∠ABC given in the adjoining figure and construct an angle DEF equal to ∠ABC.

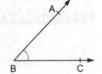

4. Draw a line segment AB = 6 cm. Take a point C on AB such that AC = 4 cm. From C, draw CD ⊥ AB.

EXERCISE 13D

OBJECTIVE QUESTIONS

Mark (✓) against the correct answer in each of the following:

1. Where does the vertex of an angle lie?
   (a) In its interior   (b) In its exterior   (c) On the angle   (d) None of these

2. The figure formed by two rays with the same initial point is called
   (a) a ray   (b) a line   (c) an angle   (d) none of these

3. An angle measuring 180° is called
   (a) a complete angle (b) a reflex angle   (c) a straight angle   (d) none of these

4. An angle measuring 90° is called
   (a) a straight angle   (b) a right angle   (c) a complete angle   (d) a reflex angle

5. An angle measuring 91° is
   (a) an acute angle   (b) an obtuse angle   (c) a reflex angle   (d) none of these

6. An angle measuring 270° is
   (a) an obtuse angle   (b) an acute angle   (c) a straight angle   (d) a reflex angle

7. The measure of a straight angle is
   (a) 90°   (b) 150°   (c) 180°   (d) 360°

8. An angle measuring 200° is
   (a) an obtuse angle   (b) an acute angle   (c) a reflex angle   (d) none of these

9. An angle measuring 360° is
   (a) a reflex angle   (b) an obtuse angle   (c) a straight angle   (d) a complete angle

10. A reflex angle measures
   (a) more than 180° but less than 270°   (b) more than 180° but less than 360°
   (c) more than 90° but less than 180°   (d) none of these

11. 2 right angles = ?
   (a) 90°   (b) 180°   (c) 270°   (d) 360°

12. $\frac{3}{2}$ right angles = ?

   (a) 115°   (b) 135°   (c) 270°   (d) 230°

13. If there are 36 spokes in a bicycle wheel, then the angle between a pair of adjacent spokes is
   (a) 15°   (b) 12°   (c) 10°   (d) 18°

═══════════════

Things to Remember

1. *The figure formed by two rays with the same initial point is called an angle. The common initial point is called the vertex, and the two rays are called the arms of the angle.*

2. *The amount of rotation through which one of the arms of a given angle must be rotated about its vertex to bring it to the position of the other is called the magnitude of the angle.*

3. *The standard unit of measuring an angle is degree.*

4. (i) *A complete turn of a ray OA about O describes a complete angle whose measure is 360°.*
   (ii) *A half turn of a ray OA about O describes a straight angle whose measure is 180°.*
   (iii) *A quarter turn of a ray OA about O describes a right angle whose measure is 90°.*

5. *A right angle = 90°, a straight angle = 180°, a complete angle = 360°.*

6. (i) *0° < acute angle < 90° < obtuse angle < 180° < reflex angle < 360°.*
   (ii) *1 right angle = 90°, and 1° = 60′ and 1′ = 60″.*

────────────────

14

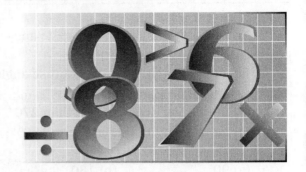

Constructions (Using Ruler and a Pair of Compasses)

TO DRAW THE PERPENDICULAR BISECTOR OF A GIVEN LINE SEGMENT

EXAMPLE 1. *Draw the perpendicular bisector of a given line segment AB of length* 5 cm.

Steps of construction

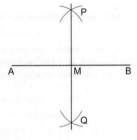

1. Draw a line segment $AB = 5$ cm.
2. With A as centre and radius more than half AB, draw arcs, one on each side of AB.
3. With B as centre and the same radius as before, draw arcs, cutting the previously drawn arcs at P and Q respectively.
4. Join PQ, meeting AB at M.
   Then, PM is the perpendicular bisector of AB.

Verification Measure AM and MB.
   You would find that $AM = MB$.
   Also, on measuring, we find that $\angle PMB = \angle PMA = 90°$.
   Hence, PM is the perpendicular bisector of AB.

TO DRAW AN ANGLE EQUAL TO A GIVEN ANGLE

EXAMPLE 2. *Draw an angle equal to a given angle $\angle ABC$.*

Steps of construction

   Let $\angle ABC$ be given.

1. Draw a ray OX.

2. With B as centre and any radius, draw an arc cutting BA and BC at P and Q respectively.

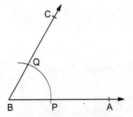
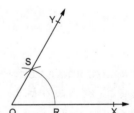

3. With O as centre and the same radius, draw an arc, cutting, OX at R.

4. With R as centre and radius as PQ, cut the arc through R at S.

5. Join OS and produce it to any point Y.
   Then, $\angle XOY$ is the required angle equal to $\angle ABC$.

Verification   Measure ∠ABC and ∠XOY.
           You would find that ∠XOY = ∠ABC.

TO BISECT A GIVEN ANGLE

EXAMPLE 3. *An angle ∠AOB is given. Draw a ray OX, bisecting ∠AOB.*

Steps of construction

Let ∠AOB be given.

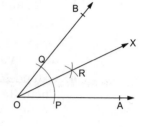

1. With *O* as centre and any convenient radius, draw an arc, cutting *OA* and *OB* at *P* and *Q* respectively.

2. With centre *P* and radius more than $\frac{1}{2}(PQ)$, draw an arc.

3. With centre *Q* and the same radius as before, draw another arc, cutting the previously drawn arc at a point *R*.

4. Join *OR* and produce it to any point *X*.
   Then, ray *OX* bisects ∠AOB.

Verification   Measure ∠AOX and ∠BOX.
           You would find that ∠AOX = ∠BOX.

TO DRAW A LINE PERPENDICULAR TO A GIVEN LINE FROM A POINT ON IT

EXAMPLE 4. *A line XY is given and P is a point on it. Draw a line through P perpendicular to XY.*

Steps of construction

Let *XY* be the given line and *P* be a point on it.

1. With centre *P* and any radius, draw a semicircle to intersect *XY* at *A* and *B*.

2. With centre *A* and any radius more than *PA*, draw an arc.

3. With centre *B* and the same radius, draw another arc, cutting the previously drawn arc at *Q*.

4. Join *PQ*.
   Then, *QP* ⊥ *XY*.

Verification   Measure ∠QPX and ∠QPY.
           You would find that ∠QPX = ∠QPY = 90°.

TO DRAW A LINE PERPENDICULAR TO A GIVEN LINE FROM A POINT OUTSIDE IT

EXAMPLE 5. *A line XY is given and P is a point outside it. Draw a line through P perpendicular to XY.*

Steps of construction

Let *XY* be the given line and *P* be a point outside it.

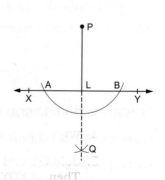

1. With *P* as centre and a convenient radius, draw an arc intersecting *XY* at *A* and *B*.

2. With *A* as centre and a radius greater than $\frac{1}{2}(AB)$, draw an arc.

3. With *B* as centre and the same radius, draw another arc, cutting the previously drawn arc at *Q*.

4. Join *PQ*, meeting *XY* at *L*.
   Then, *PL* is the required perpendicular on *XY*.

Verification   Measure ∠*PLX* and ∠*PLY*.
        You would find that ∠*PLX* = ∠*PLY* = 90°.

TO DRAW A LINE PARALLEL TO A GIVEN LINE THROUGH A POINT OUTSIDE IT

EXAMPLE 6. *A line XY is given and P is a point outside it. Draw a line through P parallel to XY.*

Steps of construction

        Let *XY* be the given line and *P* be a given point outside it.

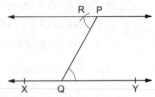

1. Take any point *Q* on *XY*.
2. Join *QP*.
3. Draw ∠*RPQ* such that ∠*RPQ* = ∠*PQY* as shown in the figure.
4. Extend *RP* on both sides.
    Then, the line *RP* passes through the point *P* and *RP* ∥ *XY*.

EXERCISE 14A

1. Draw a line segment *PQ* = 6.2 cm. Draw the perpendicular bisector of *PQ*.

2. Draw a line segment *AB* = 5.6 cm. Draw the perpendicular bisector of *AB*.

3. Draw an angle equal to ∠*AOB*, given in the adjoining figure.

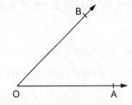

4. Draw an angle of 50° with the help of a protractor. Draw a ray bisecting this angle.

5. Construct ∠*AOB* = 85° with the help of a protractor. Draw a ray *OX* bisecting ∠*AOB*.

6. Draw a line *AB*. Take a point *P* on it. Draw a line passing through *P* and perpendicular to *AB*.

7. Draw a line *AB*. Take a point *P* outside it. Draw a line passing through *P* and perpendicular to *AB*.

8. Draw a line *AB*. Take a point *P* outside it. Draw a line passing through *P* and parallel to *AB*.

9. Draw ∠*ABC* of measure 60° such that *AB* = 4.5 cm and *BC* = 5 cm. Through *C* draw a line parallel to *AB* and through *B* draw a line parallel to *AC*, intersecting each other at *D*. Measure *BD* and *CD*.

10. Draw a line segment *AB* = 6 cm. Take a point *C* on *AB* such that *AC* = 2.5 cm. Draw *CD* perpendicular to *AB*.

11. Draw a line segment *AB* = 5.6 cm. Draw the right bisector of *AB*.

CONSTRUCTION OF SOME SPECIAL ANGLES USING A PAIR OF COMPASSES

EXAMPLE 1. *Construct an angle of* 60°, *using a pair of compasses.*

Steps of construction

        (i) Draw a ray *OA*.

(ii) With O as centre and any suitable radius, draw an arc cutting OA at a point B.

(iii) With B as centre and the same radius as before, draw another arc to cut the previous arc at C.

(iv) Join OC and produce it to D.

Now, $\angle AOD = 60°$.

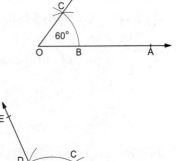

EXAMPLE 2. *Construct an angle of 120°, using a pair of compasses.*

Steps of construction

(i) Draw a ray OA.

(ii) With O as centre and any suitable radius, draw an arc cutting OA at B.

(iii) With B as centre and the same radius, cut the arc at C. Again with C as centre and the same radius, cut the arc at D.

(iv) Join OD and produce it to E.

Then, $\angle AOE = 120°$.

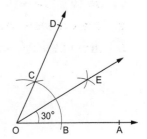

EXAMPLE 3. *Construct an angle of 30°, using a pair of compasses.*

Steps of construction

(i) Construct an angle $\angle AOD = 60°$ as above.

(ii) Draw the bisector OE of $\angle AOD$.

Then, $\angle AOE = 30°$.

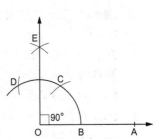

EXAMPLE 4. *Construct an angle of 90°, using a pair of compasses.*

Steps of construction

(i) Draw a ray OA.

(ii) With O as centre and any suitable radius, draw an arc, cutting OA at B.

(iii) With B as centre and the same radius, cut the previously drawn arc at C, and then with C as centre and the same radius, cut the arc at D.

(iv) With C as centre and radius more than half CD, draw an arc.

(v) With D as centre and the same radius, draw another arc to cut the previous arc at E.

(vi) Join OE.

Then, $\angle AOE = 90°$.

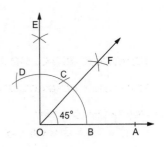

EXAMPLE 5. *Construct an angle of 45°, using a pair of compasses.*

Steps of construction

(i) Draw $\angle AOE = 90°$ as above.

(ii) Draw the bisector OF of $\angle AOE$.

Then, $\angle AOF = 45°$.

EXERCISE 14B

1. Using a pair of compasses construct the following angles:
   - (i) 60°
   - (ii) 120°
   - (iii) 90°

2. Draw an angle of 60°, using a pair of compasses. Bisect it to make an angle of 30°.

3. Draw an angle of 45°, using a pair of compasses.

4. Use a pair of compasses and construct the following angles:

   - (i) 150°
   - (ii) 15°
   - (iii) 135°
   - (iv) $22\frac{1}{2}°$

   - (v) 105°
   - (vi) 75°
   - (vii) $67\frac{1}{2}°$
   - (viii) 45°

5. Draw a rectangle whose two adjacent sides are 5 cm and 3.5 cm. Make use of a pair of compasses and a ruler only.

6. Draw a square, each of whose sides is 5 cm. Use a pair of compasses and a ruler in your construction.

CCE TEST PAPER-14

A. **1.** How many lines can be drawn to pass through

     (i) a given point   (ii) two given points   (iii) three given points?

  2. Classify the angles whose magnitudes are given below.

     (i) $50°$ (ii) $92°$ (iii) $185°$ (iv) $90°$ (v) $180°$

  3. Draw the perpendicular bisector of a given line segment *AB* of length 6 cm.

  4. Construct an angle of $120°$ and bisect it.

  5. Construct an angle of $90°$ and bisect it.

  6. Draw a rectangle whose two adjacent sides are 5.4 cm and 3.5 cm.

B. *Mark (✓) against the correct answer in each of the following:*

  7. Which of the following has no end points?

     (a) A line segment (b) A ray   (c) A line   (d) none of these

  8. Which of the following has one end point?

     (a) A line   (b) A ray   (c) A line segment (d) none of these

  9. Which of the following has two end points?

     (a) A line segment (b) A ray   (c) A line   (d) none of these

 10. Two planes intersect

     (a) at a point   (b) in a line   (c) in a plane   (d) none of these

 11. $\dfrac{3}{2}$ right angles = ...

     (a) $115°$ (b) $135°$ (c) $230°$ (d) $270°$

 12. Where does the vertex of an angle lie?

     (a) in its interior   (b) in its exterior   (c) on the angle   (d) none of these

 13. An angle measuring $270°$ is

     (a) an obtuse angle   (b) an acute angle

     (c) a straight line   (d) a reflex angle

C. 14. *Fill in the blanks.*

     (i) A line has ...... end point.

     (ii) A ray has ...... end point

     (iii) A line ...... be drawn on a paper.

     (iv) $0°$ ...... acute angle ...... $90° <$ obtuse angle $< 180°$.

     (v) The standard unit of measuring an angle is ....

D. 15. *Write 'T' for true and 'F' for false for each of the statements given below:*

     (i) If two line segments do not intersect, they are parallel.

     (ii) If two rays do not intersect, they are parallel.

     (iii) If two lines do not meet even when produced, they are called parallel lines.

     (iv) Two parallel lines are everywhere the same distance apart.

     (v) A ray has a finite length.

     (vi) Ray $\overrightarrow{AB}$ is the same as ray $\overrightarrow{BA}$.

15 | Polygons

IDEA OF SIMPLE CLOSED FIGURES

STRAIGHT LINE We know that by moving a pencil along the straight edge of a ruler, we get a *straight line*.

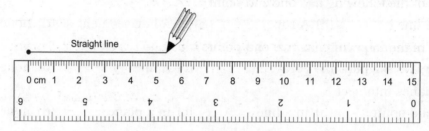

CURVE By moving a pencil along a curved edge (like that of a coin), we get a *curve*.

CLOSED FIGURES *A figure which begins and ends at the same point is called a closed figure.*

Each of the figures given below is a closed figure.

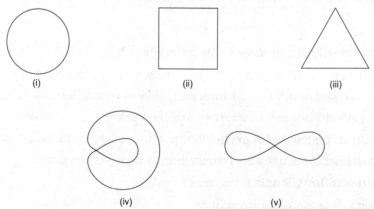

OPEN FIGURES *A figure which does not end at the starting point is called an open figure.*

Each of the figures given below is an open figure.

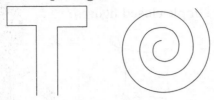

SIMPLE CLOSED FIGURES *A closed figure which does not intersect itself is called a simple closed figure.*

Thus, out of the examples given above for closed figures (i), (ii) and (iii) are simple closed figures.

POLYGONS *A simple closed figure formed of three or more line segments is called a polygon.*

SIDES, VERTICES AND DIAGONALS OF A POLYGON

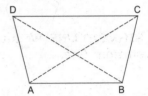

SIDES *The line segments forming a polygon are called its sides.*

In the given figure, *ABCD* is a polygon in which *AB*, *BC*, *CD* and *DA* are its four sides.

VERTICES *The meeting point of a pair of sides of a polygon is called its vertex.*

Thus, *A*, *B*, *C*, *D* are the four vertices of the given polygon *ABCD*.

ADJACENT SIDES *Any two sides of a polygon having a common end point are called its adjacent sides.*

Thus, (*AB*, *BC*), (*BC*, *CD*), (*CD*, *DA*) and (*DA*, *AB*) are four pairs of adjacent sides in the given polygon *ABCD*.

Here (*A*, *B*), (*B*, *C*), (*C*, *D*) and (*D*, *A*) are the pairs of *adjacent vertices*.

DIAGONALS *A line segment joining two non-adjacent vertices of a polygon is called its diagonal.*

Thus, *AC* and *BD* are the diagonals of the given polygon *ABCD*.

TRIANGLE *A polygon of 3 sides is called a triangle.*

QUADRILATERAL *A polygon of 4 sides is called a quadrilateral.*

PENTAGON *A polygon of 5 sides is called a pentagon.*

HEXAGON *A polygon of 6 sides is called a hexagon.*

HEPTAGON *A polygon of 7 sides is called a heptagon.*

OCTAGON *A polygon of 8 sides is called an octagon.*

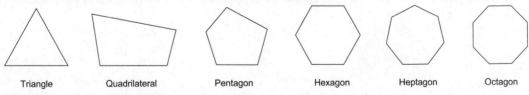

| Triangle | Quadrilateral | Pentagon | Hexagon | Heptagon | Octagon |

A triangle has 3 sides, 3 angles and 3 vertices.

A quadrilateral has 4 sides, 4 angles and 4 vertices.

A pentagon has 5 sides, 5 angles and 5 vertices.

A hexagon has 6 sides, 6 angles and 6 vertices.

A heptagon has 7 sides, 7 angles and 7 vertices.

An octagon has 8 sides, 8 angles and 8 vertices.

EXERCISE 15

1. Which of the following are simple closed figures?

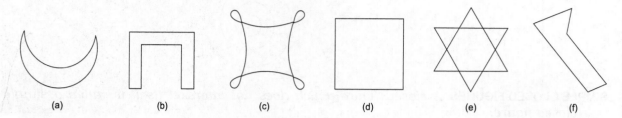

   (a)   (b)   (c)   (d)   (e)   (f)

2. Which of the following are polygons?

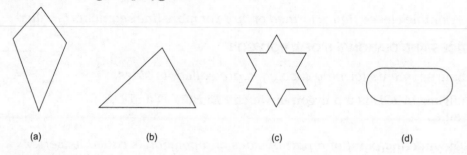

   (a)   (b)   (c)   (d)

3. Fill in the blanks:
    (i) A polygon is a simple closed figure formed by more than ...... line segments.
    (ii) A polygon formed by three line segments is called a ....
    (iii) A polygon formed by four line segments is called a ....
    (iv) A triangle has ...... sides and ...... angles.
    (v) A quadrilateral has ...... sides and ...... angles.
    (vi) A figure which ends at the starting point is called a ....

16

Triangles

Triangle Let A, B and C be three noncollinear points.

Then, *the figure formed by the three line segments AB, BC and CA is called a triangle with vertices A, B and C.*

Such a triangle is denoted by the symbol $\triangle ABC$.

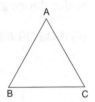

A $\triangle ABC$ has:

(i) *three sides,* namely, AB, BC and CA;

(ii) *three angles,* namely, $\angle BAC$, $\angle ABC$ and $\angle BCA$ to be denoted by $\angle A$, $\angle B$ and $\angle C$ respectively.

The three sides and three angles of a triangle are together called the *six parts* or *six elements* of the triangle.

In $\triangle ABC$, the points A, B and C are called its *vertices*.

Clearly, A is the vertex opposite to the side BC.

Similarly, B is the vertex opposite to the side CA.

And, C is the vertex opposite to the side AB.

CONGRUENT TRIANGLES *Two triangles are said to be congruent if every angle of one is equal to the corresponding angle of the other and every side of one is equal to the corresponding side of the other.*

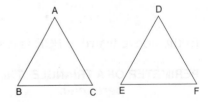

$\triangle ABC$ and $\triangle DEF$ are congruent triangles because $\angle A = \angle D$, $\angle B = \angle E$, $\angle C = \angle F$, AB = DE, BC = EF and CA = FD.

INTERIOR AND EXTERIOR OF A TRIANGLE

(i) The part of the plane enclosed by $\triangle ABC$ is called the *interior* of $\triangle ABC$.

$\triangle ABC$ *is the boundary of its interior.*

(ii) The part of the plane not enclosed by $\triangle ABC$ is called the *exterior* of $\triangle ABC$.

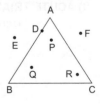

In the adjoining figure P, Q, R are the interior points of $\triangle ABC$.

E and F are the exterior points of $\triangle ABC$.

And, D lies on $\triangle ABC$.

REMARK   If P and Q are two interior points of $\triangle ABC$ then the line segment $\overline{PQ}$ lies entirely in the interior of $\triangle ABC$.

VARIOUS TYPES OF TRIANGLES

NAMING TRIANGLES BY CONSIDERING THE LENGTHS OF THEIR SIDES

(I) EQUILATERAL TRIANGLE *A triangle having all sides equal is called an equilateral triangle.*

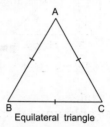
Equilateral triangle

In the figure given above, △ *ABC* is an equilateral triangle in which *AB = BC = CA*.

(II) ISOSCELES TRIANGLE *A triangle having two sides equal is called an isosceles triangle.*

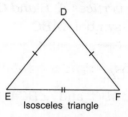
Isosceles triangle

In the above figure, △ *DEF* is an isosceles triangle in which *DE = DF*.

(III) SCALENE TRIANGLE *A triangle having three sides of different lengths is called a scalene triangle.*

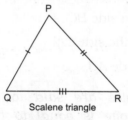
Scalene triangle

In the above figure, △ *PQR* is a scalene triangle, as *PQ ≠ PR ≠ QR*.

PERIMETER OF A TRIANGLE *The sum of the lengths of the sides of a triangle is called its perimeter.*

NAMING TRIANGLES BY CONSIDERING THEIR ANGLES

(I) ACUTE TRIANGLE *A triangle each of whose angles measures less than 90° is called an acute-angled triangle or simply an acute triangle.*

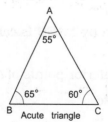
Acute triangle

In the above figure, each angle of △ *ABC* is an acute angle. So, △ *ABC* is an acute triangle.

(II) RIGHT TRIANGLE *A triangle whose one angle measures 90° is called a right-angled triangle or simply a right triangle.*

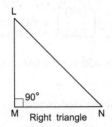

Right triangle

In the above figure, $\triangle LMN$ is a right triangle, as $\angle LMN = 90°$.

(III) OBTUSE TRIANGLE *A triangle one of whose angles measures more than 90° is called an obtuse-angled triangle or simply an obtuse triangle.*

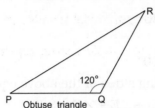

Obtuse triangle

In the above figure, $\angle PQR$ is obtuse. So, $\triangle PQR$ is an obtuse triangle.

SOME IMPORTANT RESULTS

RESULT 1. *Each angle of an equilateral triangle measures 60°.*

RESULT 2. *The angles opposite to equal sides of an isosceles triangle are equal.*

RESULT 3. *A scalene triangle has no two angles equal.*

ANGLE SUM PROPERTY OF A TRIANGLE

The sum of the angles of a triangle is 180°, or 2 right angles.

As a consequence of the above result, we can say that

  (i) a triangle cannot have more than one right angle,

 (ii) a triangle cannot have more than one obtuse angle,

(iii) in a right triangle, the sum of the two acute angles is 90°.

ILLUSTRATIVE EXAMPLES

EXAMPLE 1. *Find the angles of a triangle which are in the ratio 2 : 3 : 4.*

Solution   Let the measures of the given angles be $(2x)°, (3x)°$ and $(4x)°$.
Then, $2x + 3x + 4x = 180 \implies 9x = 180 \implies x = 20$.
Hence, the measures of the angles of the given triangle are $40°, 60°$ and $80°$.

EXAMPLE 2. *In a $\triangle ABC$, if $2\angle A = 3\angle B = 6\angle C$ then calculate $\angle A, \angle B$ and $\angle C$.*

Solution   Let $2\angle A = 3\angle B = 6\angle C = x°$.

Then, $\angle A = \left(\dfrac{x}{2}\right)°$; $\angle B = \left(\dfrac{x}{3}\right)°$ and $\angle C = \left(\dfrac{x}{6}\right)°$.

But, $\angle A + \angle B + \angle C = 180°$.

$\therefore \quad \dfrac{x}{2} + \dfrac{x}{3} + \dfrac{x}{6} = 180$

$\implies \quad 3x + 2x + x = 1080 \implies 6x = 1080 \implies x = \dfrac{1080}{6} = 180.$

$$\therefore \quad \angle A = \left(\frac{180}{2}\right)^\circ = 90^\circ; \ \angle B = \left(\frac{180}{3}\right)^\circ = 60^\circ \text{ and } \angle C = \left(\frac{180}{6}\right)^\circ = 30^\circ.$$

Hence, $\angle A = 90^\circ$, $\angle B = 60^\circ$ and $\angle C = 30^\circ$.

EXAMPLE 3. *The adjoining figure has been obtained by using two triangles.*

Prove that $\angle A + \angle B + \angle C + \angle D + \angle E + \angle F = 360^\circ$.

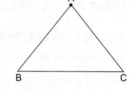

Solution   We know that the sum of the angles of a triangle is 180°.
$\therefore$ In $\triangle ACE$, we have:

$\angle A + \angle C + \angle E = 180^\circ.$

In $\triangle BDF$, we have:

$\angle B + \angle D + \angle F = 180^\circ.$

Adding the corresponding sides of the above equations, we get:

$\angle A + \angle B + \angle C + \angle D + \angle E + \angle F = 360^\circ.$

EXERCISE 16A

1. Take three noncollinear points A, B and C on a page of your notebook. Join AB, BC and CA. What figure do you get?

    Name: (i) the side opposite to $\angle C$

    (ii) the angle opposite to the side BC

    (iii) the vertex opposite to the side CA

    (iv) the side opposite to the vertex B

2. The measures of two angles of a triangle are 72° and 58°. Find the measure of the third angle.

3. The angles of a triangle are in the ratio $1 : 3 : 5$. Find the measure of each of the angles.

4. One of the acute angles of a right triangle is 50°. Find the other acute angle.

5. One of the angles of a triangle is 110° and the other two angles are equal. What is the measure of each of these equal angles?

6. If one angle of a triangle is equal to the sum of other two, show that the triangle is a right triangle.

    Hint. $\angle A = \angle B + \angle C \ \Rightarrow \ \angle A + \angle A = \angle A + \angle B + \angle C = 180^\circ.$

7. In a $\triangle ABC$, if $3\angle A = 4\angle B = 6\angle C$, calculate the angles.

8. Look at the figures given below. State for each triangle whether it is acute, right or obtuse.

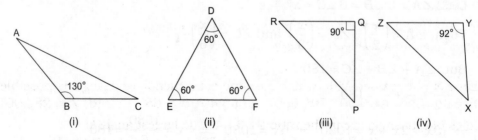

9. In the given figure some triangles have been given. State for each triangle whether it is scalene, isosceles or equilateral.

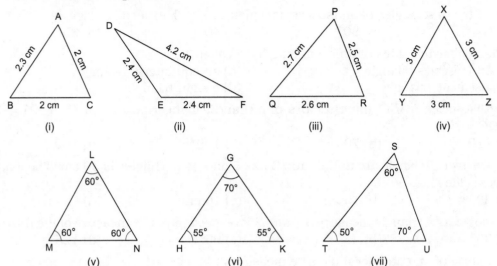

(i)   (ii)   (iii)   (iv)

(v)   (vi)   (vii)

10. Draw a △ABC. Take a point D on BC.
Join AD.
How many triangles do you get?
Name them.

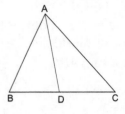

11. Can a triangle have
   (i) two right angles?
   (ii) two obtuse angles?
   (iii) two acute angles?
   (iv) each angle more than 60°?
   (v) each angle less than 60°?
   (vi) each angle equal to 60°?

12. Fill in the blanks:
   (i) A triangle has ...... sides, ... angles and ...... vertices.
   (ii) The sum of the angles of a triangle is ....
   (iii) The sides of a scalene triangle are of .... lengths.
   (iv) Each angle of an equilateral triangle measures ....
   (v) The angles opposite to equal sides of an isosceles triangle are ....
   (vi) The sum of the lengths of the sides of a triangle is called its ....

EXERCISE 16B

OBJECTIVE QUESTIONS

Mark (✓) against the correct answer in each of the following:

1. How many parts does a triangle have?
   (a) 2   (b) 3   (c) 6   (d) 9

2. With the angles given below, in which case the construction of triangle is possible?
   (a) 30°, 60°, 70°   (b) 50°, 70°, 60°   (c) 40°, 80°, 65°   (d) 72°, 28°, 90°

3. The angles of a triangle are in the ratio 2 : 3 : 4. The largest angle is
   (a) 60°   (b) 80°   (c) 76°   (d) 84°

4. The two angles of a triangle are complementary. The third angle is

    (a) 60°   (b) 45°   (c) 36°   (d) 90°

5. One of the base angles of an isosceles triangle is 70°. The vertical angle is

    (a) 60°   (b) 80°   (c) 40°   (d) 35°

6. A triangle having sides of different lengths is called

    (a) an isosceles triangle   (b) an equilateral triangle

    (c) a scalene triangle   (d) a right triangle

7. In an isosceles $\triangle ABC$, the bisectors of $\angle B$ and $\angle C$ meet at a point O. If $\angle A = 40°$, then $\angle BOC = ?$

    (a) 110°   (b) 70°   (c) 130°   (d) 150°

8. The sides of a triangle are in the ratio 3 : 2 : 5 and its perimeter is 30 cm. The length of the longest side is

    (a) 20 cm   (b) 15 cm   (c) 10 cm   (d) 12 cm

9. Two angles of a triangle measure 30° and 25° respectively. The measure of the third angle is

    (a) 35°   (b) 45°   (c) 65°   (d) 125°

10. Each angle of an equilateral triangle measures

    (a) 30°   (b) 45°   (c) 60°   (d) 80°

11. In the adjoining figure, the point P lies

    (a) in the interior of $\triangle ABC$

    (b) in the exterior of $\triangle ABC$

    (c) on $\triangle ABC$

    (d) outside $\triangle ABC$

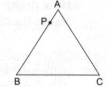

Things to Remember

1. *If A, B, C are three noncollinear points, the figure made up by three line segments AB, BC and CA is called a triangle with vertices A, B, C.*

2. *The three line segments forming a triangle are called the sides of the triangle.*

3. *The three sides and the three angles of a triangle are together called the six parts or elements of the triangle.*

4. *Two triangles are said to be congruent if every angle of one is equal to the corresponding angle of the other and every side of one is equal to the corresponding side of the other.*

5. *A triangle is said to be*
    (i) *an equilateral triangle if all of its sides are equal;*
    (ii) *an isosceles triangle if two of its sides are equal;*
    (iii) *a scalene triangle if its three sides are of different lengths.*

6. *A triangle is said to be*
    (i) *an acute triangle if each one of its angles measures less than 90°;*
    (ii) *a right triangle if one of its angles measures 90°;*
    (iii) *an obtuse triangle if one of its angles measures more than 90°.*

7. *The sum of the angles of a triangle is 180°.*

17 | Quadrilaterals

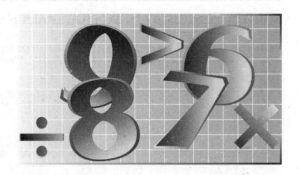

QUADRILATERAL *A simple closed figure bounded by four line segments is called a quadrilateral.*

In the adjacent figure, *ABCD* is a quadrilateral.

A quadrilateral *ABCD* has:

 (i) *Four vertices*, namely, *A, B, C* and *D*.
 (ii) *Four sides*, namely, *AB, BC, CD* and *DA*.
 (iii) *Four angles*, namely, ∠*DAB*, ∠*ABC*, ∠*BCD* and ∠*CDA*, to be denoted by ∠*A*, ∠*B*, ∠*C* and ∠*D* respectively.
 (iv) *Two diagonals*, namely, *AC* and *BD*.

ADJACENT SIDES *Two sides of a quadrilateral which have a common end point are called its adjacent sides.*

Thus, *AB, BC; BC, CD; CD, DA*, and *DA, AB* are four pairs of adjacent sides of the quadrilateral *ABCD*.

OPPOSITE SIDES *Two sides of a quadrilateral are called its opposite sides if they do not have a common end point.*

Thus, *AB, DC*, and *AD, BC* are two pairs of opposite sides of the quadrilateral *ABCD*.

ADJACENT ANGLES *Two angles of a quadrilateral having a common side are called its adjacent angles.*

Thus, ∠*A*, ∠*B*; *B*, ∠*C*; ∠*C*, ∠*D*; and ∠*D*, ∠*A* are four pairs of adjacent angles of the quadrilateral *ABCD*.

OPPOSITE ANGLES *Two angles of a quadrilateral which are not adjacent angles are known as the opposite angles of the quadrilateral.*

Thus, ∠*A*, ∠*C*, and ∠*B*, ∠*D* are two pairs of opposite angles of the quadrilateral *ABCD*.

REMARK   The figure given below is also a figure obtained by joining four line segments *AB, BC, CD* and *DA*. But *ABCD* is not a quadrilateral, since these line segments intersect at points other than their end points.

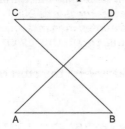

CONVEX AND CONCAVE QUADRILATERALS

CONVEX QUADRILATERAL *A quadrilateral in which the measure of each angle is less than 180° is called a convex quadrilateral.*

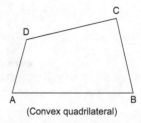

(Convex quadrilateral)

CONCAVE QUADRILATERAL *A quadrilateral in which the measure of one of the angles is more than 180° is called a concave quadrilateral.*

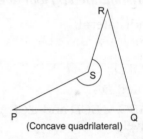

(Concave quadrilateral)

In the above figure, *PQRS* is a concave quadrilateral in which $\angle S > 180°$.

In this chapter, by a quadrilateral we would mean a convex quadrilateral.

INTERIOR AND EXTERIOR OF A QUADRILATERAL

Consider a quadrilateral *ABCD*. It divides the whole plane into three parts.

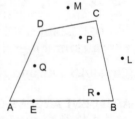

(i) The part of the plane lying inside the boundary *ABCD* is called the *interior* of the quadrilateral *ABCD*. Each point of this part is called an *interior point* of the quadrilateral. In the given figure, the points *P, Q, R* are the interior points of the quadrilateral *ABCD*.

(ii) The part of the plane lying outside the boundary *ABCD* is called the *exterior* of the quadrilateral *ABCD*. Each point of this part is called an *exterior point* of the quadrilateral.

In the given figure, the points *L* and *M* are the exterior points of the quadrilateral *ABCD*.

(iii) The boundary *ABCD*.

Clearly, the point *E* lies on the quadrilateral *ABCD*.

QUADRILATERAL REGION *The interior of the quadrilateral ABCD together with its boundary is called the quadrilateral region ABCD.*

ANGLE SUM PROPERTY OF A QUADRILATERAL *The sum of the angles of a quadrilateral is 360°.*

EXAMPLE. *The angles of a quadrilateral are in the ratio 1 : 2 : 3 : 4. Find the measure of each of the four angles.*

Solution   Let the measure of the angles of the given quadrilateral be $x°, (2x)°, (3x)°$ and $(4x)°$. Then,

$x + 2x + 3x + 4x = 360$ [∵ the sum of the angles of a quadrilateral is 360°]

$\Rightarrow 10x = 360 \Rightarrow x = 36.$

Hence, the required angles are 36°, 72°, 108° and 144°.

VARIOUS TYPES OF QUADRILATERALS

1. TRAPEZIUM *A quadrilateral having one and only one pair of parallel sides is called a trapezium.*

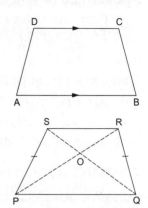

In the adjacent figure, *ABCD* is a trapezium in which *AB* || *DC*.

A trapezium is said to be an isosceles trapezium if its nonparallel sides are equal.

In the adjoining figure, *PQRS* is an isosceles trapezium in which *PQ* || *SR* and *PS* = *QR*.

REMARK   The diagonals of an isosceles trapezium are always equal.

2. PARALLELOGRAM *A quadrilateral in which both pairs of opposite sides are parallel is called a parallelogram.*

In the given figure, *ABCD* is a parallelogram in which *AB* || *DC* and *AD* || *BC*. We denote it by ||gm *ABCD*.

PROPERTIES OF A PARALLELOGRAM

(i)   *The opposite sides of a ||gm are equal and parallel.*

(ii) *The opposite angles of a ||gm are equal.*

(iii) *The diagonals of a ||gm bisect each other.*

Thus, in a ||gm *ABCD*, we have:

(i)   *AB* = *DC*, *AD* = *BC* and *AB* || *DC*, *AD* || *BC*.

(ii) ∠*BAD* = ∠*BCD* and ∠*ABC* = ∠*ADC*.

(iii) If the diagonals *AC* and *BD* intersect at *O*, then *OA* = *OC* and *OB* = *OD*.

3. RHOMBUS *A parallelogram in which all the sides are equal is called a rhombus.*

In the given figure, *ABCD* is a rhombus in which *AB* || *DC*, *AD* || *BC* and *AB* = *BC* = *CD* = *DA*.

PROPERTIES OF A RHOMBUS

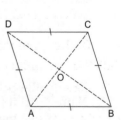

(i)   *The opposite sides of a rhombus are parallel.*

(ii) *All the sides of a rhombus are equal.*

(iii) *The opposite angles of a rhombus are equal.*

(iv) *The diagonals of a rhombus bisect each other at right angles.*

Thus, in a rhombus *ABCD*, we have:

(i)   *AB* || *DC* and *AD* || *BC*.

(ii) *AB* = *BC* = *CD* = *DA*.

(iii) ∠*DAB* = ∠*BCD* and ∠*ABC* = ∠*CDA*.

(iv) Let the diagonals *AC* and *BD* intersect at *O*. Then, *OA* = *OC*, *OB* = *OD* and ∠*AOB* = ∠*COD* = ∠*BOC* = ∠*AOD* = 1 right angle.

4. RECTANGLE *A parallelogram in which each angle is a right angle is called a rectangle.*

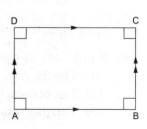

In the given figure, *ABCD* is a rectangle in which *AB* || *DC*, *AD* || *BC* and ∠*A* = ∠*B* = ∠*C* = ∠*D* = 90°.

PROPERTIES OF A RECTANGLE

(i) *Opposite sides of a rectangle are equal and parallel.*

(ii) *Each angle of a rectangle is 90°.*

(iii) *Diagonals of a rectangle are equal.*

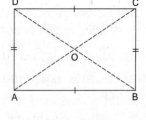

Thus, in a rectangle *ABCD*, we have:

(i) $AB = DC$, $AD = BC$ and $AB \parallel DC$, $AD \parallel BC$.

(ii) $\angle A = \angle B = \angle C = \angle D = 1$ right angle.

(iii) Diagonal AC = diagonal BD.

5. SQUARE *A parallelogram in which all the sides are equal and each angle is a right angle, is called a square.*

In the given figure, *ABCD* is a square in which $AB = BC = CD = DA$ and $\angle A = \angle B = \angle C = \angle D = 90°$.

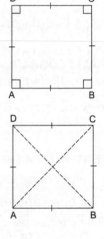

PROPERTIES OF A SQUARE

(i) *The sides of a square are all equal.*

(ii) *Each angle of a square is 90°.*

(iii) *The diagonals of a square are equal and bisect each other at right angles.*

Thus, in a square *ABCD*, we have:

(i) $AB = BC = CD = DA$.

(ii) $\angle A = \angle B = \angle C = \angle D = 90°$.

(iii) Diagonal AC = diagonal BD.

6. KITE *A quadrilateral which has two pairs of equal adjacent sides but unequal opposite sides, is called a kite.*

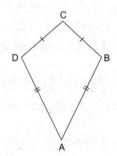

In the given figure *ABCD* is a kite in which $CB = CD$ and $AB = AD$ but $AD \neq BC$ and $AB \neq CD$.

EXERCISE 17A

1. In the adjacent figure, a quadrilateral has been shown. Name: (i) its diagonals,
   (ii) two pairs of opposite sides,
   (iii) two pairs of opposite angles,
   (iv) two pairs of adjacent sides,
   (v) two pairs of adjacent angles.

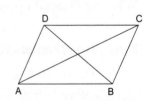

2. Draw a parallelogram *ABCD* in which $AB = 6.5$ cm, $AD = 4.8$ cm and $\angle BAD = 70°$. Measure its diagonals.

3. Two sides of a parallelogram are in the ratio 4 : 3. If its perimeter is 56 cm, find the lengths of its sides.

4. Name each of the following parallelograms:
   (i) The diagonals are equal and the adjacent sides are unequal.
   (ii) The diagonals are equal and the adjacent sides are equal.
   (iii) The diagonals are unequal and the adjacent sides are equal.

5. What is a trapezium? When do you call a trapezium an isosceles trapezium? Draw an isosceles trapezium. Measure its sides and angles.

6. Which of the following statements are true and which are false?
   (a) The diagonals of a parallelogram are equal.
   (b) The diagonals of a rectangle are perpendicular to each other.
   (c) The diagonals of a rhombus are equal.

7. Give reasons for the following:
   (a) A square can be thought of as a special rectangle.
   (b) A square can be thought of as a special rhombus.
   (c) A rectangle can be thought of as a special parallelogram.
   (d) A square is also a parallelogram.

8. A figure is said to be regular if its sides are equal in length and angles are equal in measure. What do you mean by a regular quadrilateral?

EXERCISE 17B

OBJECTIVE QUESTIONS

Mark (✓) against the correct answer in each of the following:

1. The sum of all the angles of a quadrilateral is
   (a) 180°   (b) 270°   (c) 360°   (d) 400°

2. The three angles of a quadrilateral are 80°, 70° and 120°. The fourth angle is
   (a) 110°   (b) 100°   (c) 90°   (d) 80°

3. The angles of a quadrilateral are in the ratio 3 : 4 : 5 : 6. The largest of these angles is
   (a) 90°   (b) 120°   (c) 150°   (d) 102°

4. A quadrilateral having one and only one pair of parallel sides is called
   (a) a parallelogram   (b) a kite   (c) a rhombus   (d) a trapezium

5. A quadrilateral whose opposite sides are parallel is called
   (a) a rhombus   (b) a kite   (c) a trapezium   (d) a parallelogram

6. An isosceles trapezium has
   (a) equal parallel sides   (b) equal nonparallel sides
   (c) equal opposite sides   (d) none of these

7. If the diagonals of a quadrilateral bisect each other at right angles, then this quadrilateral is
   (a) a rectangle   (b) a rhombus   (c) a kite   (d) none of these

8. A square has
   (a) all sides equal and diagonals unequal   (b) all sides equal and diagonals equal
   (c) all sides unequal and diagonals equal   (d) none of these

9. A quadrilateral having two pairs of equal adjacent sides but unequal opposite sides, is called a
   (a) trapezium   (b) parallelogram   (c) kite   (d) rectangle

10. What do you mean by a regular quadrilateral?
    (a) A rectangle   (b) A rhombus   (c) A square   (d) A trapezium

Things to Remember

1. (i) *A quadrilateral which has exactly one pair of parallel sides is called a trapezium.*
   (ii) *A quadrilateral in which both pairs of opposite sides are parallel is called a parallelogram.*
   (iii) *A parallelogram in which all the sides are equal is called a rhombus.*
   (iv) *A parallelogram in which each angle is a right angle is called a rectangle.*
   (v) *A parallelogram in which all the sides are equal and each angle is equal to a right angle is called a square.*
   (vi) *A quadrilateral which has two pairs of equal adjacent sides but unequal opposite sides is called a kite.*
2. *A quadrilateral is a parallelogram if*
   (i) *its opposite sides are equal, or*
   (ii) *its opposite angles are equal, or*
   (iii) *its diagonals bisect each other, or*
   (iv) *it has one pair of opposite sides equal and parallel.*
3. *The diagonals of a rhombus bisect each other at right angles.*
4. *The diagonals of a rectangle are equal.*
5. *The diagonals of a square are equal and bisect each other at right angles.*

18 | Circles

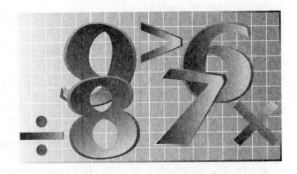

We see around us a large number of objects which are circular in shape. The wheel, the rupee coin, the 50-paisa coin, the 25-paisa coin, the full moon, etc., are all examples of circular objects.

Here, we shall learn about figures bounded by circles.

CIRCLE *A circle is the collection of all those points in a plane whose distance from a fixed point remains constant.*

The fixed point is called the *centre* of the circle, and the constant distance is known as the *radius* of the circle.

Let O be the centre of a circle of radius r, and let P be a point on the circle. Then, the line segment OP is the radius of the circle. If Q is another point on the circle then the line segment OQ is also a radius of the circle.

Clearly, $OP = OQ = r$.

In general, *all the radii of a circle are equal.*

INTERIOR AND EXTERIOR OF A CIRCLE Let us consider a circle with centre O and radius r. The circle divides the plane containing it into three parts:

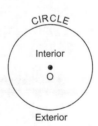

  (i) The part of the plane, consisting of those points P for which $OP < r$, is called the *interior of the circle*.

  (ii) The part of the plane, consisting of those points P for which $OP = r$, is the *circle itself*.

  (iii) The part of the plane, consisting of those points P for which $OP > r$ is called the *exterior of the circle*.

Clearly, the circle is the *boundary* of its interior.

The part of the plane consisting of the circle and its interior is called the *circular region*.

DIAMETER OF A CIRCLE *A line segment passing through the centre of a circle and having its end points on the circle is called a diameter of the circle.*

Clearly, *diameter* = 2 × (*radius*).

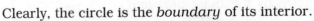

An infinite number of diameters of a circle can be drawn. Clearly, all the diameters of a circle are concurrent. The centre is their point of concurrence.

CHORD OF A CIRCLE *A line segment with its end points lying on a circle is called a chord of the circle.*

In the given figure, AB is a chord of the circle with centre O.

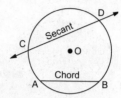

Clearly, the diameter of a circle is its largest chord.

SECANT OF A CIRCLE *A line passing through a circle and intersecting the circle at two points is called a secant of the circle.*

In above figure, CD is a secant of the circle with centre O.

CIRCUMFERENCE OF A CIRCLE *The perimeter of a circle is called its circumference.* In other words, the length of the boundary of the interior of a circle is its circumference.

SEGMENTS OF A CIRCLE A chord *AB* of a circle divides the circular region into two parts. Each part is called a *segment* of the circle.

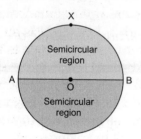

The segment containing the centre of the circle is called the *major segment*, while the segment not containing the centre is called the *minor segment* of the circle.

SEMICIRCLE *The end points of a diameter of a circle divide the circle into two equal parts; each part is called a semicircle.*

A diameter of a circle divides the circular region into two equal parts; each part is called a semicircular region.

In the figure given below, both the shaded regions are semicircular regions.

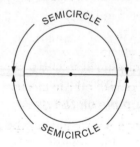

ARC *Any part of a circle is called an arc of the circle.*

In the given figure, the arc *ACB* has been shown by the thick part and denoted by $\overparen{ACB}$. If the arc of a circle is greater than a semicircle, it is called a *major arc*. On the other hand, if the arc of a circle is less than a semicircle, it is called a *minor arc*.

Thus, in the given figure, arc *ACB* is the minor arc and arc *ADB* is the major arc.

SECTOR OF A CIRCLE *The area bounded by an arc and the two radii joining the end points of the arc with the centre is called a sector.*

If the sector is formed by a major arc, it is called a *major sector*. If the sector is formed by a minor arc, it is called a *minor sector*. In the figure given below, *OACB* is a minor sector while *OADB* is the major sector.

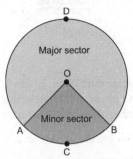

CONCENTRIC CIRCLES *Two or more circles with the same centre are called concentric circles.*

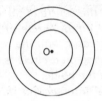

EXERCISE 18

1. Take a point *O* on your notebook and draw circles of radii 4 cm, 5.3 cm and 6.2 cm, each having the same centre *O*.

2. Draw a circle with centre *C* and radius 4.5 cm. Mark points *P*, *Q*, *R* such that *P* lies in the interior of the circle, *Q* lies on the circle, and *R* lies in the exterior of the circle.

3. Draw a circle with centre *O* and radius 4 cm. Draw a chord *AB* of the circle. Indicate by marking points *X* and *Y*, the minor arc *AXB* and the major arc *AYB* of the circle.

4. Which of the following statements are true and which are false?
   (i) Each radius of a circle is also a chord of the circle.
   (ii) Each diameter of a circle is also a chord of the circle.
   (iii) The centre of a circle bisects each chord of the circle.
   (iv) A secant of a circle is a segment having its end points on the circle.
   (v) A chord of a circle is a segment having its end points on the circle.

5. Draw a circle with centre *O* and radius 3.7 cm. Draw a sector having the angle 72°.

6. Fill in the blanks by using <, >, = or ≤.
   (i) *OP* ...... *OQ*, where *O* is the centre of the circle, *P* lies on the circle and *Q* is in the interior of the circle.
   (ii) *OP* ...... *OR*, where *O* is the centre of the circle, *P* lies on the circle and *R* lies in the exterior of the circle.
   (iii) Major arc ...... minor arc of the circle.
   (iv) Major arc ...... semicircumference of the circle.

7. Fill in the blanks:
   (i) A diameter of a circle is a chord that .... the centre.
   (ii) A radius of a circle is a line segment with one end point .... and the other end point ....
   (iii) If we join any two points of a circle by a line segment, we obtain a .... of the circle.
   (iv) Any part of a circle is called an .... of the circle.

(v) The figure bounded by an arc and the two radii joining the end points of the arc with the centre is called a .... of the circle.

═══

Things to Remember

1. *Let there be a plane and O be a point on it. Then, a 'circle' with centre O and radius r cm is the figure consisting of all those points of the plane which are at a distance of r cm from O.*
2. *A line segment with one end point at the centre of a circle and the other on the circle is called a 'radius' of the circle.*
3. *All radii of a circle are equal.*
4. *A line segment passing through the centre of a circle and having its end points on the circle is called a 'diameter' of the circle.*
5. *Diameter* $= 2 \times$ *(radius).*
6. *All the diameters of a circle meet at the centre of the circle.*
7. *A point lies in the 'interior of a circle', on the 'circle' or in the 'exterior of a circle', if its distance from the centre is less than, equal to or greater than the radius of the circle, respectively.*
8. *A line segment with its end points lying on a circle is called a 'chord' of the circle.*
9. *The diameter is the longest chord of the circle.*
10. *A line passing through a circle and intersecting the circle at two points is called a 'secant' of the circle.*
11. *The interior of a circle together with the circle itself is called the 'circular region'.*
12. *The end points of the diameter of a circle divide the circle into two equal parts; each part is called a semicircle.*
13. *A diameter of a circle divides the circular region into two equal parts; each part is called a 'semicircular region'.*
14. *The perimeter of a circle is called its 'circumference'.*
15. *Any part of a circle is called an 'arc' of the circle.*
16. *A chord of a circle divides the circular region into two parts; each part is called a 'segment'.*
17. *The segment containing the centre of the circle is called the major segment, and the other part is called the minor segment of the circle.*

CCE TEST PAPER-18

A. **1.** Define each of the following:

      (a) Closed figures   (b) Open figures   (c) Polygons

   2. Define each of the following:

      (a) A scalene triangle   (b) An isosceles triangle   (c) An obtuse triangle

   3.   (i) What do you mean by a convex quadrilateral?

      (ii) Define a regular polygon.

   4. The angles of a triangle are in the ratio 3 : 5 : 7. Find the measures of these angles.

   5. The angles of a quadrilateral are in the ratio 2 : 3 : 4 : 6. Find the measures of these angles.

   6. State the properties of a rhombus.

   7. Define (i) a trapezium (ii) a kite.

   8. Draw a circle with centre O and radius 3 cm. Draw a sector having an angle of $54°$.

B. *Mark (✓) against the correct answer in each of the following:*

   9. A quadrilateral having two pairs of equal adjacent sides but unequal opposite sides is called a

      (a) parallelogram (b) rectangle   (c) trapezium   (d) kite

  10. If the diagonals of a quadrilateral bisect each other at right angles, then this quadrilateral is a

      (a) rectangle   (b) parallelogram   (c) rhombus   (d) kite

  11. A quadrilateral having one and only one pair of parallel sides is called a

      (a) parallelogram (b) a kite   (c) a trapezium   (d) a rhombus

  12. One of the base angles of an isosceles triangle is $70°$. The vertical angle is

      (a) $35°$ (b) $40°$ (c) $70°$ (d) $80°$

C. **13.** *Write 'T' for true and 'F' for false for each of the statements given below:*

      (i) The diagonals of a rhombus are equal.

      (ii) The diagonals of a parallelogram bisect each other.

     (iii) The centre of a circle bisects each chord of a circle.

     (iv) Each diameter of a circle is a chord of the circle.

      (v) The diagonals of a rhombus bisect each other at right angles.

Three-Dimensional Shapes

CUBOID, CUBE, CYLINDER, SPHERE, CONE, PRISM AND PYRAMID

IDEA OF SPACE When we look at something empty, like a box, room or bowl, it has space. We can keep things in that space. A park has space for us to play.

SOLID *An object that has a fixed shape and size is called a solid.*

A solid occupies a fixed amount of space.

Solids occur in different shapes.

*These shapes are known as **three-dimensional shapes.***

The various types of these shapes are shown below.

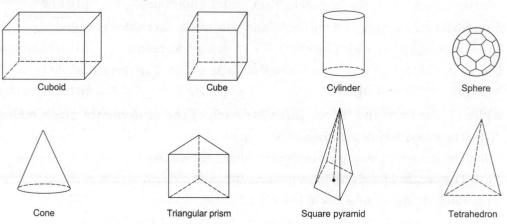

| Cuboid | Cube | Cylinder | Sphere |

| Cone | Triangular prism | Square pyramid | Tetrahedron |

CUBOID

CUBOID Solids such as *a wooden box, a matchbox, a brick, a book, an almirah,* etc., are all in the shape of a cuboid.

Some of these shapes are given below.

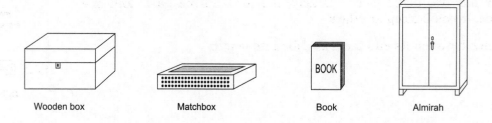

| Wooden box | Matchbox | Book | Almirah |

A cuboid has length, breadth and height.

Various parts of a cuboid are given below:

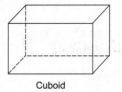
Cuboid

(i) FACES *A cuboid has six rectangular faces.*

The opposite faces of a cuboid are identical.

(ii) EDGES *Two adjacent faces of a cuboid meet in a line segment, called an edge of the cuboid. A cuboid has 12 edges.*

(iii) VERTICES *Three edges of a cuboid meet at a point, called a vertex. A cuboid has 8 vertices.*

Thus, *a cuboid has 6 rectangular faces, 12 edges and 8 vertices.*

CUBE

CUBE *A cuboid whose length, breadth and height are equal is called a cube.*

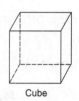
Cube

EXAMPLES Ice cubes, sugar cubes, dice, etc., are all examples of a cube.

Clearly, *a cube has 6 square faces, 12 edges and 8 vertices.*

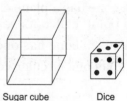
Sugar cube   Dice

CYLINDER

CYLINDER Objects such as *a circular pillar, a circular pipe, a test tube, a circular storage tank, a measuring jar, a gas cylinder, a circular powder tin,* etc., are in the shape of a cylinder.

Some of these shapes are shown below.

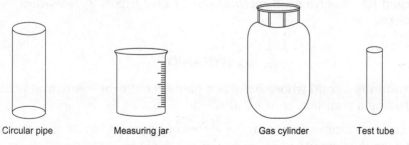
Circular pipe   Measuring jar   Gas cylinder   Test tube

A cylinder has a curved lateral surface and two circular faces at its ends.

A cylinder has no corner or vertex.

A cylinder has two plane faces, namely, the top and the base, and one curved face. It has 2 circular edges.

The distance between its end faces is called its length.

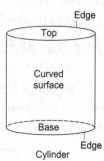
Cylinder

SPHERE

SPHERE An object which is in the shape of a ball is said
to have the shape of a sphere.

A sphere has *a curved surface.*

A sphere has no vertex and no edge.

CONE

CONE Objects such as an *ice-cream cone, a conical tent, a conical vessel, a clown's cap,* etc.,
are in the shape of a cone.

Some examples of cones are given below.

Ice-cream   Clown's cap   A conical tent
cone

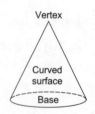

A cone has a plane circular end as the *base* and a *curved surface* tapering into
a point, called its *vertex.*

Thus, a cone has one plane face (i.e. base) and one curved face.

It has one circular edge and one vertex.

TRIANGULAR PRISM

TRIANGULAR PRISM *A solid whose lateral faces are rectangular and the bases are congruent
triangles, is called a triangular prism.*

The adjoining figure shows a triangular prism, denoted by (*ABC, PQR*).

A triangular prism has 6 *vertices*, 3 *rectangular lateral faces*, 2 *triangular
bases* and 9 *edges*.

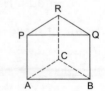

PYRAMID

PYRAMID A pyramid is a solid whose *base* is a plane rectilinear figure and whose side faces are
triangles having a common vertex, called the *vertex* of the pyramid.

The length of perpendicular drawn from the vertex of a pyramid to its base is called the *height* of
the pyramid.

The side faces of a pyramid are called its *lateral faces.*

(i) SQUARE PYRAMID *A solid whose base is a square and whose side faces
are triangles having a common vertex is called a square pyramid.*

The adjacent figure shows a square pyramid *OABCD* with *O* as *vertex*, the
square *ABCD* as its *base* and *OP* as its *height.*

A square pyramid has 4 *lateral triangular faces* and 8 *edges*.

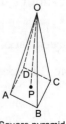

Square pyramid

(ii) TRIANGULAR PYRAMID *A solid whose base is a triangle and whose side faces are triangles having a common vertex is called a triangular pyramid.*

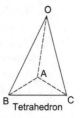

The adjacent figure shows a triangular pyramid *OABC* with *O* as vertex and △*ABC* as its base.

A triangular pyramid has 3 triangular lateral faces, one triangular base and 6 edges.

A triangular pyramid is also called a **tetrahedron.**

EXERCISE 19

Mark (✓) against the correct answer in each of Q.1 to Q.6.

1. A cuboid has
   (a) length only
   (b) length and breadth only
   (c) length, breadth and height
   (d) thickness only

2. A dice is an example of a
   (a) cuboid   (b) cube
   (c) cone   (d) cylinder

3. A gas pipe is an example of a
   (a) cuboid   (b) cube
   (c) cone   (d) cylinder

4. A football is an example of a
   (a) cylinder   (b) cone
   (c) sphere   (d) none of these

5. A brick is an example of a
   (a) cube   (b) cuboid
   (c) prism   (d) cylinder

6. An ice-cream cone is an example of a
   (a) cuboid   (b) cube
   (c) pyramid   (d) none of these

7. Fill in the blanks:
   (i) An object that occupies space is called a ....
   (ii) A cuboid has ...... faces, ... edges and ...... vertices.
   (iii) The ...... faces of a cuboid are identical.
   (iv) A ...... has no vertex and no edge.
   (v) All the faces of a ...... are identical.
   (vi) A square pyramid has ...... lateral triangular faces and ...... edges.
   (vii) A triangular pyramid has ...... triangular lateral faces and ...... edges.
   (viii) A triangular prism has ...... vertices, ... rectangular lateral faces, ... triangular bases and ...... edges.

8. Give examples of four objects which are in the shape of:
   (a) a cone   (b) a cuboid   (c) a cylinder

═══

Things to Remember

1. *An object that occupies space is called a solid.*
2. *Shapes of solids are known as three-dimensional shapes.*
3. *A matchbox, a chalk box, a brick are all examples of a cuboid.*
4. *A cuboid has length, breadth and height.*
5. *A cuboid has 6 rectangular faces, 12 edges and 8 vertices.*

6. *A cuboid in which length, breadth and height are equal is called a cube.*
7. *Ice cubes, sugar cubes, dice, etc., are examples of a cube.*
8. *Objects such as a circular pillar, a circular pipe, a measuring jar, a gas cylinder, a test tube, etc., are examples of a cylinder.*
9. *A cylinder has a curved lateral surface and two circular faces as its ends.*
10. *The distance between the two end faces is called the length of the cylinder.*
11. *Objects in the shape of a ball are known as spheres.*
12. *A sphere has a curved surface only. It has no vertex and no edge.*
13. *Objects such as ice-cream cone, a conical tent and a conical vessel are in the shape of a cone.*
14. *A cone has a circular base, a curved surface and a vertex.*
15. *A solid with rectangular lateral faces and congruent triangles as bases is called a triangular prism.*
16. *A triangular prism has 6 vertices, 3 rectangular faces, 2 triangular bases and 9 edges.*
17. *A square pyramid is a solid whose base is square and whose lateral faces are triangles having a common vertex.*
18. *A square pyramid has 4 lateral triangular faces and 8 edges.*
19. *A triangular pyramid is a solid whose base is a triangle and whose lateral faces are triangles having a common vertex.*
20. *A triangular pyramid has 3 triangular lateral faces, one triangular base and 6 edges.*

20

Two-Dimensional Reflection Symmetry (Linear Symmetry)

LINEAR SYMMETRY *A figure is said to be symmetrical about a line l, if it is identical on either side of l.*

And, *l* is known as the *line of symmetry* or *axis of symmetry*.

Look at the design given herewith. If we fold it along the line *AB*, we shall find that the designs on two sides of *AB* exactly coincide with each other.

We say that the given figure is symmetrical about the line *AB*.

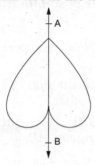

EXAMPLES OF LINEAR SYMMETRY

EXAMPLE 1. *A line segment is symmetrical about its perpendicular bisector.*

Method   Let *AB* be a given line segment and let *POQ* be the perpendicular bisector of *AB*.

Hence, the line segment *AB* is symmetrical about its perpendicular bisector *POQ*.

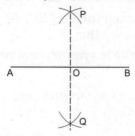

EXAMPLE 2. *A given angle having equal arms is symmetrical about the bisector of the angle.*

Method   Let ∠*AOB* be a given angle with equal arms *OA* and *OB*, and let *OC* be the bisector of ∠*AOB*.

Then, clearly ∠*AOC* and ∠*BOC* are identical.

Hence, ∠*AOB* is symmetrical about the bisector *OC*.

EXAMPLE 3.   *An isosceles triangle is symmetrical about the bisector of the angle included between the equal sides.*

Method   Let $\triangle ABC$ be an isosceles triangle in which $AB = AC$ and let AD be the bisector of $\angle BAC$.

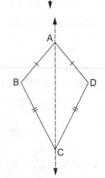

If $\triangle ABC$ be folded along AD then $\triangle ADC$ coincides exactly with $\triangle ADB$.

Thus, $\triangle ADC$ is identical with $\triangle ADB$.

Hence, AD is the line of symmetry of $\triangle ABC$.

EXAMPLE 4.   *A kite has one line of symmetry, namely, the diagonal shown dotted in the adjoining figure.*

Method   Here $ABCD$ is a kite in which $AB = AD$ and $BC = DC$.

If we fold the kite along the line AC, we find that the two parts coincide with each other.

Hence, the kite $ABCD$ is symmetrical about the diagonal AC.

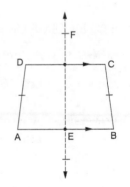

EXAMPLE 5.   *A semicircle ACB has one line of symmetry, namely, the perpendicular bisector of the diameter AB.*

Method   Here ACB is a semicircle and PQ is the perpendicular bisector of diameter AB.

If we fold the semicircle along the line PQ, we find that the two parts of it coincide with each other.

Hence, the semicircle ACB is symmetrical about the perpendicular bisector of diameter AB.

EXAMPLE 6.   *An isosceles trapezium has one line of symmetry, namely, the line joining the midpoints of the bases of the trapezium.*

Method   Let $ABCD$ be an isosceles trapezium in which $AB \parallel DC$ and $AD = BC$.

Let E and F be the midpoints of AB and DC respectively.

If we fold the trapezium along the line EF, we find that the two parts of it coincide with each other.

Hence, the trapezium $ABCD$ is symmetrical about the line EF.

EXAMPLE 7.   *A rectangle has two lines of symmetry, each one of which being the line joining the midpoints of opposite sides.*

Method   Let $ABCD$ be a given rectangle, and let P and Q be the midpoints of AB and DC respectively.

Now, if we fold the rectangle along PQ, we find that the two parts of it coincide with each other.

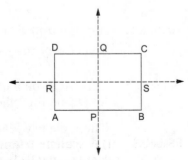

Hence, rectangle $ABCD$ is symmetrical about the line PQ.

Similarly, if R and S be the midpoints of AD and BC respectively then rectangle $ABCD$ is symmetrical about the line RS.

EXAMPLE 8. *A rhombus is symmetrical about each one of its diagonals.*

Method   Let *ABCD* be a rhombus. Now, if we fold it along the
diagonal *AC*, we find that the two parts coincide
with each other.

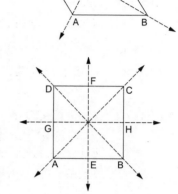

Hence, the rhombus *ABCD* is symmetrical about its
diagonal *AC*.

Similarly, the rhombus *ABCD* is symmetrical about
its diagonal *BD*.

EXAMPLE 9. *A square has four lines of symmetry, namely, the
diagonals and the lines joining the midpoints of
its opposite sides.*

Method   Let *ABCD* be the given square and *E*, *F*, *G*, *H* be the
midpoints of *AB*, *DC*, *AD* and *BC* respectively.

Then, it is easy to see that it is symmetrical about
each of the lines *AC*, *BD*, *EF* and *GH*.

EXAMPLE 10. *An equilateral triangle is symmetrical about each one of the bisectors of its
interior angles.*

Method   Let △*ABC* be an equilateral triangle and let *AD*, *BE* and *CF* be the bisectors of ∠*A*, ∠*B*
and ∠*C* respectively.

Then, it is easy to see that △*ABC* is symmetrical about each of the lines *AD*, *BE*
and *CF*.

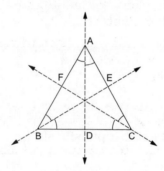

EXAMPLE 11. *A circle is symmetrical about each of its diameters. Thus, each diameter of a
circle is an axis of symmetry.*

Method   Here, a number of diameters of a circle have been drawn. It is easy to see that the
circle is symmetrical about each of the diameters drawn. Hence, a circle has an
infinite number of lines of symmetry.

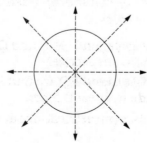

REMARKS   (i) A scalene triangle has no line of symmetry.
            (ii) A parallelogram has no line of symmetry.

EXAMPLE 12.   *Each of the following capital letters of the English alphabet is symmetrical about the dotted line or lines as shown.*

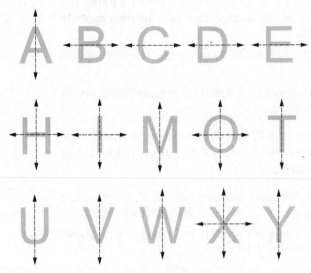

EXERCISE 20

Mark (✓) against the correct answer in each of Q.1 to Q.8.

1. A square has
   (a) one line of symmetry
   (b) two lines of symmetry
   (c) three lines of symmetry
   (d) four lines of symmetry

2. A rectangle is symmetrical about
   (a) each one of its sides
   (b) each one of its diagonals
   (c) a line joining the midpoints of its opposite sides
   (d) none of these

3. A rhombus is symmetrical about
   (a) the line joining the midpoints of its opposite sides
   (b) each of its diagonals
   (c) perpendicular bisector of each of its sides
   (d) none of these

4. A circle has
   (a) no line of symmetry
   (b) one line of symmetry
   (c) two lines of symmetry
   (d) an unlimited number of lines of symmetry

5. A scalene triangle has
   (a) no line of symmetry
   (b) one line of symmetry
   (c) two lines of symmetry
   (d) three lines of symmetry

6. *ABCD* is a kite in which *AB* = *AD* and *BC* = *DC*.
   The kite is symmetrical about
   (a) the diagonal *AC*   (b) the diagonal *BD*   (c) none of these

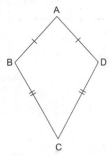

7. The letter O of the English alphabet has
   (a) no line of symmetry   (b) one line of symmetry
   (c) two lines of symmetry   (d) none of these

8. The letter Z of the English alphabet has
   (a) no line of symmetry   (b) one line of symmetry
   (c) two lines of symmetry   (d) none of these

9. Draw the line (or lines) of symmetry of each of the following figures.

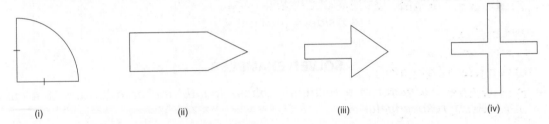

   (i)   (ii)   (iii)   (iv)

10. Which of the following statements are true and which are false?
    (i) A parallelogram has no line of symmetry.
    (ii) An angle with equal arms has its bisector as the line of symmetry.
    (iiii) An equilateral triangle has three lines of symmetry.
    (iv) A rhombus has four lines of symmetry.
    (v) A square has four lines of symmetry.
    (vi) A rectangle has two lines of symmetry.
    (vii) Each one of the letters H, I, O, X of the English alphabet has two lines of symmetry.

21 | Concept of Perimeter and Area

PERIMETER OF A PLANE FIGURE *The sum of the lengths of all sides of a plane figure, or the length of its boundary, is called the perimeter of the figure.*

PERIMETER OF A RECTANGLE *Perimeter of a rectangle*

$$= 2(length + breadth)$$
$$= 2(l + b) \text{ units.}$$

PERIMETER OF A SQUARE *Perimeter of a square*

$$= (4 \times side) = (4a) \text{ units.}$$

SOLVED EXAMPLES

EXAMPLE 1. *Find the perimeter of a rectangle whose length and breadth are 15.4 cm and 11.6 cm respectively.*

Solution   Length of the rectangle = 15.4 cm.

Breadth of the rectangle = 11.6 cm.

Perimeter of the rectangle = $2(l + b)$ units

$$= 2(15.4 + 11.6) \text{ cm} = (2 \times 27) \text{ cm} = 54 \text{ cm.}$$

Hence, the perimeter of the rectangle is 54 cm.

EXAMPLE 2. *Find the cost of fencing a rectangular field 260 m long and 175 m wide at ₹ 40 per metre.*

Solution   Length of the field = 260 m.

Breadth of the field = 175 m.

Perimeter of the field = $2(l + b)$ units

$$= 2(260 + 175) \text{ m} = (2 \times 435) \text{ m} = 870 \text{ m.}$$

Cost of fencing per metre = ₹ 40.

Total cost of fencing = ₹ (870×40) = ₹ 34800.

EXAMPLE 3. *The length and the breadth of a rectangular field are 240 m and 180 m respectively. It is fenced with three rounds of a rope. Find the length of the rope.*

Solution   Length of the field = 240 m and its breadth = 180 m.

Perimeter of the field = $2 \times$ (length + breadth) units

$$= \{2 \times (240 + 180)\} \text{ m} = (2 \times 420) \text{ m} = 840 \text{ m.}$$

Total length of rope = (3×840) m = 2520 m.

EXAMPLE 4. *The length and the breadth of a rectangle are in the ratio 3 : 2. If its perimeter is 1 m 40 cm, find its dimensions.*

Solution Let the length of the rectangle be $3x$ cm.

Then, its breadth = $2x$ cm.

∴ perimeter of the rectangle = {2 × (length + breadth)} units

$$= \{2 \times (3x + 2x)\} \text{ cm} = (2 \times 5x) \text{ cm} = (10x) \text{ cm}.$$

But, perimeter of the rectangle = 1 m 40 cm = 140 cm (given).

∴ $10x = 140 \Rightarrow x = \dfrac{140}{10} \Rightarrow x = 14.$

∴ length = (3×14) cm = 42 cm and breadth = (2×14) cm = 28 cm.

EXAMPLE 5. *The cost of fencing a rectangular field at ₹ 24 per metre is ₹ 1920. If its length is 23 m, find its breadth.*

Solution Total cost of fencing = ₹ 1920.

Rate of fencing = ₹ 24 per metre.

Perimeter of the field = $\left(\dfrac{\text{total cost}}{\text{rate}}\right) = \dfrac{₹\ 1920}{₹\ 24/m}$

$$= \left(\dfrac{1920}{24}\right) \text{m} = 80 \text{ m}.$$

Let the breadth of the field be x metres.

Then, perimeter of the field = $[2 \times (23 + x)]$ m.

∴ $2(23 + x) = 80 \Rightarrow (23 + x) = 40$

$$\Rightarrow x = (40 - 23) = 17.$$

Hence, the breadth of the field is 17 m.

EXAMPLE 6. *Find the perimeter of a square, each of whose sides measures 3.6 cm.*

Solution Each side of the square = 3.6 cm.

Perimeter of the square = $(4 \times \text{side})$

$$= (4 \times 3.6) \text{ cm} = 14.4 \text{ cm}.$$

EXAMPLE 7. *The cost of fencing a square field at ₹ 125 per metre is ₹ 8000. Find the length of each side of the field.*

Solution Total cost of fencing = ₹ 8000.

Rate of fencing = ₹ 125 per metre.

Length of boundary of the field = $\left(\dfrac{\text{total cost}}{\text{rate}}\right) = \dfrac{₹\ 8000}{₹\ 125/m}$

$$= \left(\dfrac{8000}{125}\right) \text{m} = 64 \text{ m}.$$

Let the length of each side of the field be x metres.

Then, its perimeter = $(4x)$ metres.

∴ $4x = 64 \Rightarrow x = \dfrac{64}{4} = 16.$

Hence, the length of each side of the field is 16 m.

EXAMPLE 8. *Find the perimeter of an equilateral triangle with each side measuring* 5.8 cm.

Solution   Length of each side of the triangle = 5.8 cm.

∴   perimeter of the triangle = (3 × 5.8) cm = 17.4 cm.

EXAMPLE 9. *Find the perimeter of a regular hexagon having each side equal to* 6.5 cm.

Solution   Length of each side of the given hexagon = 6.5 cm.

∴   perimeter of the hexagon = (6 × 6.5) cm = 39 cm.

EXERCISE 21A

1. Find the perimeter of a rectangle in which:
    (i) length = 16.8 cm and breadth = 6.2 cm
    (ii) length = 2 m 25 cm and breadth = 1 m 50 cm
    (iii) length = 8 m 5 dm and breadth = 6 m 8 dm

2. Find the cost of fencing a rectangular field 62 m long and 33 m wide at ₹ 16 per metre.

3. The length and the breadth of a rectangular field are in the ratio 5 : 3. If its perimeter is 128 m, find the dimensions of the field.

4. The cost of fencing a rectangular field at ₹ 18 per metre is ₹ 1980. If the width of the field is 23 m, find its length.

5. The length and the breadth of a rectangular field are in the ratio 7 : 4. The cost of fencing the field at ₹ 25 per metre is ₹ 3300. Find the dimensions of the field.

6. Find the perimeter of a square, each of whose sides measures:
    (i) 3.8 cm   (ii) 4.6 m   (iii) 2 m 5 dm

7. The cost of putting a fence around a square field at ₹ 35 per metre is ₹ 4480. Find the length of each side of the field.

8. Each side of a square field measures 21 m. Adjacent to this field, there is a rectangular field having its sides in the ratio 4 : 3. If the perimeters of both the fields are equal, find the dimensions of the rectangular field.

9. Find the perimeter of
    (i) a triangle of sides 7.8 cm, 6.5 cm and 5.9 cm,
    (ii) an equilateral triangle of side 9.4 cm,
    (iii) an isosceles triangle with equal sides 8.5 cm each and third side 7 cm.

10. Find the perimeter of
    (i) a regular pentagon of side 8 cm,
    (ii) a regular octagon of side 4.5 cm,
    (iii) a regular decagon of side 3.6 cm.

11. Find the perimeter of each of the following figures:

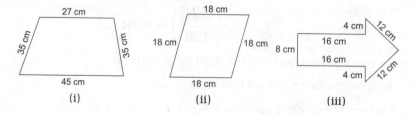

(i)   (ii)   (iii)

CIRCUMFERENCE OF A CIRCLE

CIRCUMFERENCE OF A CIRCLE *The perimeter of a circle is called its circumference.*

The length of the thread that winds around the circle exactly once gives the circumference of the circle.

AN IMPORTANT RESULT *The ratio of the circumference of a circle and its diameter is always constant.*

This result can be verified with the help of the experiment given below.

EXPERIMENT Draw any three circles of different radii.

   Measure the diameter of each one of them.

   With the help of a tape or a thread, measure the circumference of each of them.

   Record them as given below.

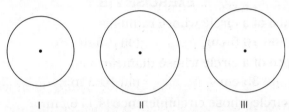

Circle	Radius (r)	Diameter $(2r)$	Circumference (C)	$\dfrac{\text{Circumference}}{\text{Diameter}} \left(\dfrac{C}{2r}\right)$
I				
II				
III				

You will find in each case that:

$$\frac{\text{Circumference}}{\text{Diameter}} = 3.14 \text{ (nearly)}.$$

This ratio is denoted by π (called pi).

$$\frac{\text{Circumference}}{\text{Diameter}} = \pi \;\Rightarrow\; \frac{C}{2r} = \pi \;\Rightarrow\; \boldsymbol{C = 2\pi r}.$$

Hence, **circumference = 2πr units,** *where r is the radius of the circle.*

REMARK Unless stated, we take $\pi = \dfrac{22}{7}$.

EXAMPLE 1. *Find the circumference of a circle of radius* 14 cm.

Solution The radius of the given circle is $r = 14$ cm.
    ∴ circumference of the circle is given by

$$C = 2\pi r = \left(2 \times \frac{22}{7} \times 14\right) \text{cm} = 88 \text{ cm}.$$

    Hence, the circumference of the given circle is 88 cm.

EXAMPLE 2. *Find the diameter of a circle whose circumference is* 66 cm.

Solution Let the radius of the given circle be r cm.
    Then, its circumference = $2\pi r$ cm.

$$\therefore \quad 2\pi r = 66 \;\Rightarrow\; r = \frac{66}{2\pi}$$

$$\Rightarrow r = \left(\frac{66}{2} \times \frac{7}{22}\right) \text{cm} = \frac{21}{2} \text{ cm} = 10.5 \text{ cm}.$$

    Hence, the diameter of the circle is (2×10.5) cm = 21 cm.

EXAMPLE 3. *The diameter of a wheel of a car is* 70 *cm. Find the distance covered by the car during the time in which the wheel makes* 1000 *revolutions.*

Solution   Radius of the wheel = $\dfrac{70}{2}$ cm = 35 cm.

Circumference of the wheel = $2\pi r$

$$= \left(2 \times \frac{22}{7} \times 35\right) \text{cm} = 220 \text{ cm} = 2.20 \text{ m}.$$

In 1 revolution, the wheel covers a distance equal to its circumference.

∴   distance covered by the wheel in 1 revolution = 2.20 m.

∴   distance covered by the wheel in 1000 revolutions

$$= (2.20 \times 1000) \text{ m} = 2200 \text{ m} = 2.2 \text{ km}.$$

EXERCISE 21B

1. Find the circumference of a circle whose radius is
   (i) 28 cm   (ii) 10.5 cm   (iii) 3.5 m

2. Find the circumference of a circle whose diameter is
   (i) 14 cm   (ii) 35 cm   (iii) 10.5 m

3. Find the radius of a circle whose circumference is 176 cm.

4. Find the diameter of a wheel whose circumference is 264 cm.

5. Find the distance covered by the wheel of a car in 500 revolutions if the diameter of the wheel is 77 cm.

6. The diameter of the wheel of a car is 70 cm. How many revolutions will it make to travel 1.65 km?

AREA

AREA *The measurement of the region enclosed by a plane figure is called the area of the figure.*

STANDARD UNIT OF AREA *We say that the area of a square of side* 1 *cm is* 1 square centimetre, *written as* 1 cm^2. *The standard unit of area is* cm^2.

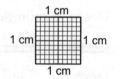

NOTE   *If a figure contains n squares, each of side* 1 *cm, we say that the area of the figure is n* cm^2.

EXAMPLE 1.   Consider the following regions:

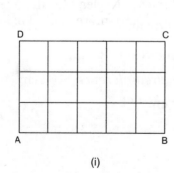

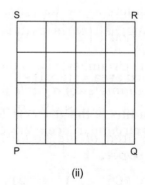

(i)   (ii)

In figure (i) *ABCD* is a rectangle containing $5 \times 3 = 15$ squares, each having an area of 1 cm^2.

∴   area of rectangle *ABCD* = $15 \times 1 \text{ cm}^2 = 15 \text{ cm}^2$.

In figure (ii) $PQRS$ is a square containing $4 \times 4 = 16$ squares, each having an area of $1\ \mathrm{cm}^2$.

$\therefore$ area of square $PQRS = 16 \times 1\ \mathrm{cm}^2 = 16\ \mathrm{cm}^2$.

TO FIND AREA USING SQUARED PAPER

Suppose we have to find the area of a given figure.

We take a trace copy of the figure on a transparent paper and place it on a sheet of squared paper.

Let the given figure enclose m complete squares, n more-than-half squares and p exactly half squares.

Then, **area of the figure** $= \left(m + n + \dfrac{1}{2}p \right) \mathbf{cm}^2.$

NOTE   We consider a more-than-half square as a complete square and neglect each less-than-half square.

SOLVED EXAMPLES

EXAMPLE 1.   *The following figures are drawn on squared paper. Count the number of squares enclosed by each figure and find its area, taking the area of each square as* $1\ \mathrm{cm}^2$.

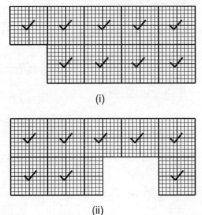

(i)

(ii)

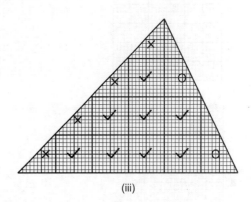

(iii)

Solution   Figure (i) contains 9 complete squares, so its area is 9 sq cm.

Figure (ii) contains 8 complete squares and 1 half part of a square.

So, its area $= \left[(8 \times 1) + \left(1 \times \dfrac{1}{2} \right) \right]$ sq cm $= 8\dfrac{1}{2}$ sq cm.

Figure (iii) contains 8 complete squares, 2 more-than-half parts, 4 half parts and some less-than-half parts of a square. Neglecting the less-than-half parts, considering half parts as half squares and more than half parts as complete squares, we have:

$$\text{required area} = \left[(8 \times 1) + (2 \times 1) + \left(4 \times \dfrac{1}{2} \right) \right] \text{sq cm}$$

$$= (8 + 2 + 2)\ \text{sq cm} = 12\ \text{sq cm}.$$

EXAMPLE 2.   *Find the area of the figure given, using a sheet of squared paper.*

Solution   Make a trace copy of the given figure on a transparent paper and put it on a sheet of squared paper, as shown in the figure given along side.

We find that the given figure contains 2 complete squares and 5 more-than-half parts of squares and some less-than-half parts.

Neglecting the less-than-half parts and considering each more-than-half part as a complete square, we find that the area of the given figure is 7 cm^2.

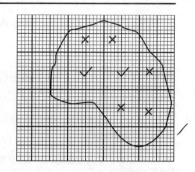

EXERCISE 21C

The following figures are drawn on a sheet of squared paper. Count the number of squares enclosed by each figure and find its area, taking the area of each square as 1 cm^2.

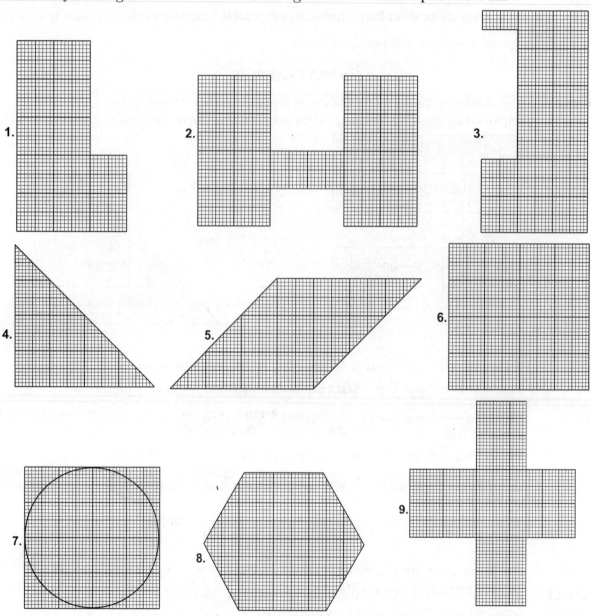

Hint. 5. *This figure contains 9 complete squares and 6 half squares.*

7. *It contains 4 complete squares and 8 more-than-half sqaures.*

AREA OF A RECTANGLE AND A SQUARE

EXPERIMENT Draw a rectangle *ABCD* of length 5 cm and breadth 3 cm on a sheet of graph paper, as shown in the given figure.

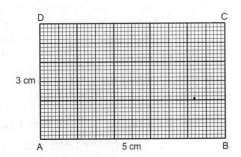

Count the number of squares of area 1 cm^2 each, contained in this rectangle.

Clearly, it contains (5×3) such squares.

∴ area of the rectangle *ABCD*

$= (5 \times 3)$ cm$^2 = 15$ cm^2.

Repeat the experiment with a rectangle of length 6 cm and breadth 5 cm.

You will find that its area $= (6 \times 5)$ cm$^2 = 30$ cm^2.

Thus, **area of a rectangle = (length × breadth) sq units.**

Similarly, **area of a square = (side)^2 sq units.**

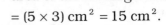

SUMMARY

I. For a rectangle, we have:

(i) *Area = (length × breadth) sq units*

(ii) *Length* $= \left(\dfrac{area}{breadth} \right)$ *units*

(iii) *Breadth* $= \left(\dfrac{area}{length} \right)$ *units*

(iv) *Perimeter* $= 2 \times$ *(length + breadth) units*

II. For a square, we have:

(i) *Area = (side)^2 sq units* $= \left\{ \dfrac{1}{2} \times (diagonal)^2 \right\}$ *sq units*

(ii) *Perimeter* $= (4 \times$ *side) units*

REMARKS In calculating the area of a rectangle, we must express the length and breadth in the same unit.

SOLVED EXAMPLES

EXAMPLE 1. *Find the area of a rectangle whose length and breadth are 45 cm and 18 cm respectively. Also, find the perimeter of the rectangle.*

Solution Here, length = 45 cm and breadth = 18 cm.

Area of the rectangle = (length × breadth) sq units

$= (45 \times 18)$ cm$^2 = 810$ cm^2.

Perimeter of the rectangle = [2 × (length + breadth)] units

$= [2 \times (45 + 18)]$ cm $= (2 \times 63)$ cm $= 126$ cm.

EXAMPLE 2. *Find the area and perimeter of a rectangular plot of land whose length and breadth are 28.5 m and 20 m respectively.*

Solution Here, length = 28.5 m and breadth = 20 m.

∴ area of the plot = (length × breadth) sq units

$= (28.5 \times 20)$ m$^2 = \left(\dfrac{285}{10} \times 20 \right)$ m$^2 = 570$ m^2.

Perimeter of the plot = [2 × (length + breadth] units

$$= [2 \times (28.5 + 20)]\, m$$

$$= [2 \times 48.5]\, m = \left(2 \times \frac{485}{10}\right) m = 97\ m.$$

EXAMPLE 3. *Find the cost of cultivating a rectangular field 80 m long and 35 m wide at ₹ 15 per square metre. Also, find the cost of fencing the field at ₹ 24 per metre.*

Solution   Length = 80 m and breadth = 35 m.

Area of the field = (length × breadth) sq units

$$= (80 \times 35)\, m^2 = 2800\ m^2.$$

Rate of cultivation = ₹ 15 per m^2.

∴   cost of cultivation = ₹ (2800 × 15) = ₹ 42000.

Perimeter of the field = [2 × (length + breadth)] units

$$= [2 \times (80 + 35)]\, m = (2 \times 115)\, m = 230\ m.$$

Rate of fencing = ₹ 24 per metre.

∴   cost of fencing = ₹ (230 × 24) = ₹ 5520.

EXAMPLE 4. *The area of a rectangle is 630 cm^2 and its length is 35 cm. Find the perimeter of the rectangle.*

Solution   Area = 630 cm^2 and length = 35 cm.

$$\text{Breadth of the rectangle} = \frac{\text{area in } cm^2}{\text{length in cm}} = \frac{630\ cm^2}{35\ cm}$$

$$= \left(\frac{630}{35}\right) cm = 18\ cm.$$

Perimeter of the rectangle = [2 × (length + breadth)] units

$$= [2 \times (35 + 18)]\, cm = (2 \times 53)\, cm = 106\ cm$$

$$= 1\ m\ 6\ cm.$$

EXAMPLE 5. *A room is 20 m long and 18 m broad. Find the cost of carpeting the room with a carpet of width 1.5 m at the rate of ₹ 60 per metre.*

Solution   Length of the room = 20 m and its breadth = 18 m.

Area of the floor of the room = $(20 \times 18)\, m^2 = 360\ m^2$.

Area of the carpet required = 360 m^2.

Width of the carpet = 1.5 m.

$$\text{Length of the carpet} = \frac{\text{area of the carpet}}{\text{width of the carpet}} = \frac{360\ m^2}{1.5\ m}$$

$$= \left(\frac{360}{1.5}\right) m = \left(360 \times \frac{2}{3}\right) m = 240\ m.$$

Rate of carpeting = ₹ 60 per metre.

Cost of carpeting = ₹ (240 × 60) = ₹ 14400.

EXAMPLE 6. *The total cost of flooring a room at ₹ 85/m^2 is ₹ 5100. If the length of the room is 8 metres, find its breadth.*

Solution   Total cost of flooring = ₹ 5100.

Rate of flooring = ₹ 85/m^2.

$$\text{Area of the floor} = \frac{\text{total cost of flooring}}{\text{rate of flooring}} = \frac{₹\,5100}{₹\,85/m^2}$$

$$= \left(\frac{5100}{85}\right)m^2 = 60\ m^2.$$

Length of the floor = 8 m.

$$\therefore\quad \text{breadth of the floor} = \frac{\text{area}}{\text{length}} = \frac{60\ m^2}{8\ m}$$

$$= \left(\frac{60}{8}\right)m = 7.5\ m.$$

Hence, the breadth of the floor is 7.5 m.

EXAMPLE 7. *A room is 8 m long and 6 m wide. Its floor is to be covered with rectangular tiles of size 25 cm by 20 cm. How many tiles will be required? Find the cost of these tiles at ₹ 25 per tile.*

Solution   Here, length of the room = 8 m and its width = 6 m.

$$\therefore\quad \text{area of the floor} = (8 \times 6)\ m^2 = 48\ m^2.$$

$$\text{Area of each tile} = \left(\frac{25}{100} \times \frac{20}{100}\right)m^2 = \frac{1}{20}\ m^2.$$

$$\therefore\quad \text{number of tiles required} = \frac{\text{area of the floor}}{\text{area of each tile}}$$

$$= \left(48 \div \frac{1}{20}\right) = (48 \times 20) = 960.$$

Cost of tiles = ₹ (960 × 25) = ₹ 24000.

EXAMPLE 8. *How many square tiles each of side 0.5 m will be required to pave the floor of a room which is 4 m long and 3 m broad?*

Solution   Length of the room = 4 m and its breadth = 3 m.

Area of the floor of the room = $(4 \times 3)\ m^2 = 12\ m^2.$

Each side of the square tile = 0.5 m = $\frac{1}{2}$ m.

Area of each square tile = $\left(\frac{1}{2} \times \frac{1}{2}\right)m^2 = \frac{1}{4}\ m^2.$

Required number of tiles = $\left(12 \div \frac{1}{4}\right) = \left(12 \times \frac{4}{1}\right) = 48.$

Hence, 48 tiles are required to pave the floor of the room.

EXERCISE 21D

1. Find the area of a rectangle whose
    (i) length = 46 cm and breadth = 25 cm
    (ii) length = 9 m and breadth = 6 m
    (iii) length = 14.5 m and breadth = 6.8 m
    (iv) length = 2 m 5 cm and breadth = 60 cm
    (v) length = 3.5 km and breadth = 2 km

2. Find the area of a square plot of side 14 m.

3. The top of a table measures 2 m 25 cm by 1 m 20 cm. Find its area in square metres.

4. A carpet is 30 m 75 cm long and 80 cm wide. Find its cost at ₹ 150 per square metre.

5. How many envelopes can be made out of a sheet of paper 3 m 24 cm by 1 m 72 cm, if each envelope requires a piece of paper of size 18 cm by 12 cm?

6. A room is 12.5 m long and 8 m wide. A square carpet of side 8 m is laid on its floor. Find the area of the floor which is not carpeted.

7. A lane, 150 m long and 9 m wide, is to be paved with bricks, each measuring 22.5 cm by 7.5 cm. Find the number of bricks required.

8. A room is 13 m long and 9 m broad. Find the cost of carpeting the room with a carpet 75 cm broad at the rate of ₹ 65 per metre.

9. The length and the breadth of a rectangular park are in the ratio 5 : 3 and its perimeter is 128 m. Find the area of the park.

10. Two plots of land have the same perimeter. One is a square of side 64 m and the other is a rectangle of length 70 m. Find the breadth of the rectangular plot. Which plot has the greater area and by how much?

11. The cost of cultivating a rectangular field at ₹ 35 per square metre is ₹ 71400. If the width of the field is 40 m, find its length. Also, find the cost of fencing the field at ₹ 50 per metre.

12. The area of a rectangle is 540 cm^2 and its length is 36 cm. Find its width and perimeter.

13. A marble tile measures 12 cm × 10 cm. How many tiles will be required to cover a wall of size 4 m by 3 m? Also, find the total cost of the tiles at ₹ 22.50 per tile.

14. Find the perimeter of a rectangle whose area is 600 cm^2 and breadth is 25 cm.

15. Find the area of a square whose diagonal is $5\sqrt{2}$ cm.

   Hint. *Area* $= \left[\dfrac{1}{2} \times (diagonal)^2\right]$ *sq units.*

16. Calculate the area of each one of the shaded regions given below:

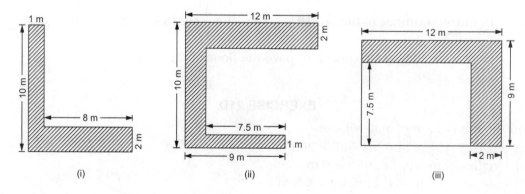

(i)   (ii)   (iii)

17. Calculate the area of each one of the shaded regions given below (all measures are given in cm):

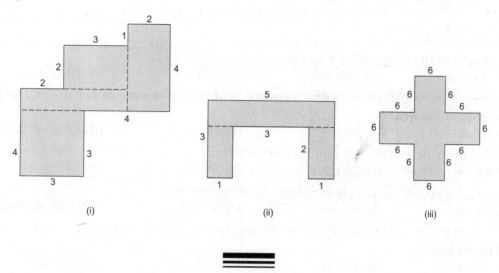

(i)   (ii)   (iii)

EXERCISE 21E

OBJECTIVE QUESTIONS

Mark (✓) against the correct answer in each of the following:

1. The sides of a rectangle are in the ratio 7 : 5 and its perimeter is 96 cm. The length of the rectangle is
   (a) 21 cm   (b) 28 cm   (c) 35 cm   (d) 14 cm

2. The area of a rectangle is 650 cm^2 and its breadth is 13 cm. The perimeter of the rectangle is
   (a) 63 cm   (b) 130 cm   (c) 100 cm   (d) 126 cm

3. The cost of fencing a rectangular field 34 m long and 18 m wide at ₹ 22.50 per metre is
   (a) ₹ 2430   (b) ₹ 2340   (c) ₹ 2400   (d) ₹ 3340

4. The cost of fencing a rectangular field at ₹ 30 per metre is ₹ 2400. If the length of the field is 24 m, then its breadth is
   (a) 8 m   (b) 16 m   (c) 18 m   (d) 24 m

5. The area of a rectangular carpet is 120 m^2 and its perimeter is 46 m. The length of its diagonal is
   (a) 15 m   (b) 16 m   (c) 17 m   (d) 20 m

   Hint. $l + b = 23$ and $lb = 120$.
   $(l^2 + b^2) = (l + b)^2 - 2lb = (23)^2 - 2 \times 120 = 289.$
   $Diagonal = \sqrt{l^2 + b^2} = \sqrt{289} = \sqrt{17 \times 17} = 17.$

6. The length of a rectangle is three times its width and the length of its diagonal is $6\sqrt{10}$ cm. The perimeter of the rectangle is
   (a) 48 cm   (b) 36 cm   (c) 24 cm   (d) $24\sqrt{10}$ cm

7. If the ratio between the length and perimeter of a rectangular plot is 1 : 3, then the ratio between the length and breadth of the plot is
   (a) 1 : 2   (b) 2 : 1   (c) 3 : 2   (d) 2 : 3

Hint. *Let the length be x cm. Then, its perimeter is 3x cm.*

$$\therefore \ 2(x+b) = 3x \ \Rightarrow \ 2b = (3x-2x) = x \ \Rightarrow \ b = \frac{x}{2}.$$

$$\therefore \ l:b = x:\frac{x}{2} = 2x:x = 2:1.$$

8. The length of the diagonal of a square is 20 cm. Its area is
   (a) 400 cm^2 (b) 200 cm^2 (c) 300 cm^2 (d) $100\sqrt{2} \text{ cm}^2$

9. The cost of putting a fence around a square field at ₹ 25 per metre is ₹ 2000. The length of each side of the field is
   (a) 80 m   (b) 40 m   (c) 20 m   (d) none of these

10. The diameter of a circle is 7 cm. Its circumference is
    (a) 44 cm   (b) 22 cm   (c) 28 cm   (d) 14 cm

11. The circumference of a circle is 88 cm. Its diameter is
    (a) 28 cm   (b) 42 cm   (c) 56 cm   (d) none of these

12. The diameter of a wheel of a car is 70 cm. How much distance will it cover in making 50 revolutions?
    (a) 350 m   (b) 110 m   (c) 165 m   (d) 220 m

13. A lane 150 m long and 9 m wide is to be paved with bricks, each measuring 22.5 cm by 7.5 cm. How many bricks are required?
    (a) 65000   (b) 70000   (c) 75000   (d) 80000

14. A room is 5 m 40 cm long and 4 m 50 cm broad. Its area is
    (a) 23.4 m^2 (b) 24.3 m^2 (c) 25 m^2 (d) 98.01 m^2

15. How many envelopes can be made out of a sheet of paper 72 cm by 48 cm, if each envelope requires a paper of size 18 cm by 12 cm?
    (a) 4   (b) 8   (c) 12   (d) 16

Things to Remember

I. Perimeter:

1. *The sum of the lengths of all sides of a plane figure, or the length of its boundary, is called the perimeter of the figure.*

2. *Perimeter of a rectangle = 2(l + b) units, where l is its length and b is its breadth.*

3. *Perimeter of a square = (4a) units, where a is one of its four sides.*

4. *Perimeter of a circle is called its circumference. If the radius of a circle is r, then its perimeter (circumference) = 2πr units.*

II. Area:

1. *The measurement of the region enclosed by a plane figure is called the area of the figure.*

2. *Area of a rectangle = (length × breadth) sq units.*

3. *Area of a square = (side)^2 sq units = $\left\{\frac{1}{2} \times (diagonal)^2\right\}$ sq units.*

CCE TEST PAPER-21

A. 1. Find the perimeter of the following shapes:

    (i) a triangle whose sides are 5.4 cm, 4.6 cm and 6.8 cm

    (ii) a regular hexagon of side 8 cm

    (iii) an isosceles triangle with equal sides 6 cm each and third side 4.5 cm.

2. The perimeter of a rectangular field is 360 m and its breadth is 75 m. Find its length.

3. The length and breadth of a rectangular field are in the ratio 5 : 4. If its perimeter is 108 m, find the dimensions of the field.

4. Find the area of a square whose perimeter is 84 cm.

5. The area of a room is 216 m^2 and its breadth is 12 m. Find the length of the room.

6. Find the circumference of a circle of radius 7 cm. [Take $\pi = \dfrac{22}{7}$]

7. The diameter of a wheel of a car is 77 cm. Find the distance covered by the wheel in 500 revolutions.

8. Find the diameter of a wheel whose circumference is 176 cm.

9. Find the area of a rectangle whose length is 36 cm and breadth 15 cm.

B. *Mark (✓) against the correct answer in each of the following:*

10. Perimeter of a square of side 16 cm is

    (a) 256 cm   (b) 64 cm   (c) 32 cm   (d) 48 cm

11. The area of a rectangle is 240 m^2 and its length is 16 m. Then, its breadth is

    (a) 15 m   (b) 16 m   (c) 30 m   (d) 40 m

12. The area of a square lawn of side 15 m is

    (a) 60 m^2 (b) 225 m^2 (c) 45 m^2 (d) 120 m^2

13. The area of a square is 256 cm^2. The perimeter of the square is

    (a) 16 cm   (b) 32 cm   (c) 48 cm   (d) 64 cm

14. The area of a rectangle is 126 m^2 and its length is 12 m. The breadth of the rectangle is

    (a) 10 m   (b) 10.5 m   (c) 11 m   (d) 11.5 m

C. 15. *Fill in the blanks.*

    (i) A polygon having all sides equal and all angles equal is called a ...... polygon.

    (ii) Perimeter of a square = ... × side.

    (iii) Area of a rectangle = (......) × (......).

    (iv) Area of a square = ...

    (v) If the length of a rectangle is 5 m and its breadth is 4 m, then its area is ....

D. 16. *Match the following:*

    (a) Area of a rectangle   (i) πr^2

    (b) Area of a square   (ii) $4 \times$ side

    (c) Perimeter of a rectangle   (iii) $l \times b$

    (d) Perimeter of a square   (iv) $(\text{side})^2$

    (e) Area of a circle   (v) $2(l + b)$

22

Data Handling

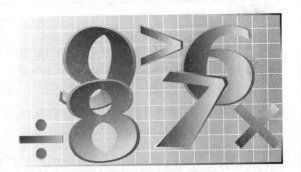

DATA *The word data means information in the form of numerical figures.*

EXAMPLE 1. *The marks obtained by 10 pupils of a class in a monthly test are given below:*
37, 21, 43, 16, 25, 21, 28, 32, 45, 14.
We call it the data related to the marks obtained by 10 pupils of a class in a monthly test.

EXAMPLE 2. *The ages (in years) of 12 teachers in a school are:*
35, 43, 38, 45, 32, 54, 39, 43, 39, 54, 24, 31.
We call it the data related to the ages of 12 teachers in a school.

RAW DATA *Data obtained in the original form is called raw data.*

Data given in the above examples are raw data.

ARRAY *Arranging the numerical figures in an ascending or a descending order is called an array.*

TABULATION OF DATA *Arranging the data in a systematic form in the form of a table is called tabulation or presentation of the data.*

OBSERVATIONS *Each numerical figure in a data is called an observation.*

FREQUENCY OF AN OBSERVATION *The number of times a particular observation occurs is called its frequency.*

STATISTICS *It is the science which deals with the collection, presentation, analysis and interpretation of numerical data.*

ILLUSTRATIVE EXAMPLES

EXAMPLE 1. *Given below is the data showing the number of children in 20 families of a colony:*
2, 1, 3, 1, 2, 1, 1, 3, 2, 3, 2, 3, 2, 2, 4, 3, 1, 4, 3, 2.
Arrange the above data in an ascending order and then put it in the tabular form.

Solution Arranging the data in an ascending order, we get the given data as

1, 1, 1, 1, 1, 2, 2, 2, 2, 2, 2, 2, 3, 3, 3, 3, 3, 3, 4, 4.

For counting purposes, we use tally marks. After putting 4 tally marks vertically, we put a cross as shown below and again we take the tally marks in the same manner, counting in sets of fives.

Now, we may prepare the frequency table, as shown below.

Observation	Tally marks	No. of families (Frequency)
1	卌	5
2	卌 II	7
3	卌 I	6
4	II	2

EXAMPLE 2. *A dice was thrown* 30 *times and the following outcomes were noted:*
4, 3, 3, 2, 5, 4, 4, 6, 1, 2, 2, 3, 4, 6, 2, 3, 3, 4, 1, 2, 3, 3, 4, 5, 6, 3, 2, 1, 3, 4.
Represent the above data in the form of frequency distribution.

Solution We may present the data, as shown below:

Outcome	Tally marks	No. of outcomes
1	III	3
2	卌 I	6
3	卌 IIII	9
4	卌 II	7
5	II	2
6	III	3

EXERCISE 22

1. Define the terms:
   (i) Data   (ii) Raw data   (iii) Array
   (iv) Tabulation of data   (v) Observations
   (vi) Frequency of an observation   (vii) Statistics

2. The number of children in 25 families of a colony are given below:
   2, 0, 2, 4, 2, 1, 3, 3, 1, 0, 2, 3, 4, 3, 1, 1, 1, 2, 2, 3, 2, 4, 1, 2, 2.
   Represent the above data in the form of a frequency distribution table.

3. The sale of shoes of various sizes at a shop on a particular day is given below:
   6, 9, 8, 5, 5, 4, 9, 8, 5, 6, 9, 9, 7, 8, 9, 7, 6, 9, 8, 6, 7, 5, 8, 9, 4, 5, 8, 7.
   Represent the above data in the form of a frequency distribution table.

4. Construct a frequency table for the following:
   3, 2, 5, 4, 1, 3, 2, 2, 5, 3, 1, 2, 1, 1, 2, 2, 3, 4, 5, 3, 1, 2, 3.

5. Construct a frequency table for the following:
   7, 8, 6, 5, 6, 7, 7, 9, 8, 10, 7, 6, 7, 8, 8, 9, 10, 5, 7, 8, 7, 6.

6. Fill in the blanks:
   (i) Data means information in the form of ....
   (ii) Data obtained in the ...... form is called raw data.
   (iii) Arranging the numerical figures in an ascending or a descending order is called an ....
   (iv) The number of times a particular observation occurs is called its ....
   (v) Arranging the data in the form of a table is called ....

23

Pictograph

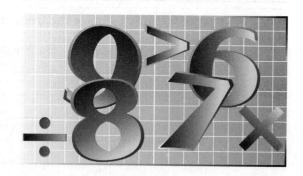

An information regarding the number of certain things can be nicely conveyed through pictures.

PICTOGRAPH *The representation of an information through pictures is called a pictograph.*

ILLUSTRATIVE EXAMPLES

EXAMPLE 1. *The number of cricket bats sold by a shop during a week are given below.*

Day	Monday	Tuesday	Wednesday	Thursday	Friday	Saturday
No. of bats sold	20	12	24	32	8	16

Draw a pictograph.

Solution Scale: ≡ 4 bats sold

Now, we may draw the pictograph, as shown below.

Day	No. of bats sold
Monday	
Tuesday	
Wednesday	
Thursday	
Friday	
Saturday	

EXAMPLE 2. *The modes of travelling to school by 160 students are given below:*

Mode	By Walking	On Bicycle	By Car	By Bus
No. of students	30	50	10	70

Draw a pictograph.

Solution Let us choose the scale as given below:

 ≡ 10 students (walking)

 ≡ 10 students (using bicycles)

 ≡ 10 students (using car)

 ≡ 10 students (using bus)

Now, we may draw the pictograph as shown below.

Mode	Number of students
Walking	🧍🧍🧍
Using bicycles	🚲🚲🚲🚲🚲
Using cars	🚗
Using bus	🚌🚌🚌🚌🚌🚌🚌

EXAMPLE 3. *The following pictograph shows the number of computers sold by a company during a week.*

The scale used: 🖥 ≡ 6 computers

Monday	🖥🖥🖥🖥🖥
Tuesday	🖥🖥🖥
Wednesday	🖥🖥
Thursday	🖥🖥🖥🖥🖥🖥
Friday	🖥🖥🖥🖥
Saturday	🖥

Look at the pictograph and answer the questions given below.
(i) How many computers were sold on Friday?
(ii) How many computers were sold on Monday?
(iii) How many computers were sold during the week?
(iv) On which day was the sale maximum?

Solution   We have:
(i) Number of computers sold on Friday = (4 × 6) = 24.
(ii) Number of computers sold on Monday = (5 × 6) = 30.
(iii) Number of computers sold during the week
= [(5 + 3 + 2 + 6 + 4 + 1) × 6] = (21 × 6) = 126.
(iv) Clearly, the sale was maximum on Thursday.

EXERCISE 23

1. The number of students who absented from the class during a week are given below:

Day	Monday	Tuesday	Wednesday	Thursday	Friday
No. of absentees	6	2	4	2	8

Take the scale ≡ 2 absentees.

Draw the pictograph.

2. The number of stools in five rooms of a school are given below:

Room number	I	II	III	IV	V
Number of stools	30	40	60	50	20

Taking the scale ≡ 10 stools, draw the pictograph.

3. In a class test, the number of students passed in various subjects are given below.

Subject	English	Mathematics	Hindi	Drawing
Number of students passed	15	25	10	20

Taking the scale ≡ 5 successful students, draw the pictograph.

4. The number of fans sold by a shopkeeper during 6 months are given below:

Month	March	April	May	June	July	August
Number of fans sold	30	40	60	50	20	30

Taking the scale 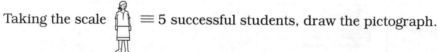 ≡ 10 fans sold, draw the pictograph.

5. The following pictograph shows different kinds of trees planted in a park. Each symbol represents 8 trees. Look at the pictograph and answer the questions given below.

Banyan tree	🌳 🌳 🌳 🌳
Neem tree	🌱 🌱 🌱 🌱 🌱
Mango tree	🌳 🌳 🌳

    (i) How many mango trees are there?

    (ii) How many banyan trees are there?

    (iii) How many neem trees are there?

    (iv) How many trees are there in all?

6. The following pictograph shows the number of scooters sold by a company during a week.

Scale used is 🏍 ≡ 6 scooters sold.

Day	Number of scooters sold
Monday	🏍 🏍 🏍 🏍 🏍
Tuesday	🏍 🏍 🏍 🏍
Wednesday	🏍 🏍 🏍
Thursday	🏍 🏍 🏍 🏍 🏍
Friday	🏍 🏍 🏍 🏍 🏍 🏍 🏍
Saturday	🏍 🏍

Study the pictograph carefully and answer the questions given below.

    (i) How many scooters were sold on Monday?

    (ii) How many scooters were sold on Tuesday?

    (iii) On what day of the week was the sale of the scooters maximum? How many scooters were sold on that day?

    (iv) On what day of the week was the sale of the scooters minimum? How many scooters were sold on that day?

24

Bar Graph

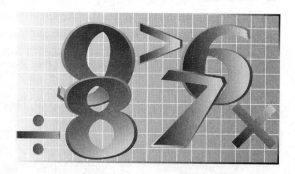

BAR GRAPH (OR COLUMN GRAPH) *A bar graph is a pictorial representation of numerical data in the form of rectangles (or bars) of equal width and varying heights.*

READING AND INTERPRETATION OF A BAR GRAPH

From a given bar graph we may answer various questions based on it, as shown below.

EXAMPLE 1. *Given below is a bar graph showing the marks obtained by Tarun in five subjects in an annual examination.*

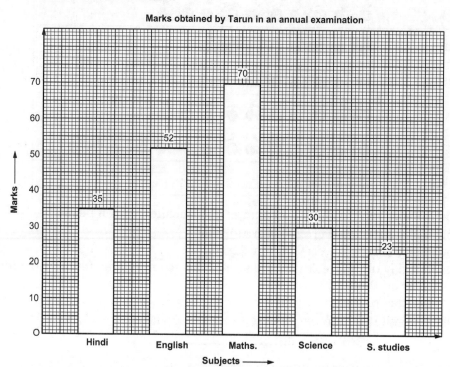

Read the bar graph carefully and answer the questions given below:

  (i) In which subject does Tarun get the lowest marks?

  (ii) In which subject does Tarun get the highest marks?

  (iii) How many marks does he get in English?

  (iv) In which subjects does Tarun get less than 50 marks?

Solution It is clear from the bar graph that:

  (i) Tarun gets the lowest marks in Social studies.

240

   (ii) Tarun gets the highest marks in Mathematics.
   (iii) Tarun gets 52 marks in English.
   (iv) Tarun gets less than 50 marks in each of the subjects Hindi, Science and Social
        studies.

EXAMPLE 2.   *In a survey of 130 families of a colony, the number of children in each family was*
                  recorded and the data has been represented by the bar graph, given below.

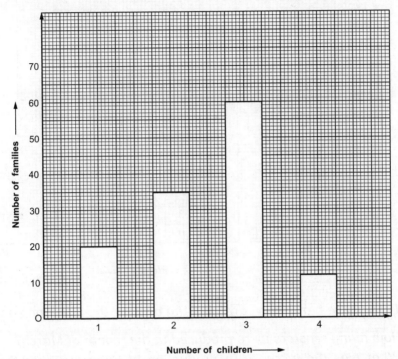

        Read the bar graph carefully and answer the questions given below:
           (i) What information does the bar graph give?
          (ii) How many families have 2 children?
         (iii) How many families have no child?
          (iv) What percentage of families have 4 children?

Solution   (i) The given bar graph shows the number of children in each of the 130 families of
                 a colony.

                (ii) Clearly, 35 families have 2 children each.

               (iii) Number of families having 1 or more children

                          $= (20 + 35 + 60 + 12) = 127.$

                    $\therefore$ number of families having no child

                          $= (130 - 127) = 3.$

                (iv) Number of families having 4 children = 12.

                    $\therefore$ required percentage

                          $= \left(\dfrac{12}{130} \times 100 \right) \% = 9.23\%.$

EXAMPLE 3.   *Given below is the bar graph showing the number of scooters produced in a factory during the first five months of a year.*

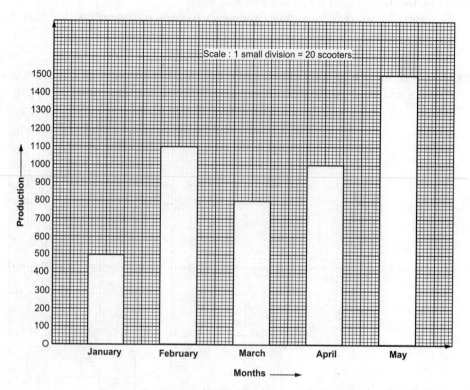

Read the above bar graph carefully and answer the questions given below:

(i) How many scooters were produced in the month of March?

(ii) What was the increase in production in February over the production in January?

(iii) What was the decrease in production in March in comparison to the production in February?

(iv) In which month was the production minimum and what was it?

Solution

(i) Clearly, 800 scooters were produced in the month of March.

(ii) Production in January = 500.

Production in February = 1100.

Increase in production = (1100 – 500) = 600.

(iii) Production in February = 1100.

Production in March = 800.

Decrease in production = (1100 – 800) = 300.

(iv) Clearly, the production was minimum in January.

Production in January = 500.

EXERCISE 24

1. Look at the bar graph given below.

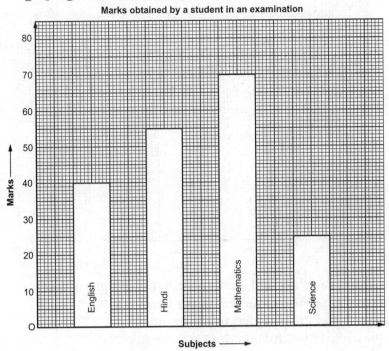

Marks obtained by a student in an examination

Read it carefully and answer the questions given below:
   (i) What information does the bar graph give?
   (ii) In which subject is the student poorest?
   (iii) In which subject is the student best?
   (iv) In which subjects did he get more than 40 marks?

2. In a survey of 60 families of a colony, the number of members in each family was recorded and the data has been represented by the bar graph given below:

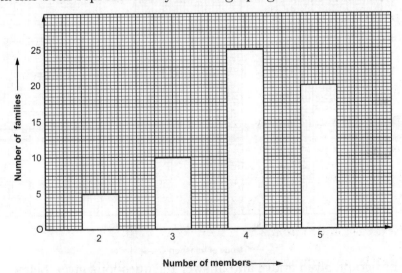

Read the bar graph carefully and answer the following questions:
   (i) What information does the bar graph give?
   (ii) How many families have 3 members?
   (iii) How many couples have no child?
   (iv) Which type of family is the most common?

3. Look at the bar graph given below:

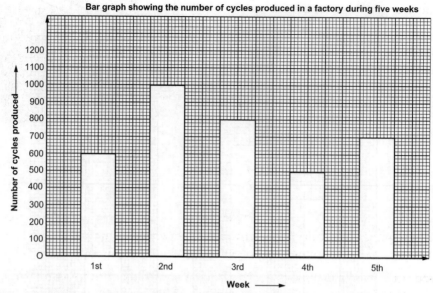

Bar graph showing the number of cycles produced in a factory during five weeks

Study the bar graph carefully and answer the questions given below:
  (i) In which week was the production maximum?
  (ii) In which week was the production minimum?
  (iii) What is the average production during these five weeks?
  (iv) How many cycles were produced in the first 3 weeks?

4. 51 students from a locality use different modes of transport to school, as shown by the bar graph given below:

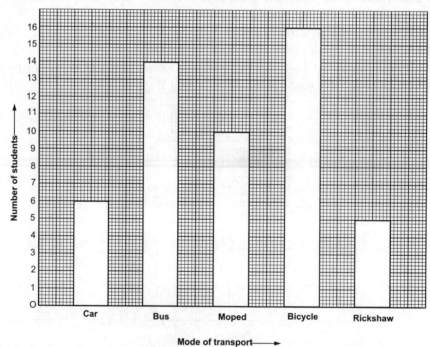

Look at the bar graph given above and answer the questions given below:
  (i) What does the above bar graph show?
  (ii) Which mode of transport is used by maximum number of students?
  (iii) How many students use bus for going to school?
  (iv) How many students of the locality do not use bus for going to school?

25

Activities

Activity–1

Objective (i) To verify that addition is commutative for whole numbers, and
(ii) to verify that multiplication is commutative for whole numbers

Materials Required (a) Two grid papers in which each square is of dimension 1 cm × 1 cm
(b) Slips of paper in two different colours (red and green) and measuring 1 cm × 1 cm
(c) Glue

Theory (i) Addition of whole numbers is commutative, e.g., 4 + 5 = 5 + 4.
(ii) Multiplication of whole numbers is commutative, e.g., 3 × 4 = 4 × 3.

Procedure **Step 1.** Take a grid paper, a few red-coloured slips and a few green-coloured slips.

Step 2. In one row of squares on the grid paper, paste 4 red-coloured slips followed by 5 green-coloured slips.

Step 3. In another row of squares below the above-mentioned row, paste 5 green-coloured slips followed by 4 red-coloured slips.

Step 4. We observe that the number of squares covered in the first row is equal to the number of squares covered in the second row. This shows that 4 + 5 = 5 + 4.

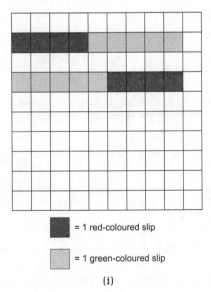

■ = 1 red-coloured slip

▢ = 1 green-coloured slip

(i)

Step 5. Take another grid paper, some red-coloured slips and some green-coloured slips.

245

Step 6. Paste red-coloured slips in 3 rows of 4 squares each on the grid paper.

Step 7. Moving below, paste green-coloured slips in 4 rows of 3 squares each.

Step 8. We observe that the number of squares covered by the red-coloured slips is equal to the number of squares covered by the green-coloured slips. This shows that $3 \times 4 = 4 \times 3$.

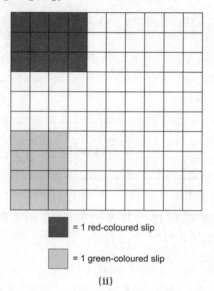

      ■ = 1 red-coloured slip

      □ = 1 green-coloured slip

(ii)

Result   It is verified that:
(i) Addition is commutative for whole numbers.
(ii) Multiplication is commutative for whole numbers.

Remarks The above procedure can be repeated for other numbers, to verify the commutative property of addition and multiplication of whole numbers.

Activity-2

Objective To find prime numbers from 1 to 100 by the method 'sieve of Eratosthenes'

Materials Required (a) Grid paper having squares of dimension 1 cm × 1 cm
(b) A black sketch pen
(c) A pair of scissors

Theory To check whether a number less than 100 is a prime number or not, we have to test its divisibility by 2, 3, 5 and 7 only.

Procedure **Step 1.** Cut out a 10 × 10 grid from the grid paper.

Step 2. Write numbers from 1 to 100 in this grid, as shown in the figure (i).

Step 3. Cross out 1.

Step 4. Encircle 2 and cross out remaining multiples of 2, i.e., 4, 6, 8, 10, ..., 100.

Step 5. Encircle 3 and cross out remaining multiples of 3, i.e., 6, 9, 12, 15, ..., 99.

Step 6. Encircle 5 and cross out remaining multiples of 5, i.e., 10, 15, 20, 25, ..., 95.

Step 7. Encircle 7 and cross out remaining multiples of 7, i.e., 14, 21, 28, 35, ..., 91.

Step 8. Encircle each one of the remaining numbers.

Step 9. The grid appears as shown in the figure (ii).

1	2	3	4	5	6	7	8	9	10
11	12	13	14	15	16	17	18	19	20
21	22	23	24	25	26	27	28	29	30
31	32	33	34	35	36	37	38	39	40
41	42	43	44	45	46	47	48	49	50
51	52	53	54	55	56	57	58	59	60
61	62	63	64	65	66	67	68	69	70
71	72	73	74	75	76	77	78	79	80
81	82	83	84	85	86	87	88	89	90
91	92	93	94	95	96	97	98	99	100

(i)

~~1~~	2	3	~~4~~	5	~~6~~	7	~~8~~	~~9~~	~~10~~
11	~~12~~	13	~~14~~	~~15~~	~~16~~	17	~~18~~	19	~~20~~
~~21~~	~~22~~	23	~~24~~	~~25~~	~~26~~	~~27~~	~~28~~	29	~~30~~
31	~~32~~	~~33~~	~~34~~	~~35~~	~~36~~	37	~~38~~	~~39~~	~~40~~
41	~~42~~	43	~~44~~	~~45~~	~~46~~	47	~~48~~	~~49~~	~~50~~
~~51~~	~~52~~	53	~~54~~	~~55~~	~~56~~	~~57~~	~~58~~	59	~~60~~
61	~~62~~	~~63~~	~~64~~	~~65~~	~~66~~	67	~~68~~	~~69~~	~~70~~
71	~~72~~	73	~~74~~	~~75~~	~~76~~	~~77~~	~~78~~	79	~~80~~
~~81~~	~~82~~	83	~~84~~	~~85~~	~~86~~	~~87~~	~~88~~	89	~~90~~
~~91~~	~~92~~	~~93~~	~~94~~	~~95~~	~~96~~	97	~~98~~	~~99~~	~~100~~

(ii) Sieve of Eratosthenes

Result In the sieve of Eratosthenes shown in the figure (ii), all the encircled numbers are prime numbers and all the crossed numbers except 1 are composite numbers.

Activity–3

Objective (i) To make a cube using a net and count the number of faces, vertices and edges
(ii) To check which of the given nets can be folded to get a cube

Materials Required (a) Net of a cube (given)
(b) Squared paper
(c) A pair of scissors
(d) An adhesive tape

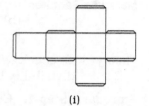

(i)

Theory There are only a small number of nets, each composed of 6 squares arranged suitably, which can be cut and folded to form a cube.

Procedure **Step 1.** Take the given net of a cube, drawn on a chart paper, and cut along its outer boundary.

Step 2. Label the squares in the net with numbers from 1 to 6, as shown in the figure (ii).

Step 3. Fold the net inwards along the lines. Join its ends with the help of an adhesive tape.

1	2	3	4

(with 5 above 3 and 6 below 3)

(ii)

Step 4. A cube is obtained whose face 1 lies opposite face 3, face 2 lies opposite face 4 and face 5 lies opposite face 6. Count the number of vertices and edges of the cube. Record your observations.

Step 5. Now draw the given nets on a squared paper, as shown in the figures (iii) to (xxi).

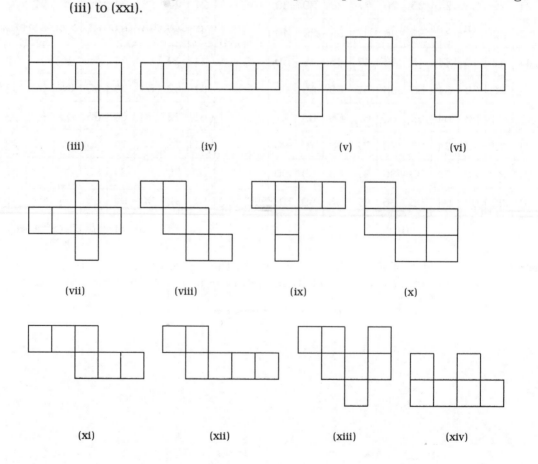

(iii)   (iv)   (v)   (vi)

(vii)   (viii)   (ix)   (x)

(xi)   (xii)   (xiii)   (xiv)

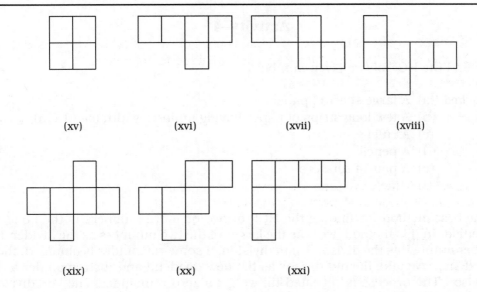

(xv)   (xvi)   (xvii)   (xviii)

(xix)   (xx)   (xxi)

Step 6. Cut each net along its boundary and fold it inwards along the lines. Observe which of these nets can be folded to form a cube. Record your observations.

Observations (i) In the cube obtained in Step 4, we have:

  (a) Number of faces = 6

  (b) Number of vertices = 8

  (c) Number of edges = 12

  (ii) Out of the given nets, we can obtain cubes only from the nets shown in the figures (iii), (vi), (vii), (viii), (xi), (xviii), (xix) and (xx).

Result   (i) A cube has 6 faces, 8 vertices and 12 edges.

  (ii) Nets having less than or greater than six squares cannot form cubes.

  (iii) Not all nets having six squares can form cubes when folded.

Remarks   (i) The students must practise forming cubes from nets different from those given in the above activity.

  (ii) The students must practise forming different types of nets which can form cubes when folded.

Activity–4

Objective   To find the HCF of two given numbers

Materials Required   (a) A large sheet of paper
(b) A few long strips of paper having uniform width (say 1 cm)
(c) A ruler
(d) A pencil
(e) A pair of scissors
(f) Glue

Theory   The best method for finding the HCF of two or more numbers is the Long Division Method. In this method, we take the larger of the two numbers as the dividend and the other number as the divisor. Upon division, if some remainder is obtained, then in the next step, we take the old divisor as the new dividend and the remainder as the new divisor. The process is repeated till we get a zero remainder. The last divisor is the requisite HCF.

Procedure   Suppose we have to find the HCF of the numbers 64 and 28.

Step 1.   Take a long strip of paper and cut a length of 64 cm from it.

Step 2.   Paste it on a large paper sheet and label it as Strip A. Label its ends P and Q.

Step 3.   Take another strip of paper, cut a length of 28 cm from it, paste it below the Strip A and label it as Strip B. Label its ends R and S.

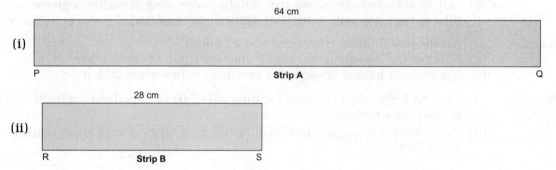

Step 4.   Cut another strip equal to Strip B. Call it Strip C. Place it at P on Strip A and mark X_1 where Strip C ends. Measure the length of the remaining part X_1Q of Strip A. We find that X_1Q is neither zero nor less than the length of Strip C. So, we place Strip C at X_1 on Strip A and mark X_2 where Strip C ends. Measure the length of the remaining part X_2Q of Strip A. We find that X_2Q is less than the length of Strip C and is not equal to zero.

Step 5.   Take another strip of paper. Measure and cut a length equal to X_2Q (equal to 8 cm). Paste it on the paper and label it as Strip D. Label its ends T and U.

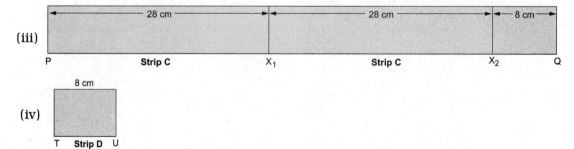

(v)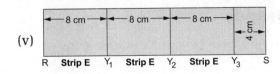

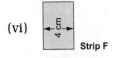

(vi)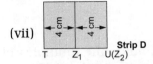

(vii)

Step 6. Cut another strip of length 8 cm (equal to Strip D). Call it Strip E. Place it at R on Strip B and mark Y_1 where the Strip E ends. Measure the length of the remaining part Y_1S of Strip B. We find that Y_1S is neither zero nor less than the length of Strip E. So, we place Strip E at Y_1 on Strip B and mark Y_2 where the strip E ends.

Measure the length of the remaining part Y_2S of Strip B. We find that Y_2S is neither zero nor less than the length of Strip E. So, we place Strip E at Y_2 on Strip B and mark Y_3 where the strip E ends. We find that Y_3S is less than the length of Strip E and is not equal to zero.

Step 7. Take another strip of paper. Measure and cut a length equal to Y_3S (equal to 4 cm). Paste it on the paper and label it as Strip F.

Step 8. Cut another strip of length 4 cm (equal to Strip F). Call it Strip G. Place it at T on Strip D and mark Z_1 where the Strip G ends. Measure the length of the remaining part Z_1U of Strip D. We find that Z_1U is neither zero nor less than the length of Strip G. So, we place Strip G at Z_1 on Strip D and mark Z_2 where the Strip G ends. We find that Z_2 lies exactly at U on the Strip D.

Step 9. The length of Strip F (or Strip G), i.e., 4 cm is the HCF of the lengths of Strip A (i.e., 64 cm) and Strip B (i.e., 28 cm).

Result   The HCF of the numbers 64 and 28 is 4.

Remarks The students must practise using this method to find the HCF of other pairs of numbers.

Activity–5

Objective To find the LCM of two or more given numbers by using number grids

Materials Required (a) Ten grid papers
                                  (b) A cardboard sheet
                                  (c) A grey colour pencil
                                  (d) A pencil
                                  (e) A pair of scissors
                                  (f) Glue
                                  (g) A ruler

Theory For smaller numbers the LCM may be determined by finding the multiples of each number and then selecting the common multiples of the given numbers. The smallest of the common multiples is the LCM of the given numbers.

Procedure Suppose we have to find the LCM of the numbers:
              (i) 2, 5, and 9
              (ii) 4, 6 and 8

Step 1. Take a grid paper and draw a square enclosing 100 squares such that we obtain a 10×10 grid. Similarly, from all the remaining 9 grid papers cut out 10×10 grids.

Step 2. Write numbers from 1 to 100 on each grid, as shown in the figure (i). Paste one of the grids on a cardboard and colour it lightly with the grey colour pencil. This forms the **Base Board.**

1	2	3	4	5	6	7	8	9	10
11	12	13	14	15	16	17	18	19	20
21	22	23	24	25	26	27	28	29	30
31	32	33	34	35	36	37	38	39	40
41	42	43	44	45	46	47	48	49	50
51	52	53	54	55	56	57	58	59	60
61	62	63	64	65	66	67	68	69	70
71	72	73	74	75	76	77	78	79	80
81	82	83	84	85	86	87	88	89	90
91	92	93	94	95	96	97	98	99	100

(i) Base Board

Step 3. Take another grid and mark all the multiples of 2. Cut out all the marked squares (squares containing the multiples of 2). This sheet forms a template for the multiples of 2. This template is shown in the figure (ii).

Step 4. Take another grid and mark all the multiples of 3. Cut out all the marked squares (squares containing the multiples of 3). This sheet forms a template for the multiples of 3. This template is shown in the figure (iii).

1		3		5		7		9	
11		13		15		17		19	
21		23		25		27		29	
31		33		35		37		39	
41		43		45		47		49	
51		53		55		57		59	
61		63		65		67		69	
71		73		75		77		79	
81		83		85		87		89	
91		93		95		97		99	

(ii) The template for the multiples of 2

1	2		4	5		7	8		10
11		13	14		16	17		19	20
	22	23		25	26		28	29	
31	32		34	35		37	38		40
41		43	44		46	47		49	50
	52	53		55	56		58	59	
61	62		64	65		67	68		70
71		73	74		76	77		79	80
	82	83		85	86		88	89	
91	92		94	95		97	98		100

(iii) The template for the multiples of 3

Step 5. Similarly, convert the remaining grids to the templates for the multiples of 4, 5, 6, 7, 8 and 9, as shown in the figures (iv) to (ix).

1	2	3		5	6	7		9	10
11		13	14	15		17	18	19	
21	22	23		25	26	27		29	30
31		33	34	35		37	38	39	
41	42	43		45	46	47		49	50
51		53	54	55		57	58	59	
61	62	63		65	66	67		69	70
71		73	74	75		77	78	79	
81	82	83		85	86	87		89	90
91		93	94	95		97	98	99	

(iv) The template for the multiples of 4

1	2	3	4		6	7	8	9	
11	12	13	14		16	17	18	19	
21	22	23	24		26	27	28	29	
31	32	33	34		36	37	38	39	
41	42	43	44		46	47	48	49	
51	52	53	54		56	57	58	59	
61	62	63	64		66	67	68	69	
71	72	73	74		76	77	78	79	
81	82	83	84		86	87	88	89	
91	92	93	94		96	97	98	99	

(v) The template for the multiples of 5

1	2	3	4	5		7	8	9	10
11		13	14	15	16	17		19	20
21	22	23		25	26	27	28	29	
31	32	33	34	35		37	38	39	40
41		43	44	45	46	47		49	50
51	52	53		55	56	57	58	59	
61	62	63	64	65		67	68	69	70
71		73	74	75	76	77		79	80
81	82	83		85	86	87	88	89	
91	92	93	94	95		97	98	99	100

(vi) The template for the multiples of 6

1	2	3	4	5	6		8	9	10
11	12	13		15	16	17	18	19	20
	22	23	24	25	26	27		29	30
31	32	33	34		36	37	38	39	40
41		43	44	45	46	47	48		50
51	52	53	54	55		57	58	59	60
61	62		64	65	66	67	68	69	
71	72	73	74	75	76		78	79	80
81	82	83		85	86	87	88	89	90
	92	93	94	95	96	97		99	100

(vii) The template for the multiples of 7

1	2	3	4	5	6	7		9	10
11	12	13	14	15		17	18	19	20
21	22	23		25	26	27	28	29	30
31		33	34	35	36	37	38	39	
41	42	43	44	45	46	47		49	50
51	52	53	54	55		57	58	59	60
61	62	63		65	66	67	68	69	70
71		73	74	75	76	77	78	79	
81	82	83	84	85	86	87		89	90
91	92	93	94	95		97	98	99	100

(viii) The template for the multiples of 8

1	2	3	4	5	6	7	8		10
11	12	13	14	15	16	17		19	20
21	22	23	24	25	26		28	29	30
31	32	33	34	35		37	38	39	40
41	42	43	44		46	47	48	49	50
51	52	53		55	56	57	58	59	60
61	62		64	65	66	67	68	69	70
71		73	74	75	76	77	78	79	80
	82	83	84	85	86	87	88	89	
91	92	93	94	95	96	97	98		100

(ix) The template for the multiples of 9

Step 6. Place the template for the multiples of 2 over the base board, followed by the template for the multiples of 5 and the template for the multiples of 9. See the figure (x). What do you observe?

Step 7. Now, replace the templates over the base board with the templates for the multiples of 4, 6 and 8. See the figure (xi). What do you observe?

1	2	3	4	5	6	7	8	9	10
11	12	13	14	15	16	17	18	19	20
21	22	23	24	25	26	27	28	29	30
31	32	33	34	35	36	37	38	39	40
41	42	43	44	45	46	47	48	49	50
51	52	53	54	55	56	57	58	59	60
61	62	63	64	65	66	67	68	69	70
71	72	73	74	75	76	77	78	79	80
81	82	83	84	85	86	87	88	89	90
91	92	93	94	95	96	97	98	99	100

(x) The templates for the multiples of 2, 5 and 9 placed over the base board

1	2	3	4	5	6	7	8	9	10
11	12	13	14	15	16	17	18	19	20
21	22	23	24	25	26	27	28	29	30
31	32	33	34	35	36	37	38	39	40
41	42	43	44	45	46	47	48	49	50
51	52	53	54	55	56	57	58	59	60
61	62	63	64	65	66	67	68	69	70
71	72	73	74	75	76	77	78	79	80
81	82	83	84	85	86	87	88	89	90
91	92	93	94	95	96	97	98	99	100

(xi) The templates for the multiples of 4, 6 and 8 placed over the base board

Observations (i) When the templates for the multiples of 2, 5 and 9 are placed over the base board, the only number that appears in grey is 90.

(ii) When the templates for the multiples of 4, 6 and 8 are placed over the base board, the numbers that appear in grey are 24, 48, 72 and 96. The smallest of these numbers is 24.

Result (i) The LCM of the numbers 2, 5 and 9 is 90.

(ii) The LCM of the numbers 4, 6 and 8 is 24.

Remarks The base board and the templates prepared in the above activity may be used to find the LCM of other sets of numbers.

Activity-6(a)

Objective To draw a line segment of length 5 cm on a paper and do the following:
  (i) Make a perpendicular line from a point on the given line
  (ii) Make a line intersecting the given line at a given point
  (iii) Make a line parallel to the given line

Materials Required (a) Three sheets of white paper
  (b) A ruler
  (c) A pencil

Procedure **Step 1.** Take a sheet of paper. Measure and draw a line segment *AB* of length 5 cm.

  Step 2. Mark any point *P* on the line segment *AB*.

  Step 3. Fold the paper along a line passing through the point *P* such that the part of the line segment *AB* that lies on one side of the line of fold falls exactly over the part on the other side of the line of fold. Make a crease and unfold the paper.

  Step 4. Draw a line *XY* along the crease as shown in the figure (i). Then, line *XY* is perpendicular to the given line segment at the given point *P*.

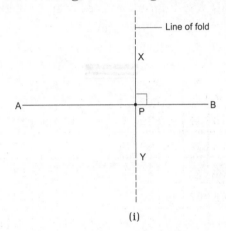

(i)

  Step 5. Take a sheet of paper. Measure and draw a line segment *AB* of length 5 cm.

  Step 6. Mark any point *P* on this line segment.

  Step 7. Fold the paper along a line passing through the point *P*. Make a crease and unfold the paper.

  Step 8. Draw a line *XY* along the crease as shown in the figure (ii). Then, *XY* is a line intersecting the given line at a given point *P*.

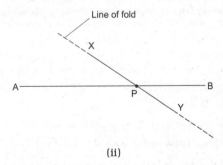

(ii)

  Step 9. Take a sheet of plain paper. Measure and draw a line segment *AB* of length 5 cm.

  Step 10. Mark any point *P* on this line segment and draw a perpendicular *XY* through *P* (as described in Step 3 and Step 4).

Step 11. Mark a point Q on the line XY.

Step 12. Fold the paper along a line passing through the point Q such that the part of the line XY on one side of the line of fold falls exactly over the part on the other side of the line of fold. Make a crease and unfold the paper.

Step 13. Draw a line X_1Y_1 along the crease, as shown in the figure (iii). Then, line X_1Y_1 is a line parallel to the given line AB.

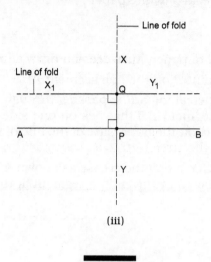

(iii)

Activity–6(b)

Objective To perform the following activity using a circular cut-out:

      (i) Make a chord   (ii) Make the diameter

     (iii) Shade the minor and major segments   (iv) Make a sector of the circle

Materials Required (a) Four sheets of plain paper

                        (b) A pair of compasses

                        (c) A pencil

                        (d) A ruler

Procedure **Step 1.** Take a sheet of plain paper. Mark a point O on this paper. With O as centre and any radius draw a circle and make a cut-out of this circle.

            Step 2. Fold the paper along a line passing through the circle. Make a crease and unfold the paper.

            Step 3. Draw a line PQ along the crease such that the points P and Q lie on the boundary of the circle. PQ is a chord of the circle.

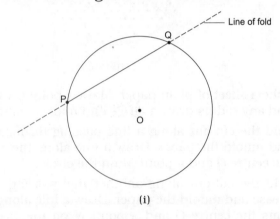

(i)

            Step 4. Take a sheet of plain paper. Mark a point O on this paper. With O as centre and any radius draw a circle and make a cut-out of this circle.

            Step 5. Fold the paper along a line that goes through the point O. The part of the circle that lies on one side of the line of fold will fall exactly over the part on the other side of the line of fold. Make a crease and unfold the paper.

            Step 6. Draw a line AB along the crease such that the points A and B lie on the boundary of the circle. Then, AB is a diameter of the circle.

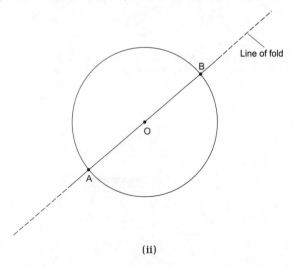

(ii)

            Step 7. Take a sheet of plain paper. Mark a point O on this paper. With O as centre and any radius draw a circle and make a cut-out of this circle.

Step 8. Draw a diameter *AB* of this circle.

Step 9. Draw a chord *PQ* in any of the semicircles such that the line segment *PQ* does not intersect the diameter *AB* inside the circle. Two segments of the circle are formed with one of the segments being smaller in area than the other. The smaller segment is the minor segment and the larger one is the major segment.

Step 10. Shade the major segment with dots and the minor segment with straight lines, as shown in the figure (iii).

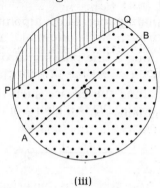

(iii)

Step 11. Take a sheet of plain paper. Mark a point *O* on this paper. With *O* as centre and any radius draw a circle and make a cut-out of this circle.

Step 12. Fold the cut-out along a line passing through the point *O*. Make a crease and unfold the paper. Draw a line along the crease such that the line joins the centre *O* and a point *M* on the circle.

Step 13. Fold the cut-out along another line passing through the point *O*. Make a crease and unfold the paper. Draw a line along the crease such that the line joins the centre *O* and a point *N* on the circle. The portion *MON* of the circle represents a sector of the circle, as shown in the figure (iv).

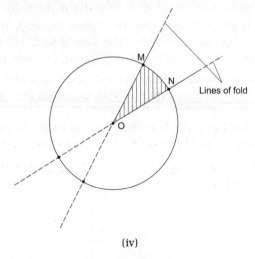

Lines of fold

(iv)

Activity–6(c)

Objective To represent the following by paper folding:

    (i) A straight angle, (ii) A right angle, (iii) An acute angle, (iv) An obtuse angle,
    (v) A reflex angle

Materials Required (a) A sheet of plain paper
               (b) A pencil
               (c) A ruler

Theory   (i) A straight angle = 180°, (ii) A right angle = 90°, (iii) An acute angle < 90°,
     (iv) An obtuse angle > 90°, (v) A reflex angle > 180°

Procedure **Step 1.** Take a sheet of plain paper. Mark a point O on it.

          Step 2. Fold the paper along a line passing through the point O. Make a crease and unfold the paper.

          Step 3. Draw a line segment AB along the crease. Then $\angle AOB$ is a straight angle, as shown in the figure (i).

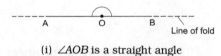

(i) $\angle AOB$ is a straight angle

          Step 4. Fold the paper along a line passing through the point O so that the part of the line segment AB that lies on one side of the line of fold falls exactly over the part that lies on the other side of the line of fold. Make a crease along the line of fold and then unfold the paper.

          Step 5. Draw a line CO along the crease. Then, $\angle COB$ is a right angle, as shown in the figure (ii).

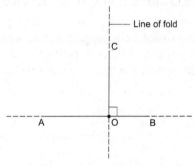

(ii) $\angle COB$ is a right angle

          Step 6. Fold the sheet along a line that passes through the point O and lies between the line segments OB and OC. Make a crease and unfold the paper.

          Step 7. Draw a line DO along the crease. Then, $\angle DOB$ is an acute angle, as shown in the figure (iii).

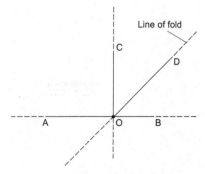

(iii) $\angle DOB$ is an acute angle

Step 8. Fold the sheet along a line that passes through the point O and lies between the line segments OA and OC. Make a crease and unfold the paper.

Step 9. Draw a line EO along the crease. Then, ∠EOB is an obtuse angle, as shown in the figure (iv).

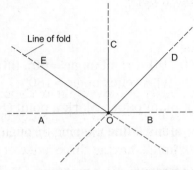

(iv) ∠EOB is an obtuse angle

Step 10. Fold the sheet along a line that passes through the point O and lies between the line segments OA and OB. Make a crease and unfold the paper.

Step 11. Draw a line FO along the crease such that point E lies on the other side of the line AB (opposite to the side in which OC, OD and OE lie). Then, ∠FOB is a reflex angle, shown in the figure (v).

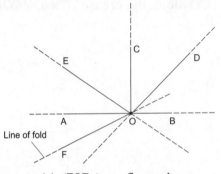

(v) ∠FOB is a reflex angle

Activity–7

Objective To classify the triangles on the basis of their sides and angles from the given set of triangles

Materials Required (a) A sheet of plain paper
                          (b) A pencil
                          (c) A ruler
                          (d) A protractor

Theory

The triangles are classified on the basis of the lengths of their sides as:

    (i) Equilateral triangle—a triangle having all sides of equal length
    (ii) Isosceles triangle—a triangle having two equal sides
    (iii) Scalene triangle—a triangle having three sides of three different lengths

The triangles are classified on the basis of their angles as:

    (i) Acute triangle—a triangle having all angles less than 90°
    (ii) Obtuse triangle—a triangle having one of the angles greater than 90°
    (iii) Right triangle—a triangle having one of the angles equal to 90°

Procedure **Step 1.** Take a sheet of plain paper. Draw all the given triangles on this paper.

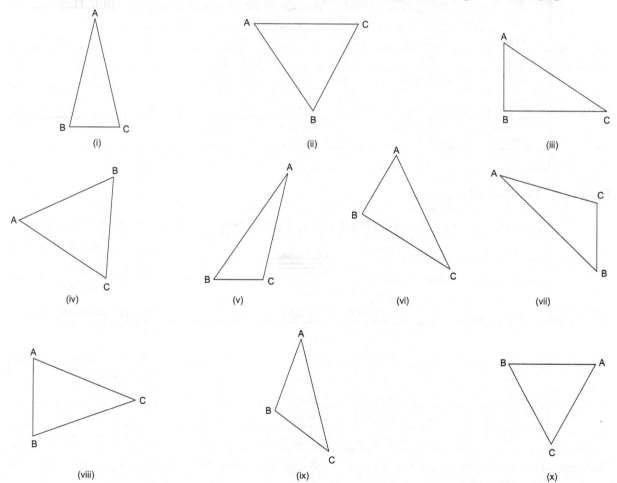

Step 2. Measure all the sides of each of the given ten triangles. Record your observations in Observation Table 1.

Step 3. Measure all the angles of each of the given ten triangles using a protractor. Record your observations in Observation Table 2.

Observation Table 1.

Triangle	Length of sides	Triangle type
(i)	$AB = $____, $BC = $____, $CA = $____	
(ii)	$AB = $____, $BC = $____, $CA = $____	
(iii)	$AB = $____, $BC = $____, $CA = $____	
(iv)	$AB = $____, $BC = $____, $CA = $____	
(v)	$AB = $____, $BC = $____, $CA = $____	
(vi)	$AB = $____, $BC = $____, $CA = $____	
(vii)	$AB = $____, $BC = $____, $CA = $____	
(viii)	$AB = $____, $BC = $____, $CA = $____	
(ix)	$AB = $____, $BC = $____, $CA = $____	
(x)	$AB = $____, $BC = $____, $CA = $____	

Observation Table 2.

Triangle	Measure of angles	Triangle type
(i)	$\angle A = $____, $\angle B = $____, $\angle C = $____	
(ii)	$\angle A = $____, $\angle B = $____, $\angle C = $____	
(iii)	$\angle A = $____, $\angle B = $____, $\angle C = $____	
(iv)	$\angle A = $____, $\angle B = $____, $\angle C = $____	
(v)	$\angle A = $____, $\angle B = $____, $\angle C = $____	
(vi)	$\angle A = $____, $\angle B = $____, $\angle C = $____	
(vii)	$\angle A = $____, $\angle B = $____, $\angle C = $____	
(viii)	$\angle A = $____, $\angle B = $____, $\angle C = $____	
(ix)	$\angle A = $____, $\angle B = $____, $\angle C = $____	
(x)	$\angle A = $____, $\angle B = $____, $\angle C = $____	

Result The given triangles are:

Triangle	Type based on the length of the sides	Type based on the angles
(i)	Isosceles triangle	Acute triangle
(ii)	Isosceles triangle	Acute triangle
(iii)	Scalene triangle	Right triangle
(iv)	Equilateral triangle	Acute triangle
(v)	Scalene triangle	Obtuse triangle
(vi)	Scalene triangle	Right triangle
(vii)	Scalene triangle	Obtuse triangle
(viii)	Isosceles triangle	Acute triangle
(ix)	Scalene triangle	Obtuse triangle
(x)	Equilateral triangle	Acute triangle

Remarks The students must practise identifying the types of more triangles provided by the teachers.

Activity–8

Objective To make the following shapes using a pair of set squares:

    (i) Square,   (ii) Rectangle,   (iii) Parallelogram

    (iv) Rhombus,   (v) Trapezium

Materials Required (a) Five sheets of plain paper

                (b) A pencil

                (c) A ruler

                (d) A geometry box

Theory   There are two set squares in a geometry box.

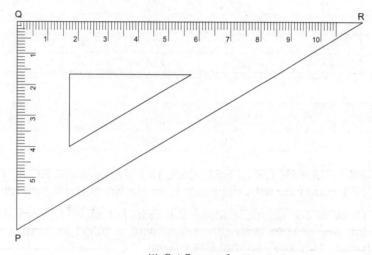

(i) Set Square 1

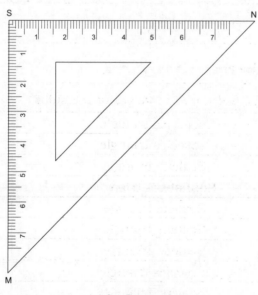

(ii) Set Square 2

    The set squares are the most useful instruments to draw parallel and perpendicular lines. In this activity we shall use SS1 for Set Square 1 and SS2 for Set Square 2.

Procedure **Step 1.**   Take one plain sheet and draw a line segment AB = 5 cm. Extend it on both sides to form a line XY.

       Step 2.   Place the side QR of SS1 along the line segment AB so that the point Q of SS1 coincides with point B, as shown in the figure (iii).

Step 3. Draw a line segment along the side *PQ* of SS1. Extend the line segment in both directions (with the help of a ruler) to form a line X_1Y_1. Mark a point *C* on X_1Y_1 so that *BC* = 5 cm. See the figure (iii).

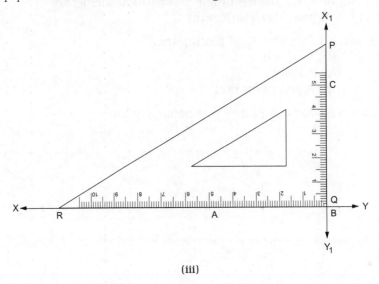

(iii)

Step 4. Place the side *QR* of SS1 along the line segment *BC* so that the point *Q* of SS1 coincides with the point *C* as shown in the figure (iv).

Step 5. Draw a line segment along the side *PQ* of SS1. Remove SS1. Extend the line segment in both directions (with a ruler) to form a line X_2Y_2. Mark a point *D* on X_2Y_2 so that *CD* = 5 cm.

Step 6. Join *DA* to form a square *ABCD* (each side measuring 5 cm) shown in the figure (v).

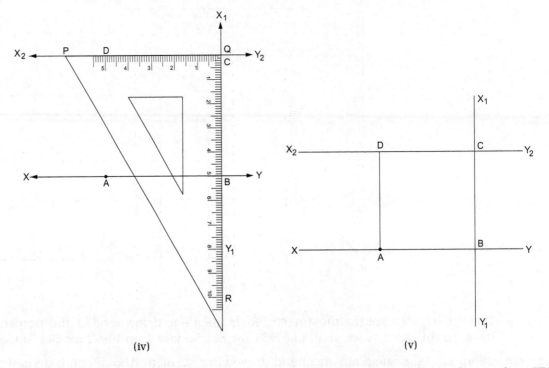

(iv)   (v)

Step 7. Draw a line segment *AB* = 6 cm. Extend it on both sides to form a line *XY*.

Step 8. Place the side *QR* of SS1 along the line segment *AB* so that point *Q* of SS1 coincides with the point *B*, as shown in the figure (vi).

Step 9. Draw a line segment along the side PQ of SS1. Extend the line segment in both directions (with the help of a ruler) to form a line X_1Y_1. Mark a point C on X_1Y_1 so that $BC = 4$ cm.

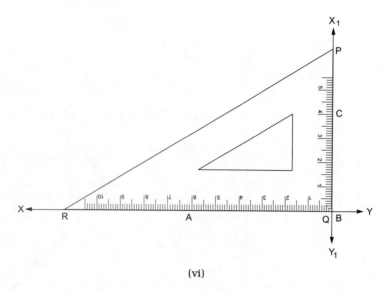

(vi)

Step 10. Place the side QR of SS1 along line segment BC so that the point Q of SS1 coincides with the point C as shown in the figure (vii).

Step 11. Draw a line segment along the side PQ of SS1. Remove SS1. Extend the line segment in both directions to form a line X_2Y_2. Mark a point D on X_2Y_2 so that $CD = 6$ cm.

Step 12. Join DA to form a rectangle $ABCD$ (of length 6 cm and breadth 4 cm), shown in the figure (viii).

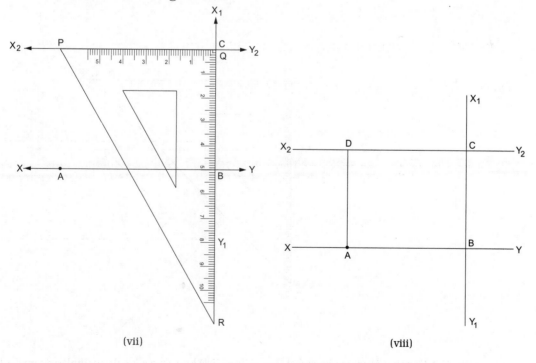

(vii)   (viii)

Step 13. Draw a line segment $AB = 5$ cm. Extend it on both sides to form a line XY.

Step 14. Place the side NS of SS2 along line segment AB such that its vertex N lies

exactly at point B as shown in the figure (ix). Place the side QR of SS1 along
the side MN of SS2, as shown in the figure (ix).

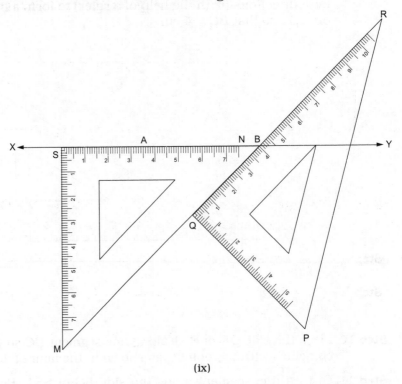

(ix)

Step 15. Slide SS2 along SS1 and move 4 cm along QR. Stop sliding SS2 further.
Draw a line segment along the side NS. Mark a point C such that it lies at
the vertex N of SS2. See the figure (x).

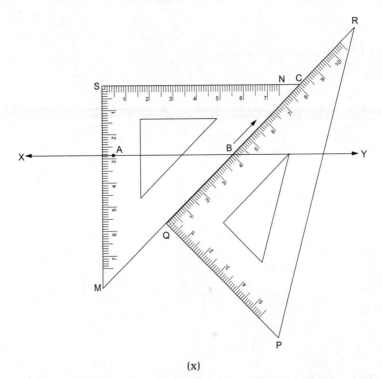

(x)

Step 16. Remove SS1 and SS2. Mark a point D on this line segment such that $DC = 5$ cm. Join BC and AD to get the required parallelogram $ABCD$, shown in the figure (xi).

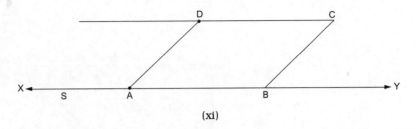

(xi)

Step 17 The steps of construction of a rhombus are the same as those of a parallelogram except that all the sides are to be taken equal to each other.

Step 18. Draw a line segment AB. Extend it on both sides to form a line XY.

Step 19. Place the side NS of SS2 along the line segment AB such that its vertex N lies exactly at point B as shown in the figure (xii). Place the side QR of SS1 along the side MN of SS2 as shown in the figure (xii).

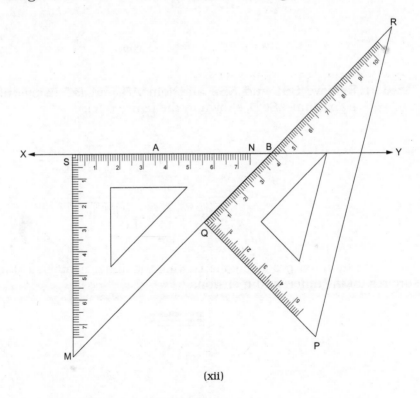

(xii)

Step 20. Slide SS2 along SS1 and move a small distance along QR. Draw a line segment DC along the side NS of SS2 (such that DC is smaller than AB). See the figure (xiii).

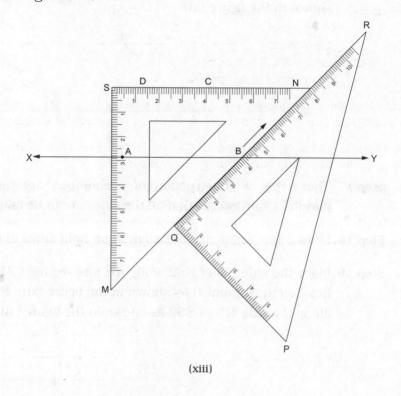

(xiii)

Step 21. Remove SS1 and SS2 and join AD and BC using ruler. We thus obtain trapezium $ABCD$, shown in the figure (xiv).

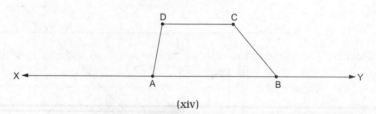

(xiv)

Remarks The students must practise constructing the above geometrical figures using the set squares taking different dimensions.

Activity–9

Objective To represent the decimal numbers 0.25, 0.5, 0.75, 0.68 and 0.09 on a 10×10 grid

Materials Required (a) Five grid papers
(b) A pencil
(c) A ruler
(d) A pair of scissors
(e) A grey colour pencil

Theory If we shade 23 squares out of 100 squares on a grid paper, the shaded region of the paper will represent the fraction $^{23}/_{100}$ and the decimal number 0.23.

Procedure **Step 1.** Take a grid paper. Cut a 10×10 grid from it. Repeat the same with each of the remaining four grid papers.

Step 2. On the first grid paper shade 25 squares. Then, the shaded portion of the grid will represent the decimal number 0.25, shown in the figure (i).

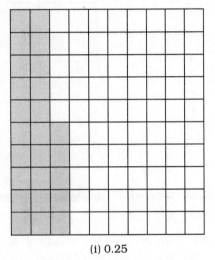

(i) 0.25

Step 3. On the second grid paper shade 50 squares. Then, the shaded portion of the grid will represent the decimal number 0.50, or 0.5, shown in the figure (ii).

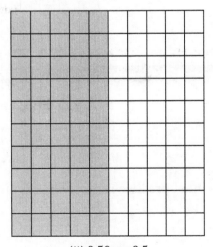

(ii) 0.50, or 0.5

Step 4. On the third grid paper shade 75 squares. Then, the shaded portion of the grid will represent the decimal number 0.75, shown in the figure (iii).

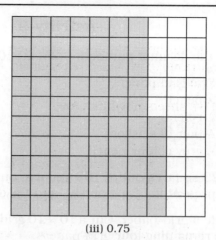

(iii) 0.75

Step 5. On the fourth grid paper shade 68 squares. Then, the shaded portion of the grid will represent the decimal number 0.68, shown in the figure (iv).

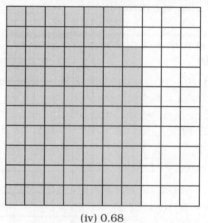

(iv) 0.68

Step 6. On the fifth grid paper shade 9 squares. Then, the shaded portion of the grid will represent the decimal number 0.09, shown in the figure (v).

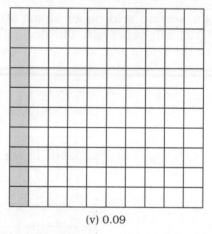

(v) 0.09

Remarks The students must practise representing more decimal numbers by shading.

Activity–10

Objective To determine the number of lines of symmetry of the following shapes:
(i) Equilateral triangle, (ii) Isosceles triangle, (iii) Square,
(iv) Rectangle, (v) Rhombus

Materials Required (a) Five sheets of white paper
(b) A pencil
(c) A ruler

Theory A figure is said to be symmetrical about a line l, if it is identical on either side of l. Thus, when a figure is folded along its line of symmetry, then the part of the figure that lies on one side of the line of fold falls exactly over the part lying on the other side of the line of fold.

Procedure **Step 1.** Take one plain sheet and draw an equilateral triangle ABC on it.

Step 2. Fold the paper along a line passing through the vertex A such that the vertex B falls exactly over the vertex C. We find that the part of the $\triangle ABC$ that lies on one side of the line of fold falls exactly over the part on the other side of the line of fold. Make a crease and unfold the paper.

Step 3. Draw a line XY along the crease. The line XY is a line of symmetry of the $\triangle ABC$.

Step 4. Fold the paper along a line passing through the vertex B such that the vertex C falls exactly over the vertex A. We find that the part of the $\triangle ABC$ that lies on one side of the line of fold falls exactly over the part on the other side. Make a crease and unfold the paper.

Step 5. Draw a line X_1Y_1 along the crease. Then, the line X_1Y_1 is another line of symmetry of the $\triangle ABC$.

Step 6. Fold the paper along a line passing through the vertex C such that the vertex A falls exactly over the vertex B. We find that the part of the $\triangle ABC$ that lies on one side of the line of fold falls exactly over the part on the other side of the line of fold. Make a crease and unfold the paper.

Step 7. Draw a line X_2Y_2 along the crease. Then, the line X_2Y_2 is the third line of symmetry of the $\triangle ABC$.

Step 8. All the three lines of symmetry of the equilateral triangle are shown in the figure (i).

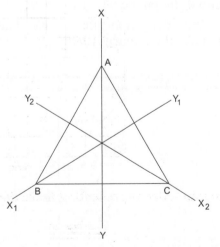

(i) Lines of symmetry of an equilateral triangle

Step 9. Take a plain sheet of paper. Draw an isosceles triangle PQR on this paper such that $PQ = PR$.

Step 10. Fold the paper along a line passing through the vertex P such that the vertex Q falls exactly over the vertex R. We find that the part of the $\triangle PQR$ that lies on one side of the line of fold falls exactly over the part on the other side of the line of fold. Make a crease and unfold the paper.

Step 11. Draw a line XY along the crease. Then, the line XY is the only line of symmetry of the $\triangle PQR$.

(ii) Line of symmetry of an isosceles triangle

Step 12. Take a plain sheet of paper. Draw a square $ABCD$ on this paper.

Step 13. Fold the paper along a line passing through the vertices A and C of the square. We find that the part of the square $ABCD$ that lies on one side of the line of fold falls exactly over the part on the other side of the line of fold. Make a crease and unfold the paper.

Step 14. Draw a line X_1Y_1 along the crease. Then, the line X_1Y_1 is a line of symmetry of the square $ABCD$.

Step 15. Fold the paper along a line passing through the vertices B and D of the square. We find that the part of the square $ABCD$ that lies on one side of the line of fold falls exactly over the part on the other side. Make a crease and unfold the paper.

Step 16. Draw a line X_2Y_2 along the crease. Then, the line X_2Y_2 is another line of symmetry of the square $ABCD$.

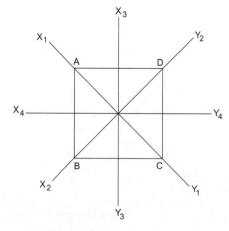

(iii) Lines of symmetry of a square

Step 17. Fold the paper along a line cutting the sides AD and BC such that the vertex A falls exactly over the vertex D and the vertex B falls exactly over the vertex C. We find that the part of the square $ABCD$ that lies on one side of the line of fold falls exactly over the part on the other side of the line of fold. Make a crease and unfold the paper.

Step 18. Draw a line X_3Y_3 along the crease. Then, the line X_3Y_3 is also a line of symmetry of the square $ABCD$.

Step 19. Fold the paper along a line cutting the sides AB and CD such that the vertex A falls exactly over the vertex B and the vertex D falls exactly over the vertex C. We find that the part of the square $ABCD$ that lies on one side of the line of fold falls exactly over the part on the other side. Make a crease and unfold the paper.

Step 20. Draw a line X_4Y_4 along the crease. Then, the line X_4Y_4 is the fourth line of symmetry of the square $ABCD$.

Step 21. The four lines of symmetry of the square $ABCD$ are shown in the figure (iii).

Step 22. Take a plain sheet of paper. Draw a rectangle $ABCD$ on this paper.

Step 23. Fold the paper along a line cutting the sides AD and BC such that the vertex A falls exactly over the vertex D and the vertex B falls exactly over the vertex C. We find that the part of the rectangle $ABCD$ that lies on one side of the line of fold falls exactly over the part lying on the other side of the line of fold. Make a crease and unfold the paper.

Step 24. Draw a line X_1Y_1 along the crease. Then, the line X_1Y_1 is a line of symmetry of the rectangle $ABCD$.

Step 25. Fold the paper along a line cutting the sides AB and CD such that the vertex A falls exactly over the vertex B and the vertex D falls exactly over the vertex C. We find that the part of the rectangle $ABCD$ that lies on one side of the line of fold falls exactly over the part on the other side. Make a crease and unfold the paper.

Step 26. Draw a line X_2Y_2 along the crease. The line X_2Y_2 is another line of symmetry of the rectangle $ABCD$.

Step 27. The two lines of symmetry of the rectangle $ABCD$ are shown in the figure (iv).

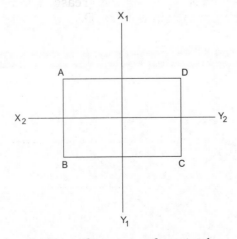

(iv) Lines of symmetry of a rectangle

Step 28. Take a plain sheet of paper. Draw a rhombus $ABCD$ on this paper.

Step 29. Fold the paper along a line passing through the vertices *A* and *C* of the rhombus. We find that the part of the rhombus *ABCD* that lies on one side of the line of fold falls exactly over the part on the other side of the line of fold. Make a crease and unfold the paper.

Step 30. Draw a line $X_1 Y_1$ along the crease. Then, the line $X_1 Y_1$ is a line of symmetry of the rhombus *ABCD*.

Step 31. Fold the paper along a line passing through the vertices *B* and *D* of the rhombus. We find that the part of the rhombus *ABCD* that lies on one side of the line of fold falls exactly over the part on the other side of the line of fold. Make a crease and unfold the paper.

Step 32. Draw a line $X_2 Y_2$ along the crease. $X_2 Y_2$ is another line of symmetry of the rhombus *ABCD*.

Step 33. The two lines of symmetry of the rhombus *ABCD* are shown in the figure (v).

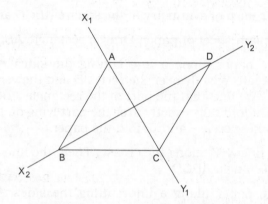

(v) Lines of symmetry of a rhombus

Remarks The teachers must explain to the students how the lines of symmetry of other geometrical figures such as an isosceles trapezium, semicircle, kite, etc., can be determined by the method of paper folding.

Answers

1. (i) 9018   (ii) 54073   (iii) 302506   (iv) 2010008
(v) 60500057   (vi) 20202202   (vii) 121212012   (viii) 155020068

2. (i) Sixty-three thousand five
(ii) Seven lakh seven thousand seventy-five
(iii) Thirty-four lakh twenty thousand nineteen
(iv) Three crore five lakh nine thousand twelve
(v) Five crore ten lakh three thousand six hundred four
(vi) Six crore eighteen lakh five thousand eight
(vii) Nineteen crore nine lakh nine thousand nine hundred
(viii) Six crore fifteen lakh thirty thousand eight hundred seven
(ix) Six crore sixty lakh sixty thousand sixty

3. (i) $15768 = (1 \times 10000) + (5 \times 1000) + (7 \times 100) + (6 \times 10) + (8 \times 1)$
(ii) $308927 = (3 \times 100000) + (8 \times 1000) + (9 \times 100) + (2 \times 10) + (7 \times 1)$
(iii) $2405609 = (2 \times 1000000) + (4 \times 100000) + (5 \times 1000) + (6 \times 100) + (9 \times 1)$
(iv) $53618493 = (5 \times 10000000) + (3 \times 1000000) + (6 \times 100000) + (1 \times 10000)$
$+ (8 \times 1000) + (4 \times 100) + (9 \times 10) + (3 \times 1)$
(v) $60606006 = (6 \times 10000000) + (6 \times 100000) + (6 \times 1000) + (6 \times 1)$
(vi) $91010510 = (9 \times 10000000) + (1 \times 1000000) + (1 \times 10000) + (5 \times 100) + (1 \times 10)$

4. (i) 62584   (ii) 581623   (iii) 20507905   (iv) 3406507

5. 8999100   **6.** 6999993   **7.** 900000   **8.** 9000000

9. 100 thousands   **10.** 10000 thousands   **11.** 99   **12.** 9548000

13. 9899999   **14.** 9999999   **15.** 234, 324, 243, 342, 423, 432

16. 10357   **17.** 964320

18.

	HM	TM	M	H Th	T Th	Th	H	T	O
(i)				7	3	5	8	2	1
(ii)			6	0	5	7	8	9	4
(iii)		5	6	9	4	3	8	2	1
(iv)		3	7	5	0	2	0	9	3
(v)		8	9	3	5	0	0	6	4
(vi)		9	0	7	0	3	0	0	6
	C	TL	L	T Th	Th	H	T	O	

In words, these numbers are:
(i) Seven hundred thirty-five thousand eight hundred twenty-one
(ii) Six million fifty-seven thousand eight hundred ninety-four
(iii) Fifty-six million nine hundred forty-three thousand eight hundred twenty-one
(iv) Thirty-seven million five hundred two thousand ninety-three
(v) Eighty-nine million three hundred fifty thousand sixty-four
(vi) Ninety million seven hundred three thousand and six

19.

	HM	TM	M	H Th	T Th	Th	H	T	O
(i)		3	0	1	0	5	0	6	3
(ii)		5	2	2	0	5	0	0	6
(iii)			5	0	0	5	0	0	5

EXERCISE 1B

1. >   **2.** <   **3.** <   **4.** <

5. >   **6.** <

7. 102345680 > 63521047 > 63514759 > 7355014 > 7354206

8. 23794206 > 23756819 > 5032790 > 5032786 > 987876

9. 16060666 > 16007777 > 1808090 > 1808088 > 190909 > 181888

10. 1712040 > 1704382 > 1702497 > 201200 > 200175 > 199988

11. 990357 < 9873426 < 9874012 < 24615019 < 24620010

12. 5694437 < 5695440 < 56943201 < 56943300 < 56944000

13. 700087 < 8014257 < 8014306 < 8015032 < 10012458

14. 893245 < 893425 < 980134 < 1020216 < 1020304 < 1021403

EXERCISE 1C

1. 26766007   **2.** 53112709   **3.** 41300000   **4.** 1316063

5. 21613495   **6.** 10144124, 18909559   **7.** 27666050, 48622530

8. 11769245   **9.** 8587868   **10.** 4356121   **11.** 8374134

12. 1782789   **13.** 6392915   **14.** 2669030   **15.** 1870770

16. ₹ 696465   **17.** ₹ 1116250   **18.** 2500630   **19.** ₹ 1365936

20. ₹ 17885075   **21.** 106920 km   **22.** 36872   **23.** ₹ 1895875

24. 15 kg 770 g   **25.** 2 m 15 cm   **26.** 44 m   **27.** 1 m 85 cm

28. 38 kg 500 g   **29.** 1 kg 325 g   **30.** 1 m 25 cm

EXERCISE 1D

1. (a) 40   (b) 170   (c) 3870   (d) 16380

2. (a) 800   (b) 1300   (c) 43100   (d) 98200

3. (a) 1000   (b) 5000   (c) 17000   (d) 28000

4. (a) 20000   (b) 30000   (c) 30000   (d) 270000

5. 90   **6.** 120   **7.** 80   **8.** 110

9. 160   **10.** 140   **11.** 640   **12.** 640

13. 820   **14.** 900   **15.** 800   **16.** 600

17. 7700   **18.** 6500   **19.** 39500   **20.** 49000

21. 58000   **22.** 130   **23.** 30   **24.** 60

25. 260   **26.** 500   **27.** 400   **28.** 4900

29. 2500   **30.** 8000   **31.** 8000

EXERCISE 1E

1. 2400   **2.** 2500   **3.** 1800   **4.** 3200

5. 3600   **6.** 600   **7.** 40000   **8.** 30000

9. 80000	**10.** 100000	**11.** 40000	**12.** 90000
13. 20000	**14.** 30000	**15.** 28000	**16.** 50000
17. 70000	**18.** 90000	**19.** 90000	**20.** 32000
21. 200000			

EXERCISE 1F

1. 3	**2.** 4	**3.** 4	**4.** 10	**5.** 35
6. 10	**7.** 20	**8.** 23	**9.** 23	**10.** 23

EXERCISE 1G

1. (i) II   (ii) VIII   (iii) XIV   (iv) XXIX
(v) XXXVI   (vi) XLIII   (vii) LIV   (viii) LXI
(ix) LXXIII   (x) LXXXI   (xi) XCI   (xii) XCV
(xiii) XCIX   (xiv) CV   (xv) CXIV

2. (i) CLXIV   (ii) CXCV   (iii) CCXXVI   (iv) CCCXLI
(v) CDLXXV   (vi) DXCVI   (vii) DCXI   (viii) DCCLIX

3. (i) 27   (ii) 34   (iii) 45   (iv) 54
(v) 74   (vi) 91   (vii) 96   (viii) 111
(ix) 154   (x) 224   (xi) 365   (xii) 414
(xiii) 464   (xiv) 506   (xv) 766

EXERCISE 1H

1. (c)	**2.** (a)	**3.** (c)	**4.** (b)
5. (b)	**6.** (b)	**7.** (c)	**8.** (b)
9. (a)	**10.** (c)	**11.** (b)	

CCE TEST PAPER-1

1. (i) Sixteen crore six lakh twenty-three thousand seven hundred eight
(ii) Fourteen crore twenty-three lakh eight thousand nine hundred fifteen

2. (i) Eighty million sixty thousand four hundred nine
(ii) Two hundred thirty-four million one hundred fifty thousand three hundred nineteen

3. 864572 < 3903216 < 6940513 < 16531079 < 19430124

4. 63240613 > 54796203 > 5125648 > 4675238 > 589623

5. 9000000   **6.** 86410, 10468, 75942

7. (i) 242   (ii) 465   (iii) 76   (iv) 741
(v) 94   (vi) 199

8. (i) LXXXIV   (ii) XCIX   (iii) CXLV   (iv) CDVI   (v) DXIX

9. 1000000, 999998,2   **10.** (i) 1000   (ii) 1000   (iii) 6000   (iv) 4000

11. (a)   **12.** (b)   **13.** (b)   **14.** (d)   **15.** (a)   **16.** (b)   **17.** (b)   **18.** (c)

19. 8,63,24,805   **20.** (i) 100   (ii) 10   (iii) 600   (iv) 1023

21. F   **22.** T   **23.** T   **24.** T   **25.** F

EXERCISE 2A

2. (i) 1, 2, 4, 5, 10, 20
(iii) 1, 2, 3, 4, 5, 6, 10, 12, 15, 20, 30, 60

(ii) 1, 2, 3, 4, 6, 9, 12, 18, 36
(iv) 1, 3, 5, 15, 25, 75

3. (i) 17, 34, 51, 68, 85
(iii) 65, 130, 195, 260, 325

(ii) 23, 46, 69, 92, 115
(iv) 70, 140, 210, 280, 350

4. (i) Even   (ii) Odd   (iii) Even   (iv) Even
(v) Odd   (vi) Even   (vii) Odd   (viii) Odd

6. (i) 11, 13, 17, 19, 23, 29, 31, 37
(iii) 41, 43, 47, 53, 59, 61, 67, 71, 73, 79

(ii) 83, 89, 97
(iv) 31, 37

7. (i) 2   (ii) 2   (iii) 3

8. 89 is a prime number

9. 90, 91, 92, 93, 94, 95, 96

10. (i) No   (ii) 1   (iii) 4, 9, 25, 49

11. Yes, 9

12. (59, 61), (71, 73)   **13.** No

14. (i) $36 = 7 + 29$ (ii) $42 = 5 + 37$ (iii) $84 = 17 + 67$ (iv) $98 = 79 + 19$

15. (i) $31 = 5 + 7 + 19$ (ii) $35 = 5 + 7 + 23$ (iii) $49 = 3 + 5 + 41$ (iv) $63 = 7 + 13 + 43$

16. (i) $36 = 17 + 19$ (ii) $84 = 41 + 43$ (iii) $120 = 59 + 61$ (iv) $144 = 71 + 73$

17. None

EXERCISE 2B

1. (i), (iii), (v), (vi) are divisible by 2.

2. (ii), (iv) are divisible by 3.

3. (iii), (iv), (vi) are divisible by 4.

4. (i), (ii), (iv), (vi) are divisible by 5.

5. (i), (iii) are divisible by 6.

6. (i), (iii), (v), (vi) are divisible by 7.

7. (iii), (v), (vi) are divisible by 8.

8. (i), (iii), (v), are divisible by 9.

9. Only (i) is divisible by 10.

10. (i), (ii), (iv), (v) are divisible by 11.

11. (i) 2   (ii) 0   (iii) 1   (iv) 2
(v) 1   (vi) 2

12. (i) 2   (ii) 7   (iii) 3   (iv) 4
(v) 8   (vi) 6

13. (i) 9   (ii) 7   (iii) 3   (iv) 2
(v) 0   (vi) 1

14. (i) Divisible   (ii) Divisible   (iii) Not divisible   (iv) Divisible
(v) Not divisible   (vi) Divisible

15. 103, 137, 179, 277, 331, 397 are prime numbers.

16. (i) 6   (ii) 12   (iii) 24   (iv) 12

17. (i) F   (ii) T   (iii) F   (iv) T
(v) F   (vi) T   (vii) T   (viii) T

EXERCISE 2C

1. $2^2 \times 3$ **2.** 2×3^2 **3.** $2^4 \times 3$ **4.** 7×2^3

5. $2 \times 3^2 \times 5$ **6.** $2^3 \times 17$ **7.** $2^2 \times 3^2 \times 7$ **8.** $2^2 \times 3 \times 5 \times 7$

9. $7^2 \times 13$ **10.** $3^3 \times 5 \times 7$ **11.** $2^3 \times 3^2 \times 17$ **12.** $7^2 \times 3^3$

13. $2^3 \times 3^2 \times 11^2$ **14.** $11^3 \times 7$ **15.** $3^2 \times 5 \times 23$ **16.** $3^2 \times 7 \times 19$

17. $3 \times 7 \times 13 \times 17$ **18.** $3 \times 5 \times 17^2$ **19.** $3^2 \times 17 \times 19$ **20.** $5 \times 11^2 \times 23$

EXERCISE 2D

1. 14	**2.** 34	**3.** 28	**4.** 36
5. 6	**6.** 53	**7.** 17	**8.** 18
9. 133	**10.** 2	**11.** 19	**12.** 95
13. 131	**14.** 83	**15.** 94	**16.** 58
17. 17	**18.** 69	**25.** 87	**26.** 154

27. 63   **28.** (i) $\dfrac{7}{9}$ (ii) $\dfrac{11}{17}$ (iii) $\dfrac{8}{13}$

29. 7 m   **30.** 31 L   **31.** 17, 113   **32.** 35 cm

33. 4290

34. (i) 1   (ii) 1   (iii) 1   (iv) 2

EXERCISE 2E

1. 126	**2.** 300	**3.** 180	**4.** 360
5. 2520	**6.** 6160	**7.** 1260	**8.** 5760
9. 1728	**10.** 13, 1989	**11.** 26, 5148	**12.** 77, 9702
13. 29, 1160	**14.** 123, 9471	**15.** 79, 119843	
17. 180	**18.** 8	**19.** 435	**20.** 1179
21. 1440	**22.** 609	**23.** 10080	**24.** 99720
25. 3 h	**26.** 4 m 32 cm	**27.** 7 min 12 s	**28.** 4.5 m
29. 7 a.m.	**30.** 3 m		

EXERCISE 2F

1. (c)	**2.** (a)	**3.** (d)	**4.** (b)	**5.** (a)
6. (c)	**7.** (d)	**8.** (c)	**9.** (c)	**10.** (b)
11. (c)	**12.** (d)	**13.** (a)	**14.** (b)	**15.** (d)
16. (d)	**17.** (c)	**18.** (d)	**19.** (c)	**20.** (c)
21. (c)	**22.** (c)	**23.** (b)	**24.** (c)	**25.** (d)

CCE TEST PAPER-2

1. Not divisible   **2.** Not divisible   **3.** 162   **4.** 110   **5.** 10200   **6.** 312

7. 725   **8.** 53, 59, 61, 67, 71, 73, 79, 83, 89, 97   **9.** 90, 91, 92, 93, 94, 95, 96

10. No, LCM should be a multiple of HCF   **11.** (a)   **12.** (c)   **13.** (b)   **14.** (d)

15. (c)   **16.** (b)   **17.** (c)   **18.** (b)

19. (i) prime, composite   (ii) 2   (iii) 4   (iv) 1   (v) 6, 28

20. (i) F   (ii) F   (iii) F   (iv) T   (v) T

EXERCISE 3A

1. 31000, 31001, 31002   **2.** 10000, 9999, 9998

3. 176   **4.** 0

5. (i) 2540802   (ii) 10000   (iii) 50905   (iv) 61640
    (v) 687891   (vi) 5386701   (vii) 6476000   (viii) 10000000

6. (i) 96   (ii) 9999   (iii) 36899   (iv) 7684319
    (v) 1566390   (vi) 2456799   (vii) 99999   (viii) 999999

7. 7510000, 7509999, 7509998

8. (i) F   (ii) T   (iii) F   (iv) T
    (v) F   (vi) T   (vii) F   (viii) T
    (ix) F   (x) F   (xi) F   (xii) T

EXERCISE 3B

1. (i) 458   (ii) 864   (iii) 984   (iv) 8063
    (v) 799

2. (i) 16623   (ii) 2907   (iii) 22620

3. 5633; 5633; yes; associative law of addition of whole numbers

4. (i) 2307   (ii) 3200   (iii) 16800   (iv) 25900
    (v) 400   (vi) 200

5. (i) 16783   (ii) 110577

6. Yes, by associative and commutative laws of addition of whole numbers

8. (i) F   (ii) T   (iii) T

EXERCISE 3C

1. (i) 5543   (ii) 10306   (iii) 21013   (iv) 353536

2. (i) 359, 558   (ii) 3269, 2903   (iii) 156987, 4844016   (iv) 29571, 970429

3. (i) 454   (ii) 5533   (iii) 7641   (iv) 3007

4. 990001   **5.** ₹ 62871   **6.** ₹ 1800   **7.** 105135

8. (i) $n = 5$ (ii) $n = 66$ (iii) $n = 57$ (iv) $n = 41971$

EXERCISE 3D

1. (i) 246   (ii) 0   (iii) 593   (iv) 753
    (v) 91   (vi) 1000   (vii) 66, 34   (viii) 5

2. (i) Commutative law for multiplication of whole numbers
    (ii) Closure property for multiplication of whole numbers
    (iii) Associative law for multiplication of whole numbers
    (iv) 1 is the multiplicative identity in whole numbers
    (v) $a \times 0 = 0$ for every whole number a
    (vi) Distributive law of multiplication over addition in whole numbers
    (vii) Distributive law of multiplication over subtraction in whole numbers

3. (i) 12940   (ii) 875900   (iii) 7459000   (iv) 987000
    (v) 56900   (vi) 168250000

4. (i) 165800   (ii) 92700   (iii) 5000000   (iv) 5740000
    (v) 6000000   (vi) 1000000

5. (i) 77700   (ii) 246960   (iii) 90912   (iv) 365532

(v) 517784	(vi) 37120	(vii) 437683	(viii) 307494

6. (i) 32184   (ii) 83853   (iii) 2434563

7. (i) 30686   (ii) 330101   (iii) 1080378   (iv) 8242736

8. 99899001   **9.** 7350 km   **10.** ₹ 3384650   **11.** ₹ 88650000

12. ₹ 102600   **13.** ₹ 445500   **14.** At least one of the given numbers is zero

15. (i) even   (ii) odd   (iii) 1

EXERCISE 3E

1. (i) 121   (ii) 423   (iii) 756   (iv) 1053
    (v) 231   (vi) 39

2. (i) Quotient = 148, remainder 15   (ii) Quotient = 119, remainder = 13
    (iii) Quotient = 236, remainder = 87   (iv) Quotient = 233, remainder = 375
    (v) Quotient = 23, remainder = 25   (vi) Quotient = 18, remainder = 385

3. (i) 65007   (ii) 0   (iii) 1553   (iv) 1482
    (v) 53   (vi) 0

4. $n = 1$ **5.** 1591   **6.** 316   **7.** 185

8. 29   **9.** 2   **10.** 9984

11. Quotient = 153, remainder = 90   **12.** 100015   **13.** 48 dozen

14. 125   **15.** 34502   **16.** ₹ 24785

EXERCISE 3F

1. (b)   **2.** (d)   **3.** (c)   **4.** (c)

5. (b)   **6.** (d)   **7.** (c)   **8.** (b)

9. (c)   **10.** (c)   **11.** (c)   **12.** (c)

13. (c)   **14.** (a)   **15.** (c)   **16.** (c)

17. (b)   **18.** (a)   **19.** (d)   **20.** (b)

21. (b)   **22.** (a)

CCE TEST PAPER-3

1. 136   **2.** 1000000   **3.** 106300   **4.** 99899001
        − 29571
        ――――――
          970429

5. Quotient = 202, Remainder = 34   **6.** 999984   **7.** ₹ 24785

8. 55   **9.** (b)   **10.** (c)   **11.** (b)

12. (c)   **13.** (c)   **14.** (d)   **15.** (d)   **16.** (c)

17. (i) 1   (ii) 0   (iii) 0   (iv) 0   (v) 1

18. (i) F   (ii) T   (iii) F   (iv) F

19. (a)→(iv)   (b)→(v)   (c)→(ii)   (d)→(i)   (e)→(iii)

EXERCISE 4A

1. (i) A decrease of 8   (ii) A gain of rupees 7

  (iii) Losing a weight of 5 kg   (iv) 10 km below sea level
  (v) 5°C above freezing point   (vi) A withdrawal of ₹ 100
  (vii) Spending ₹ 500   (viii) Going 6 m to the west
  (ix) −24   (x) 34

2. (i) +₹ 600   (ii) −₹ 800   (iii) −7°C   (iv) −9
  (v) +2 km   (vi) −3 km   (vii) +₹ 200   (viii) −₹ 300

4. (i) 0   (ii) −3   (iii) 2   (iv) 8
  (v) −365   (vi) 8

5. (i) −7   (ii) −1   (iii) −27   (iv) −26
  (v) −603   (vi) −777

6. (i) 1, 2, 3, 4, 5 (ii) −4, −3, −2, −1 (iii) −2, −1, 0, 1, 2 (iv) −6

7. (i) <   (ii) >   (iii) <   (iv) <
  (v) <   (vi) <

8. (i) −7, −2, 0, 5, 8   (ii) −100, −23, −6, −1, 0, 12
  (iii) −501, −363, −17, 15, 165   (iv) −106, −81, −16, −2, 0, 16, 21

9. (i) 36, 7, 0, −3, −9, −132   (ii) 51, 0, −2, −8, −53
  (iii) 36, 0, −5, −71, −81   (iv) 413, 102, −7, −365, −515

10. (i) 10   (ii) −1   (iii) −4   (iv) −5

11. (i) F   (ii) F   (iii) T   (iv) F
  (v) F   (vi) T   (vii) T   (viii) F
  (ix) F

12. (i) 9   (ii) 36   (iii) 0   (iv) 15
  (v) −3   (vi) 10   (vii) 3   (viii) 1

13. (i) −6, −5, −4, −3, −2   (ii) −21, −22, −23, −24, −25

EXERCISE 4B

1. (i) 3   (ii) 4   (iii) 0   (iv) −4
  (v) −11   (vi) −10   (vii) −3   (viii) −6
  (ix) −3

2. (i) −12   (ii) −15   (iii) 7   (iv) 12
  (v) −9   (vi) −10

3. (i) −452   (ii) −760   (iii) −2052   (iv) −4685

4. (i) −108   (ii) 109   (iii) 209   (iv) −204

5. (i) −217   (ii) 988   (iii) −2858   (iv) 991
  (v) −1421   (vi) 64   (vii) 2114   (viii) −30
  (ix) −81   (x) −246

6. (i) 57   (ii) −183   (iii) 0   (iv) 1001
  (v) −2054

7. (i) 202   (ii) 71   (iii) −4   (iv) −98
  (v) −499

8. (i) 119   (ii) 78   (iii) −9   (iv) −142
  (v) −301

9. (i) −20   (ii) −54   (iii) −370   (iv) 263

10. 30 km south

11. Loss = ₹ 55

12. (i) T   (ii) F   (iii) T   (iv) F
  (v) F   (vi) F

13. (i) $a = -6$ (ii) $a = -5$ (iii) $a = 4$ (iv) $a = 8$

EXERCISE 4C

1. (i) −52   (ii) 40   (iii) −15   (iv) −105
     (v) −219   (vi) 92   (vii) −115   (viii) 2481
     (ix) −6511   (x) 9262

2. 214   **3.** −24   **4.** 70   **5.** 24

6. (i) 86   (ii) 22   **7.** 106, −106, No   **8.** −183

9. 112

10. (i) True   (ii) True   (iii) False   (iv) True
     (v) False

11. 45300 m   **12.** 5°C

EXERCISE 4D

1. (i) 135   (ii) −126   (iii) −319   (iv) −234
     (v) −896   (vi) −672   (vii) 0   (viii) 0
     (ix) 108   (x) 5968   (xi) −826   (xii) 34034

2. (i) 24   (ii) 60   (iii) −120   (iv) −560
     (v) −126   (vi) −216

3. (i) −14580   (ii) 4536   (iii) 16031   (iv) −45543

6. (i) True   (ii) False   (iii) True   (iv) False

7. (i) −90   (ii) −180   (iii) −240   (iv) 300
     (v) −2150   (vi) −3600   (vii) 810

EXERCISE 4E

1. (i) −5   (ii) −4   (iii) −5   (iv) −11
     (v) −9   (vi) −7   (vii) 4   (viii) 7
     (ix) 9   (x) 125   (xi) −2067   (xii) −1
(xiii) 0   (xiv) −30

2. (i) −16   (ii) 12   (iii) −125   (iv) 0
     (v) −186   (vi) −34   (vii) −165   (viii) −73
     (ix) −1

3. (i) T   (ii) F   (iii) T   (iv) F
     (v) T   (vi) T   (vii) T   (viii) T
     (ix) F

EXERCISE 4F

1. (b)   **2.** (c)   **3.** (c)   **4.** (a)

5. (b)   **6.** (c)   **7.** (b)   **8.** (c)

9. (c)   **10.** (b)   **11.** (a)   **12.** (b)

13. (b)   **14.** (c)   **15.** (b)   **16.** (b)

17. (b)   **18.** (c)   **19.** (c)   **20.** (c)

21. (a)   **22.** (c)   **23.** (c)   **24.** (c)

25. (b)   **26.** (a)   **27.** (b)

CCE TEST PAPER-4

1. –5, –4, –3, –2, –1, 0, 1 2, 3, 4, 5

2. (i) 0   (ii) –4   (iii) 9   (iv) –385

3. –36, –18, –5, –1, 0, 1, 8, 16   **4.** (i) 3   (ii) 10   (iii) –11

5. Integers less than –6: –10, –9, –8, –7   Integers greater than –6: –5, –4, –3, –2

6. (i) –8   (ii) –11   (iii) 48   (iv) –6
     (v) 80   (vi) 4   (vii) –40   (viii) –45

7. –46   **8.** (i) –2400   (ii) –90   (iii) 7   (iv) –16

9. (b)   **10.** (b)   **11.** (c)   **12.** (b)   **13.** (c)   **14.** (c)   **15.** (d)   **16.** (d)

17. (i) –38   (ii) –1   (iii) 1   (iv) –11   (v) –201   **18.** (i) T   (ii) F   (iii) F   (iv) T   (v) T   (vi) F

EXERCISE 5A

1. (i) $\frac{3}{4}$ (ii) $\frac{1}{4}$ (iii) $\frac{2}{3}$ (iv) $\frac{3}{10}$
     (v) $\frac{4}{9}$ (vi) $\frac{3}{8}$

3. The whole rectangle is not divided into 4 equal parts.
So, the shaded part is not equal to $\frac{1}{4}$.

4. (i) $\frac{3}{4}$ (ii) $\frac{4}{7}$ (iii) $\frac{2}{5}$ (iv) $\frac{3}{10}$
     (v) $\frac{1}{8}$ (vi) $\frac{5}{6}$ (vii) $\frac{8}{9}$ (viii) $\frac{7}{12}$

5. (i) Numerator = 4, denominator = 9   (ii) Numerator = 6, denominator = 11
   (iii) Numerator = 8, denominator = 15   (iv) Numerator = 12, denominator = 17
   (v) Numerator = 5, denominator = 1

6. (i) $\frac{3}{8}$ (ii) $\frac{5}{12}$ (iii) $\frac{7}{16}$ (iv) $\frac{8}{15}$

7. (i) two-thirds   (ii) four-ninths   (iii) two-fifths   (iv) seven-tenths
   (v) one-third   (vi) three-fourths   (vii) three-eights   (viii) nine-fourteenths
   (ix) five-elevenths   (x) six-fifteenths

8. $\frac{24}{60}$ **9.** 9, $\frac{4}{9}$ **10.** (i) 10 pens   (ii) 18 balls   (iii) 24 balloons

11. (i) 12 cups   (ii) 21 rackets   (iii) 24 books   **12.** 20, 5

EXERCISE 5B

1. $\frac{1}{2}, \frac{3}{5}, \frac{0}{6}, \frac{10}{11}$ **2.** $\frac{3}{2}, \frac{9}{4}, \frac{8}{8}, 3, \frac{27}{16}, \frac{19}{18}, \frac{26}{26}$

3. $\frac{6}{5}, \frac{7}{5}, \frac{8}{5}, \frac{9}{5}, \frac{11}{5}, \frac{12}{5}$ **4.** $\frac{13}{2}, \frac{13}{3}, \frac{13}{4}, \frac{13}{5}, \frac{13}{6}, \frac{13}{7}$

5. (i) $\frac{40}{7}$ (ii) $\frac{75}{8}$ (iii) $\frac{63}{10}$ (iv) $\frac{38}{11}$
   (v) $\frac{149}{14}$ (vi) $\frac{187}{15}$ (vii) $\frac{112}{13}$ (viii) $\frac{155}{3}$

6. (i) $3\frac{2}{5}$ (ii) $8\frac{6}{7}$ (iii) $12\frac{5}{8}$ (iv) $7\frac{4}{13}$
   (v) $7\frac{4}{11}$ (vi) $5\frac{7}{16}$ (vii) $8\frac{7}{12}$ (viii) $5\frac{17}{20}$

7. (i) <   (ii) <   (iii) >   (iv) =
   (v) =   (vi) >

EXERCISE 5C

1. (i) $\dfrac{4}{6}, \dfrac{6}{9}, \dfrac{8}{12}, \dfrac{10}{15}, \dfrac{12}{18}$

   (ii) $\dfrac{8}{10}, \dfrac{12}{15}, \dfrac{16}{20}, \dfrac{20}{25}, \dfrac{24}{30}$

   (iii) $\dfrac{10}{16}, \dfrac{15}{24}, \dfrac{20}{32}, \dfrac{25}{40}, \dfrac{30}{48}$

   (iv) $\dfrac{14}{20}, \dfrac{21}{30}, \dfrac{28}{40}, \dfrac{35}{50}, \dfrac{42}{60}, \dfrac{49}{70}$

   (v) $\dfrac{6}{14}, \dfrac{9}{21}, \dfrac{12}{28}, \dfrac{15}{35}, \dfrac{18}{42}, \dfrac{21}{49}$

   (vi) $\dfrac{12}{22}, \dfrac{18}{33}, \dfrac{24}{44}, \dfrac{30}{55}, \dfrac{36}{66}, \dfrac{42}{77}$

   (vii) $\dfrac{14}{18}, \dfrac{21}{27}, \dfrac{28}{36}, \dfrac{35}{45}, \dfrac{42}{54}, \dfrac{49}{63}$

   (viii) $\dfrac{10}{24}, \dfrac{15}{36}, \dfrac{20}{48}, \dfrac{25}{60}, \dfrac{30}{72}, \dfrac{35}{84}$

2. (i), (ii), (iv)   **3.** (i) $\dfrac{18}{30}$ (ii) $\dfrac{24}{40}$ **4.** (i) $\dfrac{30}{54}$ (ii) $\dfrac{35}{63}$ **5.** (i) $\dfrac{42}{77}$ (ii) $\dfrac{60}{110}$

6. $\dfrac{4}{5}$ **7.** (i) $\dfrac{9}{12}$ (ii) $\dfrac{3}{4}$ **8.** (i) $\dfrac{4}{5}$ (ii) $\dfrac{8}{10}$

9. (i) $\dfrac{3}{5}$ (ii) $\dfrac{4}{5}$ (iii) $\dfrac{6}{7}$ (iv) $\dfrac{5}{2}$

   (v) $\dfrac{4}{5}$

11. (i) 28   (ii) 21   (iii) 32   (iv) 12
   (v) 5   (vi) 9

EXERCISE 5D

2. $\dfrac{18}{30}, \dfrac{21}{30}, \dfrac{16}{30}, \dfrac{11}{30}$ **3.** $\dfrac{6}{24}, \dfrac{15}{24}, \dfrac{14}{24}, \dfrac{13}{24}$

4. (i) >   (ii) >   (iii) <   (iv) >
   (v) >   (vi) <

5. (i) >   (ii) >   (iii) <   (iv) >
   (v) <   (vi) >

6. $\dfrac{4}{5} > \dfrac{5}{7}$ **7.** $\dfrac{3}{8} < \dfrac{5}{6}$ **8.** $\dfrac{7}{11} < \dfrac{6}{7}$ **9.** $\dfrac{5}{6} > \dfrac{9}{11}$

10. $\dfrac{2}{3} > \dfrac{4}{9}$ **11.** $\dfrac{6}{13} < \dfrac{3}{4}$ **12.** $\dfrac{3}{4} < \dfrac{5}{6}$ **13.** $\dfrac{5}{8} > \dfrac{7}{12}$

14. $\dfrac{4}{9} < \dfrac{5}{6}$ **15.** $\dfrac{4}{5} > \dfrac{7}{10}$ **16.** $\dfrac{7}{8} < \dfrac{9}{10}$ **17.** $\dfrac{11}{12} > \dfrac{13}{15}$

18. $\dfrac{1}{2} < \dfrac{3}{4} < \dfrac{5}{6} < \dfrac{7}{8}$ **19.** $\dfrac{11}{18} < \dfrac{2}{3} < \dfrac{7}{9} < \dfrac{5}{6}$ **20.** $\dfrac{2}{5} < \dfrac{17}{30} < \dfrac{7}{10} < \dfrac{11}{15}$ **21.** $\dfrac{11}{16} < \dfrac{23}{32} < \dfrac{3}{4} < \dfrac{7}{8}$

22. $\dfrac{11}{12} > \dfrac{3}{4} > \dfrac{17}{24} > \dfrac{5}{8}$ **23.** $\dfrac{7}{9} > \dfrac{11}{18} > \dfrac{17}{36} > \dfrac{5}{12}$ **24.** $\dfrac{7}{10} > \dfrac{2}{3} > \dfrac{3}{5} > \dfrac{8}{15}$ **25.** $\dfrac{17}{21} > \dfrac{31}{42} > \dfrac{5}{7} > \dfrac{9}{14}$

26. $\dfrac{1}{7} > \dfrac{1}{9} > \dfrac{1}{12} > \dfrac{1}{17} > \dfrac{1}{23} > \dfrac{1}{50}$ **27.** $\dfrac{3}{4} > \dfrac{3}{5} > \dfrac{3}{7} > \dfrac{3}{11} > \dfrac{3}{13} > \dfrac{3}{17}$

28. Sarita   **29.** Rohit   **30.** Both have the same result

EXERCISE 5E

1. $\dfrac{3}{4}$ **2.** $1\dfrac{1}{4}$ **3.** $4\dfrac{2}{5}$ **4.** $1\dfrac{1}{18}$

5. $1\dfrac{7}{48}$ **6.** $1\dfrac{7}{60}$ **7.** $8\dfrac{7}{12}$ **8.** $4\dfrac{13}{24}$

9. $6\frac{7}{30}$ **10.** $7\frac{1}{2}$ **11.** $5\frac{5}{12}$ **12.** $13\frac{3}{4}$

13. $10\frac{1}{3}$ **14.** 10   **15.** $7\frac{13}{16}$ **16.** ₹$6\frac{1}{10}$

17. $7\frac{1}{6}$ m   **18.** $6\frac{1}{4}$ km   **19.** $31\frac{7}{15}$ kg

EXERCISE 5F

1. $\frac{1}{2}$ **2.** $\frac{1}{6}$ **3.** $1\frac{6}{7}$ **4.** $\frac{7}{18}$ **5.** $\frac{1}{8}$

6. $\frac{1}{24}$ **7.** $1\frac{11}{45}$ **8.** $1\frac{5}{24}$ **9.** $\frac{5}{6}$ **10.** $2\frac{11}{12}$

11. $1\frac{1}{3}$ **12.** $3\frac{5}{8}$ **13.** $1\frac{1}{18}$ **14.** $\frac{19}{24}$ **15.** $2\frac{8}{45}$

16. $4\frac{1}{2}$ **17.** $3\frac{23}{30}$ **18.** $2\frac{1}{4}$ **19.** $8\frac{1}{24}$ **20.** $4\frac{3}{10}$

21. $4\frac{2}{5}$ **22.** $9\frac{1}{3}$ **23.** $1\frac{11}{15}$ **24.** $3\frac{1}{18}$

25. $\frac{3}{4} > \frac{5}{7}$ by $\frac{1}{28}$ **26.** $1\frac{3}{4}$ L   **27.** $1\frac{7}{12}$ h   **28.** ₹$80\frac{3}{4}$ **29.** $2\frac{1}{8}$ m

EXERCISE 5G

1. (c)   **2.** (c)   **3.** (b)   **4.** (a)   **5.** (a)

6. (c)   **7.** (d)   **8.** (a)   **9.** (b)   **10.** (c)

11. (b)   **12.** (a)   **13.** (d)   **14.** (b)   **15.** (c)

16. (b)   **17.** (b)   **18.** (a)   **19.** (d)   **20.** (a)

CCE TEST PAPER-5

2. $\frac{7}{12}$ **3.** $\frac{35}{56}$ **5.** $7\frac{1}{6}$ **6.** pen, by ₹$12\frac{1}{2}$

7. $\frac{3}{4} > \frac{5}{7}$ by $\frac{1}{28}$ **8.** $\frac{9}{18}, \frac{12}{18}, \frac{8}{18}, \frac{15}{18}$ **9.** $\frac{18}{30}$ **10.** $\frac{6}{7}$

11. (b)   **12.** (a)   **13.** (b)   **14.** (a)

15. (b)   **16.** (c)   **17.** (d)

18. (i) $9\frac{1}{3}$ (ii) $5\frac{1}{5}$ (iii) $1\frac{1}{3}$ (iv) $\frac{4}{5}$ (v) 9

19. (a) T   (b) F   (c) F   (d) F   (e) T

EXERCISE 6A

1. 13   **2.** 12   **3.** 3   **4.** 9

5. 21   **6.** 23   **7.** $1\frac{16}{25}$ **8.** $\frac{1}{6}$

9. 4   **10.** $3\frac{4}{7}$ **11.** 3   **12.** 2

13. 3   **14.** 3   **15.** $3\frac{9}{14}$

EXERCISE 6B

1. (c)   **2.** (b)   **3.** (b)   **4.** (a)

5. (b)   **6.** (a)   **7.** (b)   **8.** (b)

9. (a)   **10.** (a)

CCE TEST PAPER-6

1. 1   **2.** 12   **3.** 21   **4.** (c)

5. (c)   **6.** (b)

EXERCISE 7A

1. (i) 58.63   (ii) 124.425   (iii) 7.76   (iv) 19.8

    (v) 404.044   (vi) 0.173   (vii) 0.015

2. (i) Place value of 1 = 10, Place value of 4 = 4,

Place value of 8 $= \dfrac{8}{10}$, Place value of 3 $= \dfrac{3}{100}$

  (ii) Place value of 2 = 200, Place value of 7 = 10,

Place value of 5 = 5, Place value of 2 $= \dfrac{2}{10}$,

Place value of 6 $= \dfrac{6}{100}$, Place value of 9 $= \dfrac{9}{1000}$

 (iii) Place value of 4 = 40, Place value of 6 = 6,

Place value of 0 = 0, Place value of 7 $= \dfrac{7}{100}$,

Place value of 5 $= \dfrac{5}{1000}$

 (iv) Place value of 3 = 300, Place value of 0 = 0,

Place value of 2 = 2, Place value of 4 $= \dfrac{4}{10}$,

Place value of 5 $= \dfrac{5}{100}$, Place value of 9 $= \dfrac{9}{1000}$

  (v) Place value of 5 = 5000, Place value of 3 = 300,

Place value of 7 = 70, Place value of 0 = 0,

Place value of 3 $= \dfrac{3}{10}$, Place value of 4 $= \dfrac{4}{100}$

 (vi) Place value of 1 = 100, Place value of 8 = 80,

Place value of 6 = 6, Place value of 2 $= \dfrac{2}{10}$,

Place value of 0 = 0, Place value of 9 $= \dfrac{9}{1000}$

3. (i) $67.83 = (6 \times 10) + (7 \times 1) + \left(8 \times \dfrac{1}{10}\right) + \left(3 \times \dfrac{1}{100}\right)$

  (ii) $283.61 = (2 \times 100) + (8 \times 10) + (3 \times 1) + \left(6 \times \dfrac{1}{10}\right) + \left(1 \times \dfrac{1}{100}\right)$

 (iii) $24.675 = (2 \times 10) + (4 \times 1) + \left(6 \times \dfrac{1}{10}\right) + \left(7 \times \dfrac{1}{100}\right) + \left(5 \times \dfrac{1}{1000}\right)$

 (iv) $0.294 = \left(2 \times \dfrac{1}{10}\right) + \left(9 \times \dfrac{1}{100}\right) + \left(4 \times \dfrac{1}{1000}\right)$

  (v) $8.006 = (8 \times 1) + \left(6 \times \dfrac{1}{1000}\right)$

 (vi) $4615.72 = (4 \times 1000) + (6 \times 100) + (1 \times 10) + (5 \times 1) + \left(7 \times \dfrac{1}{10}\right) + \left(2 \times \dfrac{1}{100}\right)$

4. (i) 46.79   (ii) 578.316   (iii) 731.84   (iv) 605.079

    (v) 805.806   (vi) 39.048

5. (i) 7.500, 64.230, 0.074   (ii) 0.600, 5.937, 2.360, 4.200
  (iii) 1.60, 0.07, 3.58, 2.90   (iv) 2.500, 0.630, 14.080, 1.637

6. (i) >   (ii) <   (iii) <   (iv) >
  (v) >   (vi) <

7. (i) 5.06 < 5.69 < 5.8 < 7.14 < 7.2   (ii) 0.06 < 0.6 < 6.06 < 6.6 < 66.6
  (iii) 6.05 < 6.4 < 6.45 < 6.5 < 6.54   (iv) 0.33 < 3.003 < 3.033 < 3.3 < 3.303

8. (i) 73.03 > 8.73 > 8.073 > 7.33 > 7.3   (ii) 30.3 > 30.03 > 3.3 > 3.03 > 3.003
  (iii) 7.2 > 2.72 > 2.7 > 2.27 > 2.02 > 2.007   (iv) 88.8 > 88.08 > 8.88 > 8.088 > 8.008

EXERCISE 7B

1. $\dfrac{9}{10}$ **2.** $\dfrac{3}{5}$ **3.** $\dfrac{2}{25}$ **4.** $\dfrac{3}{20}$

5. $\dfrac{12}{25}$ **6.** $\dfrac{53}{1000}$ **7.** $\dfrac{1}{8}$ **8.** $\dfrac{28}{125}$

9. $6\dfrac{2}{5}$ **10.** $16\dfrac{1}{2}$ **11.** $8\dfrac{9}{25}$ **12.** $4\dfrac{11}{40}$

13 $25\dfrac{3}{50}$ **14.** $7\dfrac{1}{250}$ **15.** $2\dfrac{13}{250}$ **16.** $3\dfrac{27}{250}$

17. 2.3   **18.** 1.67   **19.** 15.89   **20.** 5.413

21. 21.415   **22.** 6.25   **23.** 3.6   **24.** 1.16

25. 5.34   **26.** 12.375   **27.** 2.475   **28.** 0.95

29. 0.74   **30.** 0.408   **31.** 0.075   **32.** 0.875

33. (i) 8.640 kg   (ii) 9.037 kg   (iii) 6.008 kg

34. (i) 4.365 km   (ii) 5.087 km   (iii) 3.006 km   (iv) 0.270 km
  (v) 0.035 km   (vi) 0.006 km

35. (i) 15.850 kg   (ii) 8.096 kg   (iii) 0.540 kg   (iv) 0.008 kg

36. (i) ₹ 18.25   (ii) ₹ 9.08   (iii) ₹ 0.32   (iv) ₹ 0.05

EXERCISE 7C

1. 67.3   **2.** 229.04   **3.** 97.41   **4.** 121.395

5. 115.63   **6.** 172.591   **7.** 37.815   **8.** 139.951

9. ₹ 161.40   **10.** ₹ 11262.30   **11.** 41 km 400 m   **12.** 46 kg 30 g

13. 5 m 30 cm   **14.** 5 m 40 cm

EXERCISE 7D

1. 25.88   **2.** 38.89   **3.** 32.77   **4.** 147.2

5. 88.82   **6.** 30.805   **7.** 174.883   **8.** 141.427

9. 56.865   **10.** 2.788   **11.** 45.682   **12.** 101.715

13. 128.603   **14.** 61.864   **15.** 16.5   **16.** 6.438

17. 26.246   **18.** 56.66   **19.** Neelam's, 0.815 kg

20. ₹ 18.05   **21.** 460 g   **22.** 860 m

EXERCISE 7E

1. (c)   **2.** (d)   **3.** (b)   **4.** (a)

5. (c)	**6.** (a)	**7.** (b)	**8.** (b)
9. (b)	**10.** (c)	**11.** (a)	**12.** (b)
13. (c)	**14.** (b)	**15.** (c)	**16.** (c)
17. (d)	**18.** (b)	**19.** (a)	**20.** (b)
21. (b)	**22.** (c)	**23.** (b)	**24.** (c)
25. (c)	**26.** (a)	**27.** (b)	**28.** (c)
29. (a)	**30.** (a)		

CCE TEST PAPER-7

1. 4.625	**2.** 1.05 m	**3.** 6.005 km	**4.** 0.008 km
5. 203.8	**6.** 2.672	**7.** 7.5	**8.** 7.6

9. $6.54 > 6.5 > 6.45 > 6.4 > 6.05$ **10.** (i) $\dfrac{2}{5}$ (ii) $\dfrac{7}{20}$ (iii) $\dfrac{2}{25}$ (iv) $\dfrac{3}{40}$

11. (b)	**12.** (c)	**13.** (b)	**14.** (b)	**15.** (c)
16. (c)	**17.** (a)	**18.** (c)	**19.** (d)	

20. (i) 0.001 (ii) 0.01 (iii) 16.005 (iv) 2.08 (v) like

21. (i) T (ii) T (iii) F (iv) T (v) F

EXERCISE 8A

1. (i) $x + 12$ (ii) $y - 7$ (iii) $a - b$ (iv) $(x + y) + xy$

(v) $\dfrac{1}{3}x(a + b)$ (vi) $7y + 5x$ (vii) $x + \dfrac{y}{5}$ (viii) $4 - x$

(ix) $\dfrac{x}{y} - 2$ (x) x^2 (xi) $2x + y$ (xii) $y^2 + 3x$

(xiii) $x - 2y$ (xiv) $y^3 - x^3$ (xv) $\dfrac{x}{8} \times y$

2. $80 + x$ **3.** (i) b^{15} (ii) y^{20} (iii) $14a^4b^3$ (iv) $6x^2y^2$ (v) $3z^3y^2x$

4. (i) $x \times x \times x \times y \times y \times y \times y$ (ii) $6 \times y \times y \times y \times y \times y$ (iii) $9 \times x \times y \times y \times z$

(iv) $10 \times a \times a \times a \times b \times b \times b \times c \times c \times c$

EXERCISE 8B

1. (i) 5 (ii) 10 (iii) 2 (iv) –5
(v) 8 (vi) –19

2. (i) 19 (ii) 30 (iii) 15 (iv) 7
(v) –42 (vi) –132

3. (i) –4 (ii) 34 (iii) –4 (iv) 36
(v) –10 (vi) –64

4. (i) 13 (ii) –5 (iii) $6b$ (iv) $-7x$
(v) $-2qr$ (vi) $8xz$ (vii) 1 (viii) –1

5. (i) 1 (ii) –6 (iii) 7 (iv) –2

6. (i) 8 (ii) –9 (iii) $\dfrac{3}{5}$ (iv) $-\dfrac{8}{3}$

7. (i) Monomial (ii) Binomial (iii) Monomial (iv) Trinomial
(v) Trinomial (vi) Monomial (vii) None (viii) Monomial
(ix) Binomial

8. (i) $4x^5, -6y^4, 7x^2y, -9$ (ii) $9x^3, -5z^4, 7x^3y, -xyz$

9. (i) $a^2, -2a^2$ (ii) $-yz, \dfrac{1}{2}zy$ (iii) $-2xy^2, 5y^2x$ (iv) $ab^2c, acb^2, b^2ac, cab^2$

EXERCISE 8C

1. (i) $10x$ (ii) $-2y$ (iii) $6xy$ (iv) $3x+2y$
    (v) $6x^2$ (vi) $3xyz$ (vii) $4a^3$ (viii) $-8x^2+5a^2$

2. (i) $-x+2y+z$ (ii) $-2m^2-8$ (iii) $-x^2-7xy-7y^2$ (iv) $-3xy-6yz-3zx$

3. (i) $4a+2b-c$ (ii) $-2a-5ab$ (iii) $-4x^3+4x^2-3x-4$
   (iv) $4x^2-3xy+10y^2-5xy^2$ (v) $x^3+y^3-z^3-11xyz$ (vi) $1+3x+2x^2+2x^3$

4. (i) $-3x$ (ii) $7xy$ (iii) $5b-3a$ (iv) $9y+7x$
   (v) $-17x^2$ (vi) $2b^2-2a^2$

5. (i) $-2a-14b+6c$ (ii) $-3a+7b-c$ (iii) $2x^2+xy-5y^2$
   (iv) $7-10x+13x^2-14x^3$ (v) $2y^3-9xy^2-6x^2y-x^3$
   (vi) $20x^2y^2-13xy+15$ (vii) $7a-3b-3c-6d$

6. (i) $-4p^3-p^2+2p+1$ (ii) $8x^2+4xy+2x-y$ (iii) x^3+5x^2+x-5

7. $-6x^2-4x+1$ **9.** $-4x^3+5x^2-7x-6$

10. $5a^2+3b^2-7ab-a+6$ **11.** a^3-5a^2+7a-7

12. $-a+5b-4c$ **13.** $-x+2y+4z$

14. $-x^3+4x^2-9x+7$ **15.** $12x+7y-9z$

16. $-8y+10z-2$ **17.** $5-2x+3y$

EXERCISE 8D

1. $3a-b$ **2.** $5x-3y-2z$ **3.** $4ab$ **4.** $3a-14b$

5. x^2-7 **6.** $-5x^2-y^2+xy$ **7.** $4a-4b+3c$ **8.** $-4x+10y$

9. $3+77x$ **10.** $4x^3+2x^2+18x-4$ **11.** $5a^3+12a^2+8a$ **12.** $6-6x-2y+3x^2$

13. $xy-3y+2xz$ **14.** $-a+b-c$ **15.** $-2b$ **16.** $8a-5b$

17. $9x-11y+7z$

EXERCISE 9A

1. (i) $5x=40$ (ii) $x+8=15$ (iii) $25-x=7$ (iv) $x-5=3$
   (v) $3x-5=16$ (vi) $x-12=24$ (vii) $19-2x=11$ (viii) $\dfrac{x}{8}=7$
   (ix) $4x-3=17$ (x) $6x=x+5$

2. (i) 7 less from the number x is 14.   (ii) Twice the number y is 18.
   (iii) 11 increased by thrice the number x is 17.   (iv) 3 less from twice the number x is 13.
   (v) 12 times the number y decreased by 30 is 6. (vi) Twice the number z divided by 3 is 8.

4. (i) $y=4$ (ii) $x=17$ (iii) $x=7$ (iv) $y=12$
   (v) $x=8$ (vi) $x=12$ (vii) $x=6$ (viii) $x=8$
   (ix) $y=4$ (x) $z=2$

EXERCISE 9B

1. $x=7$ **2.** $x=-5$ **3.** $x=13$ **4.** $x=-3$

5. $x=6$ **6.** $x=2$ **7.** $x=60$ **8.** $x=25$

9. $x=5$ **10.** $x=\dfrac{7}{4}$ **11.** $x=2$ **12.** $x=3$

13. $x = 36$ **14.** $x = 6$ **15.** $x = -1$ **16.** $x = -1$

17. $x = 3$ **18.** $x = 5$ **19.** $x = 8$ **20.** $x = 1$

21. $n = 66$ **22.** $m = -54$ **23.** $x = -25$ **24.** $x = -13$

25. $x = 60$ **26.** $x = 9$

EXERCISE 9C

1. 27   **2.** 25   **3.** 20   **4.** 37, 38, 39

5. 13   **6.** 15   **7.** 37, 55   **8.** 31, 93

9. 33, 165   **10.** 36, 38   **11.** 5, 7, 9

12. Ajay's age = 11 years, Reena's age = 17 years   **13.** 22 years, 11 years

14. 46 years, 19 years   **15.** 32 years, 8 years   **16.** 45 years, 15 years   **17.** 8 years

18. 18 years   **19.** 80 and 20   **20.** ₹ 8.50   **21.** 119

22. $l = 63$ m, $b = 21$ m   **23.** $l = 21$ m , $b = 16$ m   **24.** $l = 25$ cm, $b = 18$ cm

CCE TEST PAPER-9

1. ₹ $25x$ **2.** ₹ $(16x + 5y)$ **3.** ₹ $30(x - y)$ **4.** 4

5. 17   **6.** $x = 2$ **7.** $x = -1$ **8.** $x = -25$

9. 16, 17, 18   **10.** 8 years   **11.** (c)   **12.** (b)

13. (a)   **14.** (c)   **15.** (c)   **16.** (b)

17. (c)   **18.** (c)

19. (i) monomial   (ii) binomial   (iii) trinomial   (iv) 3   (v) $2b^2$

20. (i) T   (ii) F   (iii) T   (iv) F   (v) T

EXERCISE 10A

1. (i) 3 : 7   (ii) 7 : 25   (iii) 16 : 3   (iv) 3 : 10
    (v) 4 : 5   (vi) 8 : 3

2. (i) 2 : 5   (ii) 9 : 4   (iii) 5 : 33   (iv) 5 : 4
    (v) 6 : 13   (vi) 21 : 31

3. (i) 3 : 8   (ii) 7 : 10   (iii) 61 : 7   (iv) 3 : 10
    (v) 23 : 6   (vi) 8 : 5

4. (i) 8 : 5   (ii) 5 : 8   (iii) 8 : 13

5. (i) 25 : 2   (ii) 25 : 23   (iii) 23 : 2

6. 69   **7.** 160   **8.** Kamal—₹ 1225, Madhu—₹ 350

9. A—₹ 690, B—₹ 1150, C—₹ 1610   **10.** 220, 240   **11.** 20 cm, 15 cm

12. 63   **13.** 8 : 7   **14.** 70 m   **15.** ₹ 6840

16. ₹ 2000   **17.** 9.1 kg   **18.** 4 : 5

19. (i) (9 : 16)   (ii) (17 : 30)   (iii) (4 : 9)   (iv) (1 : 2)

20. (i) 3, 20   (ii) 7, 12   (iii) 20, 49

EXERCISE 10B

1. (i) Yes   (ii) Yes   (iii) No   (iv) Yes
     (v) No   (vi) No

3. (i) $x = 30$ (ii) $x = 36$ (iii) $x = 95$ (iv) $x = 69$

4. (i) F   (ii) T   (iii) T   (iv) T
     (v) T   (vi) F

5. (i) Yes   (ii) Yes   (iii) Yes   (iv) No

6. 81   **7.** 21   **9.** $x = 21$ **10.** 15 m

11. $x = 10$

EXERCISE 10C

1. ₹ 810   **2.** ₹ 357   **3.** ₹ 1820   **4.** 19 kg

5. 156 kg   **6.** 407 km   **7.** ₹ 756   **8.** 14.7 g

9. 126   **10.** 3   **11.** 8

12. (i) 8 h   (ii) 455 km   **13.** (i) ₹ 1155   (ii) 16 days

14. (i) 16 kg   (ii) 32   **15.** 15   **16.** 40 days

17. 65 men   **18.** 22 days   **19.** 10 days

EXERCISE 10D

1. (d)   **2.** (a)   **3.** (a)   **4.** (c)

5. (b)   **6.** (b)   **7.** (b)   **8.** (a)

9. (d)   **10.** (b)   **11.** (c)   **12.** (b)

13. (b)   **14.** (a)   **15.** (b)   **16.** (a)

17. (c)   **18.** (b)   **19.** (a)   **20.** (c)

21. (b)   **22.** (a)   **23.** (d)   **24.** (b)

CCE TEST PAPER-10

1. (a) 6 : 7   (b) 7 : 12   (c) 3 : 40   (d) 6 : 5

2. 9.8 kg   **3.** ₹ 280, ₹ 420, ₹ 700   **5.** 65 men   **6.** 34 days

7. $x = 24$ **9.** (c)   **10.** (b)   **11.** (c)

12. (d)   **13.** (a)   **14.** (c)   **15.** (b)

16. (b)   **17.** (b)

18. (i) 2, 9   (ii) 3 : 5   (iii) $x = 28$ (iv) $x = 49$ (v) $x = 21$

19. (i) T   (ii) T   (iii) F   (iv) T

EXERCISE 11A

1. (i) $\overline{XY}, \overline{YZ}$ (ii) $\overline{AD}, \overline{AB}, \overline{AC}, \overline{AE}, \overline{DB}, \overline{BC}, \overline{CE}$ (iii) $\overline{PQ}, \overline{PR}, \overline{PS}, \overline{QR}, \overline{QS}, \overline{RS}$

2. (i) $\overrightarrow{AB}, \overrightarrow{AC}, \overline{BD}$ (ii) $\overline{GE}, \overline{GP}, \overline{EP}, \overrightarrow{EF}, \overrightarrow{GH}, \overrightarrow{PQ}$ (iii) $\overline{OL}, \overline{OP}, \overrightarrow{LM}, \overrightarrow{PQ}$

3. (i) $\overline{PR}, \overline{PQ}, \overline{RS}, \overline{QS}$ (ii) $\overrightarrow{PA}, \overrightarrow{QC}, \overrightarrow{RB}, \overrightarrow{SD}$ (iii) $\overline{PR}$ and $\overline{QS}$

4. (i) One only   (ii) Three, $\overline{AB}, \overline{BC}, \overline{AC}$

5. (i) $(\overleftrightarrow{AB}, \overleftrightarrow{PS}), (\overleftrightarrow{AB}, \overleftrightarrow{RS}), (\overleftrightarrow{CD}, \overleftrightarrow{PS}), (\overleftrightarrow{CD}, \overleftrightarrow{RS})$ (ii) A, Q, S, B (iii) A, C, B
     (iv) $\overleftrightarrow{AB}, \overleftrightarrow{PS}, \overleftrightarrow{RS}$ (v) $\overleftrightarrow{CD}, \overleftrightarrow{PQ}, \overleftrightarrow{PS}$

6. $\overset{\leftrightarrow}{AB}, \overset{\leftrightarrow}{BC}, \overset{\leftrightarrow}{AC}$, Three

7. (i) Six, $\overline{AB}, \overline{AC}, \overline{AD}, \overline{BD}, \overline{BC}, \overline{DC}$ (ii) Ten, $\overline{AB}, \overline{BC}, \overline{CD}, \overline{DA}, \overline{OA}, \overline{OC}, \overline{OD}, \overline{OB}, \overline{AC}, \overline{BD}$

     (iii) Six, $\overline{AB}, \overline{FA}, \overline{FB}, \overline{DE}, \overline{DC}, \overline{EC}$

     (iv) Twelve, $\overline{AB}, \overline{BC}, \overline{AD}, \overline{DC}, \overline{FB}, \overline{FG}, \overline{GC}, \overline{EF}, \overline{EH}, \overline{HG}, \overline{EA}, \overline{HD}$

8. (i) False   (ii) True   (iii) True   (iv) True   (v) True

9. (i) F   (ii) F   (iii) F   (iv) F   (v) T

     (vi) T   (vii) T   (viii) T   (ix) F   (x) F

     (xi) F   (xii) T   (xiii) T

10. (i) definite   (ii) one   (iii) no   (iv) definite

     (v) cannot

EXERCISE 11B

1. (c)   **2.** (b)   **3.** (a)   **4.** (b)

5. (b)   **6.** (d)   **7.** (a)   **8.** (c)

9. (a)   **10.** (a)   **11.** (d)   **12.** (d)

13. (c)   **14.** (b)   **15.** (c)

EXERCISE 12

1. $(AB, DC), (AD, BC)$ **2.** $(AB \,\|\, HE \,\|\, DC \,\|\, GF), (DA \,\|\, GH \,\|\, CB \,\|\, FE), (DG \,\|\, CF \,\|\, AH \,\|\, BE)$

3. (i) $(DE \,\|\, BC)$ (ii) $(AB \,\|\, DC), (DA \,\|\, CB)$ (iii) $(AB \,\|\, DC), (AD \,\|\, BC)$

     (iv) $(LM \,\|\, RQ), (SL \,\|\, QP), (RS \,\|\, PM)$ (v) $(BA \,\|\, DC \,\|\, FE), (AC \,\|\, BD)$ and $(CE \,\|\, DF)$

5. $CD = 2.3$ cm   **6.** No, No, Corresponding lines will intersect when produced in one direction

7. (i) Yes   (ii) No

8. (i) True   (ii) True   (iii) False   (iv) False

EXERCISE 13A

1. Scissors, a pair of compasses, tongs   **2.** Vertex is B and arms are $\overrightarrow{BA}$ and $\overrightarrow{BC}$

3. (i) Three; $\angle BAC, \angle ACB$ and $\angle ABC$ (ii) Four; $\angle BAD, \angle ABC, \angle BCD$ and $\angle CDA$

     (iii) Eight; $\angle ABD, \angle BAD, \angle ADB, \angle DBC, \angle BDC, \angle DCB, \angle ABC, \angle ADC$

4. (i) Q, S (ii) P, R (iii) A, O, B, T, N

5. (i) False   (ii) True   (iii) False   (iv) True   (v) False

6. (i) $\angle EPB$ (ii) $\angle PQC$ (iii) $\angle FQD$

EXERCISE 13B

1. (i) Obtuse angle   (ii) Right angle   (iii) Straight angle   (iv) Reflex angle

     (v) Acute angle   (vi) Complete angle

2. (i) Acute   (ii) Obtuse   (iii) Obtuse   (iv) Right

     (v) Reflex   (vi) Complete   (vii) Obtuse   (viii) Obtuse

     (ix) Acute   (x) Acute   (xi) Zero   (xii) Acute

3. (i) $90°$ (ii) $180°$ (iii) $270°$ (iv) $360°$

     (v) $60°$ (vi) $135°$

4. (i) $90°$ (ii) $180°$ (iii) $0°$ (iv) $90°$

EXERCISE 13D

1. (c)	**2.** (c)	**3.** (c)	**4.** (b)
5. (b)	**6.** (d)	**7.** (c)	**8.** (c)
9. (d)	**10.** (b)	**11.** (b)	**12.** (b)
13. (c)			

CCE TEST PAPER-14

1. (i) infinitely many   (ii) one only   (iii) three

2. (i) acute angle   (ii) obtuse angle   (iii) reflex angle   (iv) right angle   (v) straight angle

7. (c)	**8.** (b)	**9.** (a)	**10.** (b)
11. (b)	**12.** (c)	**13.** (d)	

14. (i) no   (ii) one   (iii) cannot   (iv) < , <   (v) degree

15. (i) F   (ii) F   (iii) T   (iv) T   (v) F   (vi) F

EXERCISE 15

1. (a), (b), (d), (f)   **2.** (a), (b), (c)

3. (i) two   (ii) triangle   (iii) quadrilateral   (iv) 3, 3

   (v) 4, 4   (vi) closed figure

EXERCISE 16A

1. (i) AB (ii) $\angle A$ (iii) B (iv) AC

2. 50°   **3.** 20°, 60°, 100°   **4.** 40°   **5.** 35°

7. $\angle A = 80°$, $\angle B = 60°$, $\angle C = 40°$

8. (i) Obtuse   (ii) Acute   (iii) Right   (iv) Obtuse

9. (i) Isosceles   (ii) Isosceles   (iii) Scalene   (iv) Equilateral

   (v) Equilateral   (vi) Isosceles   (vii) Scalene

10. Three, $\triangle ABD$, $\triangle ADC$ and $\triangle ABC$

11. (i) No   (ii) No   (iii) Yes   (iv) No

   (v) No   (vi) Yes

12. (i) 3, 3, 3   (ii) 180°   (iii) different   (iv) 60°

   (v) equal   (vi) perimeter

EXERCISE 16B

1. (c)	**2.** (b)	**3.** (b)	**4.** (d)
5. (c)	**6.** (c)	**7.** (a)	**8.** (b)
9. (d)	**10.** (c)	**11.** (c)	

EXERCISE 17A

1. (i) AC, BD (ii) (AB, DC) and (AD, BC) (iii) $(\angle A, \angle C)$, $(\angle B, \angle D)$

   (iv) (AB, BC), (AD, DC) (v) $(\angle A, \angle B)$, $(\angle B, \angle C)$

3. 16 cm, 12 cm   **4.** (i) Rectangle   (ii) Square   (iii) Rhombus

6. (a) False   (b) False   (c) False

7. (a) A rectangle with sides equal becomes a square.
(b) A rhombus with each angle a right angle becomes a square.
(c) A parallelogram with each angle a right angle becomes a rectangle.
(d) The opposite sides of a square are parallel, so it is a parallelogram.

8. A regular quadrilateral is a square.

EXERCISE 17B

1. (c)   **2.** (c)   **3.** (b)   **4.** (d)
5. (d)   **6.** (b)   **7.** (b)   **8.** (b)
9. (c)   **10.** (c)

EXERCISE 18

4. (i) False   (ii) True   (iii) False   (iv) False   (v) True
6. (i) >   (ii) <   (iii) >   (iv) >
7. (i) passes through   (ii) at the centre, on the circle   (iii) chord
(iv) arc   (v) sector

CCE TEST PAPER-18

4. 36°, 60°, 84°   **5.** 48°, 72°, 96°, 144°   **9.** (d)   **10.** (c)
11. (c)   **12.** (b)
13. (i) F   (ii) T   (iii) F   (iv) T   (v) T

EXERCISE 19

1. (c)   **2.** (b)   **3.** (d)   **4.** (c)
5. (b)   **6.** (d)
7. (i) solid   (ii) 6, 12, 8   (iii) opposite   (iv) sphere
(v) cube   (vi) 4, 8   (vii) 3, 6   (viii) 6, 3, 2, 9

8. (a) Ice-cream cone, clown's cap, conical tent, conical vessel
(b) A brick, a book, a chalk box, a matchbox
(c) Circular pillar, circular pipe, measuring jar, test tube

EXERCISE 20

1. (d)   **2.** (c)   **3.** (b)   **4.** (d)
5. (a)   **6.** (a)   **7.** (c)   **8.** (a)
10. (i) True   (ii) True   (iii) True   (iv) False
(v) True   (vi) True   (vii) True

EXERCISE 21A

1. (i) 46 cm   (ii) 7 m 50 cm   (iii) 30 m 6 dm
2. ₹ 3040   **3.** $l = 40$ m, $b = 24$ m   **4.** 32 m   **5.** $l = 42$ m, $b = 24$ m
6. (i) 15.2 cm   (ii) 18.4 m   (iii) 10 m   **7.** 32 m
8. $l = 24$ m, $b = 18$ m   **9.** (i) 20.2 cm   (ii) 28.2 cm   (iii) 24 cm
10. (i) 40 cm   (ii) 36 cm   (iii) 36 cm

11. (i) 142 cm   (ii) 72 cm   (iii) 72 cm

EXERCISE 21B

1. (i) 176 cm   (ii) 66 cm   (iii) 22 m

2. (i) 44 cm   (ii) 110 cm   (iii) 33 m

3. 28 cm   **4.** 84 cm   **5.** 1210 m   **6.** 750

EXERCISE 21C

1. 12 sq cm   **2.** 18 sq cm   **3.** 14.5 sq cm   **4.** 8 sq cm

5. 12 sq cm   **6.** 16 sq cm   **7.** 12 sq cm   **8.** 14 sq cm

9. 16 sq cm

EXERCISE 21D

1. (i) 1150 cm^2 (ii) 54 m^2 (iii) 98.6 m^2 (iv) 12300 cm^2, or 1.23 m^2
   (v) 7 km^2

2. 196 m^2 **3.** 2.7 m^2 **4.** ₹ 3690   **5.** 258

6. 36 m^2 **7.** 80000   **8.** ₹ 10140   **9.** 960 m^2

10. $b = 58$ m, square plot has more area by 36 m^2 **11.** 51 m, ₹ 9100

12. 15 cm, 1 m 2 cm   **13.** 1000, ₹ 22500   **14.** 98 cm   **15.** 25 cm^2

16. (i) 26 m^2 (ii) 43.5 m^2 (iii) 33 m^2

17. (i) 28 cm^2 (ii) 9 cm^2 (iii) 180 cm^2

EXERCISE 21E

1. (b)   **2.** (d)   **3.** (b)   **4.** (b)

5. (c)   **6.** (a)   **7.** (b)   **8.** (b)

9. (c)   **10.** (b)   **11.** (a)   **12.** (b)

13. (d)   **14.** (b)   **15.** (d)

CCE TEST PAPER-21

1. (i) 16.8 cm   (ii) 48 cm   (iii) 16.5 cm   **2.** 105 m   **3.** $l = 30$ m, $b = 24$ m

4. 441 cm^2 **5.** 18 m   **6.** 44 cm   **7.** 1210 m

8. 56 cm   **9.** 540 cm^2 **10.** (b)   **11.** (a)

12. (b)   **13.** (d)   **14.** (b)

15. (i) regular   (ii) 4   (iii) length, breadth   (iv) $(\text{side})^2$ (v) 20 m^2

16.
   a   b   c   d   e
   ↓   ↓   ↓   ↓   ↓
   (iii) (iv) (v) (ii) (i)

EXERCISE 22

2.

Number of children	Tally marks	Number of families
0	||	2
1	ⅠⅢ |	6
2	ⅠⅢ ||||	9
3	ⅠⅢ	5
4	|||	3
	Total number of families = 25	

3.

Size	Tally marks	Frequency
4	||	2
5	ⅠⅢ	5
6	||||	4
7	||||	4
8	ⅠⅢ |	6
9	ⅠⅢ ||	7

4.

Number	Tally marks	Frequency
1	ⅠⅢ	5
2	ⅠⅢ ||	7
3	ⅠⅢ |	6
4	||	2
5	|||	3
	Total	23

5.

Number	Tally marks	Frequency
5	||	2
6	||||	4
7	ⅠⅢ ||	7
8	ⅠⅢ	5
9	||	2
10	||	2
	Total	22

6. (i) numerical figures (ii) original (iii) array
(iv) frequency (v) tabulation

EXERCISE 23

5. (i) 24   (ii) 32   (iii) 40   (iv) 96

6. (i) 30   (ii) 24   (iii) Friday, 42   (iv) Saturday, 12

EXERCISE 24

1. (i) The given bar graph shows the marks obtained by a student in each of the four subjects in an examination.
   (ii) The student is poorest in Science.
   (iii) The student is best in Mathematics.
   (iv) He got more than 40 marks in Hindi and Mathematics.

2. (i) The given bar graph shows the number of members in each of the 60 families of a colony.
   (ii) 10 families have 3 members each.
   (iii) 5 couples have no child.
   (iv) A family of 4 members is most common.

3. (i) The production was maximum in the 2nd week.
   (ii) The production was minimum in the 4th week.
   (iii) The average production is 720 per week.
   (iv) 2400 cycles were produced in the first three weeks.

4. (i) The given bar graph shows the different modes of transport to school used by 51 students of a locality.
   (ii) Maximum number of students use bicycle for going to school.
   (iii) 14 students use bus for going to school.
   (iv) 37 students do not use bus for going to school.